Introduction to the soil ecosystem

Introduction to the soil ecosystem

B. N. Richards
Associate Professor, School of Natural Resources
University of New England
Armidale, NSW
Australia

Longman
London and New York

LONGMAN GROUP LIMITED
London

*Associated companies, branches and representatives
throughout the world*

Published in the United States of America by
Longman Inc., New York

First Published, 1974
Reprinted, with minor corrections, 1976

Library of Congress Cataloging in Publication Data
Richards, Bryant N
   Introduction to the soil ecosystem.
   Includes bibliographies and index.
   1. Soil ecology. I. Title
QH541.5.S6R52 1976   574.5'26   75–30993

SBN 0 582 44130

*Printed in Great Britain by
Whitstable Litho Ltd*

Preface

This book has evolved from a lecture course in microbial ecology given over a period of years in the Department of Botany at the University of New England. It aims to emphasize the role of soil microorganisms, and of their interactions with plants, in the functioning of terrestrial ecosystems. Briefly, it is designed to give students of ecology an understanding of plant—microbe relationships in an ecosystem context. Hopefully, it may also bring to students of microbiology a wider appreciation of the microbial contribution to ecological processes. While written primarily for undergraduates in the biological sciences and in such applied fields as forestry and agriculture, it may perhaps serve additionally to introduce graduate students and research workers, with a peripheral interest in the subject, to the microbiology of terrestrial ecosystems.

The book differs in several respects from standard works on soil microbiology. I have adopted what is essentially a systems approach throughout, examining the role of soil microbes both in the soil—litter subsystem and in the wider context of the ecosystem and, where applicable, the biosphere. It is for this reason that plant—microbe interactions have received proportionally more emphasis than is usual in a book of this kind. In the same vein, the idea of a 'functional, factorial' approach to the study of ecosystems is introduced and discussed, albeit briefly. This concept had its origins in the attempt by V. V. Dokuchaev to establish soil properties as functions of the factors of the environment, and was refined and extended to encompass the ecosystem as a whole by Hans Jenny. It seems to me the most appropriate means of dealing with the principle of interacting limiting factors at the ecosystem level. Its relevance as a conceptual framework for the study of ecosystems has not been widely recognized since it has yet to be incorporated in the general body of ecological theory. However, since it is well suited to the techniques of systems analysis, much more use is likely to be made of it in the future.

Because the book is not meant to be a reference work, specific literature citations have been omitted from the text, although the contributions of individual workers are acknowledged where they are judged to be especially pertinent to the topic under discussion. This policy was adopted in the interests of improving the narrative, though it is realized that it may prove inconvenient, and indeed irritating, to those readers wishing to ascertain the source of statements made in the text. To such readers I offer my apologies, but hasten to add that a diligent search through the list of selected references given at the end of each chapter will in most instances provide the information they seek.

Every author of a scientific textbook is greatly indebted to colleagues for discussions which help to clarify his ideas about particular issues. Many such discussions do not relate directly to his book, though the results may find expression therein, and thus it is often impossible to acknowledge fully the help he has received. For my part, I am particularly grateful to the following members of the academic staff of the University of New England: Dr J. F. Brown, Dr A. Bryce Lloyd and Dr R. L. Stanton, who read and commented upon part or all of earlier drafts of the manuscript; to Dr J. L. Charley for an exposition of Jenny's functional, factorial approach; and to Dr Majorie O. Ind for her assistance with the preparation of the description of the soil fauna given in Chapter 2. I also wish to express my appreciation to Dr David H. Hubbell and Dr H. T. Odum, of the University of Florida, Gainesville, for their comments; I have used Odum's 'energy circuit diagrams' extensively throughout the text. The final draft was typed by Miss Lorraine Blight.

Finally, I am deeply grateful to my wife, Yvonne, for her forebearance throughout the period in which the book was written.

Department of Botany
University of New England
Armidale, NSW

18 September 1972.

Contents

Acknowledgements

We are grateful to the following for permission to reproduce copyright material:

Academic Press Inc. (London) Ltd for an extract from *Adv. Microb. Phys.* **3**, 1969, by J. L. Harley and D. H. Lewis; Commonwealth Agricultural Bureaux for an extract from *Commonwealth Bureaux Pastures and Field Crops Bulletin*, **46**, by E. F. Henzell and D. O. Norris; *Forest Science* and the authors for Table 2 of the article by B. N. Richards and G. L. Wilson in *Forest Science*, **9**, 1963; The Institute of Foresters of Australia and the authors for Table 2, p. 4 by R. J. Lamb and B. N. Richards in *Aust. For.* **35**, 1971; John Murray and University of California Press for Table 1, p. 222 of *Ecology of Soil-Borne Plant Pathogens: Prelude to Biological Control*, ed. by Kenneth F. Baker and William C. Snyder, University of California Press, 1965; National Research Council of Canada for Table 1, p. 378 from a paper entitled 'The rhizosphere effect of mycorrhizal and non-mycorrhizal roots of yellow birch seedlings', by H. Katznelson *et al.* from the *Canadian Journal of Botany*, **40**, pp. 377–82 (1962); Martinus Nijhoff for Table 1, p. 613 of *Plant Soil*, **32**, 1970, by J. G. Becking; North-Holland Publishing Company for Table 1, p. 8, of *Soil Organisms* (ed. by J. Doeksen and J. van der Drift) 1963 by A. Macfadyen; Pitman Publishing Ltd, London, for Table 11, p. 234 from *Animal Ecology: Aims and Methods* by A. Macfadyen, 1963; Pergamon Press Ltd and the author for table on p. 97 of *Soil Fungi and Fertility* (1963) by S. D. Garrett; The authors for Table 4, pp. 2–4 and Tables 26 and 29 on pp. 9–26 and 9–29: 'Vesicular-arbuscular mycorrhizas of *Araucaria*: aspects of their ecology and physiology and role in nitrogen fixation' by D. I. Bevege. PhD thesis, University of New England, 1971 and two tables by J. M. Jones from 'Effect of *Pinus* on soil microorganisms and microbiological processes with special reference to the nitrogen cycle.' PhD thesis, University of New England, 1968; Unesco for Table 1, p. 167 of 'Soil metabolism in relation to ecosystem energy flow and to primary and secondary production' by A. Macfadyen in *Methods of Study in*

Soil Ecology, 1970, reproduced by permission of Unesco, © Unesco; The Williams & Wilkins Co., Baltimore, and the authors for Table 1, p. 65 of *Soil Science*, **67**, 1949, by R. H. Wallace and A. G. Lochhead.

1 Soil organisms and the ecosystem concept

A major task confronting ecologists is to characterize ecological systems, or ecosystems, in terms of their structure and function, and to relate structural characteristics to functional processes. Characterization of ecosystems in terms of **structure** involves a study of the numbers and kinds of organisms present and their spatial relationships; it also requires a knowledge of the amounts of various inorganic substances in the system and how these are distributed among its component parts. Even to a casual observer, a grassland has a very different structure from a forest: not only does it possess a very different assemblage of plants and animals, but it clearly contains a great deal less matter than the forest; in ecological terminology, it has a smaller biomass. Less obvious is the fact that the amount of energy stored in the two systems, in the form of organic compounds, is quite different also.

Functional differences between ecosystems are not so readily discernible as structural differences, nevertheless they do exist. Functional processes include the capture and transfer of energy, and the uptake and circulation of nutrients and water. **Function** is expressed in terms of the rates at which these processes take place, that is the rates at which energy and materials enter and leave the system, and the rates at which they are transformed, circulated or stored within it. Ecosystems differ very greatly in these respects.

Where do the organisms which inhabit the soil fit into the picture? The answer to this question lies in part in the functional classification of organisms as producers, consumers or decomposers. **Producers,** chiefly green plants, utilize the energy of sunlight to build up complex organic molecules from simpler inorganic ones. **Consumers** are the animals which harvest plants as food, either directly as herbivores or indirectly as carnivores. **Decomposers** are the microorganisms and small animals that reside in or on the soil, and which reduce the carbonaceous residues of dead organisms to the inorganic state. These three categories not only represent the three major functional components of the ecosystem, but in a sense they are structural units also. In addition, a fourth structural component may be added, viz. abiotic or non-living substances, such as water, the mineral fraction of the soil, dead organic matter, and the gases of the atmosphere.

Although these major structural and functional divisions are common to all ecosystems, each system has its own characteristic make-up. The contrast between typical terrestrial and marine ecosystems illustrates this point. The atmosphere is common to both systems, but in the former the remainder of the abiotic fraction comprises soil and surface detritus, while in the latter it is water containing dissolved salts and particulate organic matter together with the bottom sediments. On land, the autotrophic component is represented by green plants, while in the sea the autotrophs are microorganisms collectively known as phytoplankton. A similar array of consumers and decomposers is found in both marine and terrestrial ecosystems, except that there are clearly differences in the numbers and kinds of organisms present.

Soil organisms in relation to ecosystem structure

Most of the microbes in terrestrial ecosystems are found in the soil, and indeed the microbiology of such ecosystems can be largely equated with soil microbiology. This is not to say that microorganisms do not occur elsewhere, such as on the surfaces of leaves of green plants, but their numbers and biomass are small compared to the corresponding figures for soil. Except in extreme habitats restricted to lichens, algae and mosses, the primary producers in terrestrial ecosystems are vascular plants. In most mature ecosystems of this kind, the greater part of the organic matter fixed each year by the higher plants is returned directly to the soil. This is true irrespective of whether the system is a natural grassland, a grazed pasture, a virgin forest, or a forest managed for timber production. Only under intensive grazing is a significant amount of the primary production diverted from the producer—decomposer pathway. The organic residues are decomposed and incorporated in the soil by the combined activities of microorganisms and soil animals. The major groups of soil organisms are described in Chapter 2; in the meantime, an estimate of the numbers and biomass of decomposer microbes and of the soil fauna, for a square metre of hypothetical grassland soil in the Northern Hemisphere, is given in Table 1.1. It should be noted that animals, like microbes, are far more numerous in the soil than elsewhere.

It must be stressed that the values shown in Table 1.1 represent

TABLE 1.1 Maximum number and biomass (live weight) of soil organisms in a hypothetical grassland soil of high fertility*

Kind of organism	Abundance (no./m^2)	Biomass (g/m^2)
Bacteria	3×10^{14}	300
Fungi		400
Protozoa	5×10^8	38
Nematodes	10^7	12
Earthworms and related forms	10^5	132
Mites	2×10^5	3
Springtails	5×10^4	5
Other invertebrates†	2×10^3	36

* After Macfadyen, A. (1963) *Animal Ecology: Aims and Methods*, Pitman. No numbers are given for fungi because, being filamentous, absolute numbers have little meaning for comparisons such as this; however, the estimate would seem a reasonable one for the live weight of both fungal spores and vegetative hyphae. Macfadyen's figures for bacteria have been reduced from 10^{15} cells/m^2 and 1 000 g/m^2 on the basis of estimates made by F. E. Clark in 1967.
† Snails, millipedes, woodlice, spiders, beetles, fly larvae, etc.

situations where the respective groups are abundant, that is, no one soil would contain such high populations of all these organisms. In terms of numbers of individuals, microbes (bacteria, fungi and protozoa) are seen to constitute a very significant structural component of this hypothetical ecosystem. No other group of organisms is ever present in such high numbers. It is not sufficient, however, to consider only this aspect of structure if we are interested in structure as a guide to ecosystem function. If function is to be related to structure, then structure should be described by parameters which have some meaning for functional processes. The study of function concerns chemical transformations of matter and energy, and numbers alone are rarely an adequate guide to the contribution of microorganisms to these processes. **Biomass** is a somewhat better measure of ecological significance, and on this basis microorganisms are again seen to be the dominant group: biomass of the invertebrate soil fauna is always much less than the microbial biomass. Relative to the total biomass of many terrestrial ecosystems, however, microbes are a minor structural component. In the hypothetical grassland ecosystem illustrated in Table 1.1, the biomass of all microorganisms totals about 7.4×10^2 g/m^2, and this would be equivalent to 15–20 per cent of the total biomass of such a system. In real grassland ecosystems, the microbial biomass would be an even smaller proportion of the whole, while in forest ecosystems, with their massive woody stems, the microbial contribution to total biomass is unlikely to exceed 2 or 3 per cent. There is no way of knowing for certain, since the biomass of microorganisms can only be determined indirectly, from measurements of population density or through some index of microbial activity such as the rate of carbon dioxide evolution from soil.

Soil organisms in ecosystem function

Biomass itself is an unreliable index of the functional activities of organisms, since it is not always well correlated with metabolic activity. Thus while microbes and soil animals form only a small part of the total biomass of most terrestrial ecosystems, they are nevertheless very active metabolically and therefore of prime importance in the turnover and transport of chemical elements. The cycling of the elements is one of two major functional processes in ecosystems, the other being the flow of energy. Soil organisms are vitally concerned in this second process also. An important distinction between the two processes is that whereas energy is gradually dissipated as heat and lost from the system, material substances such as chemical elements may be re-used again and again. This is not to say that the cycle of materials is completely closed: losses occur through leaching, for example, and these losses must be made good if ecosystem function is to be maintained.

Energy flow and organic matter decomposition

The flow of energy through the system is closely related to the processes of accumulation and decomposition of organic matter. The amount of organic matter fixed by an ecosystem per unit of time is a measure of its **productivity**. Primary productivity is that fixed by photosynthesis, and it has two components: net productivity which is the rate at which organic matter accumulates within the system, and gross productivity which is the rate at which it is fixed by the system. Gross productivity is therefore equivalent to net productivity plus the amount of photosynthate used per unit of time through respiration by the primary producers. These definitions ignore any part of the gross production which might be excreted into the environment. In terms of mass this may be relatively insignificant, yet it can be of great importance functionally in terrestrial ecosystems, because microorganisms in the vicinity of plant roots (i.e. in the rhizosphere) use plant exudates as a source of energy and nutrients. This topic will be discussed more fully in Chapter 7, while the contribution of soil organisms to the energy budget of ecosystems is dealt with in Chapter 5.

The process of organic matter decomposition in soils is greatly influenced by environmental factors. An increase in soil temperature can stimulate metabolic activity of the microflora and hasten mineralization (i.e. conversion to carbon dioxide) of the organic matter; concomitantly, there is an increase in the rate of energy flow through the system. Subjecting a soil to alternate cycles of wetting and drying can also promote the breakdown of organic matter, and such a pattern of decomposition may be of particular significance in regions which experience a monsoonal climate. The question of organic matter breakdown in soil is treated in some detail in Chapter 5; for the present it will suffice to say that the decay of plant and animal residues is a complex process, involving both microbes and the soil fauna (Fig. 1.1). Animals

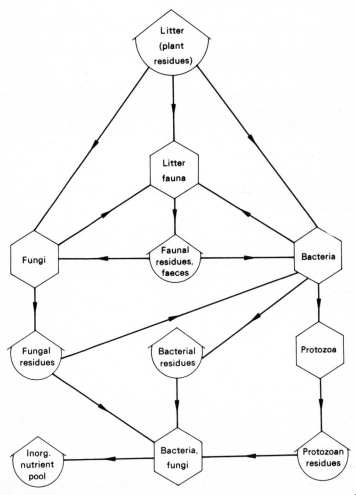

FIG. 1.1 Diagrammatic representation of the detritus food web in soils, greatly simplified.

occupy the dual roles of consumers and decomposers, some preying on other animals or grazing on plants and microorganisms, others being detritus feeders.

Two major groups of microbes are involved in organic matter decomposition, the fungi and the bacteria. Both use the same basic mechanisms to decompose insoluble substrates, viz. the hydrolysis of complex compounds by exoenzymes (see Chapter 3). As S. D. Garrett has pointed out, however, the physical organization of fungi gives them an advantage over bacteria in the breakdown of cellulosic plant remains, which constitute a major fraction of the organic matter component of terrestrial ecosystems. Bacteria have no intrinsic mechanism for penetrating plant tissues, and their progress as cellulose decomposers is limited to surface erosion, because the rate at which they break down their substrate is proportional to the rate at which exoenzymes are produced and diffuse out from the bacterial colonies. Fungi, on the other hand, supplement the action of exoenzymes with mechanical pressure from their elongating hyphae, and furthermore their filamentous habit permits them to ramify throughout dead plant tissues with relative ease. Only in anaerobic habitats, such as waterlogged peats and in the rumen of cattle, do cellulolytic bacteria predominate over fungi.

It would be a gross oversimplification, however, to assert that organic matter decomposition is the only contribution of fungi and bacteria to ecosystem function. As will be seen in Chapter 8, there are some fungi, the so-called mycorrhizal fungi, which are incapable of decomposing organic matter, yet which greatly influence the process of nutrient cycling in many forest ecosystems. These fungi satisfy their energy requirements by entering into a close anatomical and physiological association with the roots of certain trees, so that a small fraction of the photosynthate produced by the trees is passed directly to the fungi. This sacrifice on the part of the plants is recompensed by the fungi providing them with mineral nutrients at rates greatly in excess of those pertaining in the absence of the mycorrhizal fungi. In turn, enhanced growth of the trees results in a greater deposition of leaf litter on the soil, so that the soil system receives an increased input of energy as a result of the presence of mycorrhizal fungi, even though these fungi cannot themselves release the energy contained in the plant residues.

There are many other processes in soils which involve microorganisms. Bacteria in particular contribute in numerous ways. The oxidation of organic compounds is only one of many means at the disposal of bacteria for the purpose of satisfying their energy needs. A study of macroscopic organisms, i.e. plants and animals, could leave one with the impression that only two kinds of energy-yielding metabolic processes existed in the living world, photosynthesis and respiration, but various groups of bacteria have evolved other mechanisms for capturing and utilizing energy for biosynthesis and growth. These will be described in Chapter 3, and their functional significance in ecosystems will be considered in subsequent chapters, but reference to Table 1.2 will indicate something of the range of energy-yielding processes which exists in the microbial world.

Nutrient cycles

The exchanges of chemical elements between the living and non-living parts of the ecosystem constitute what are known as nutrient cycles. On a global scale they are referred to as **biogeochemical cycles**. Although microbial biomass may be a relatively small fraction of the total system biomass, microbial activity is of paramount importance in the circulation of the elements. This will be discussed again in Chapter 6, but for the present it can be inferred, from the great variety of microbial oxidations shown in Table 1.2, that bacteria, in company with fungi, not only make a major contribution to nutrient cycling (and energy flow) in particular ecosystems, but also have great significance for the geochemical cycles of the elements in the biosphere as a whole. There are several reasons, apart from their metabolic diversity, why bacteria and fungi are such potent agents of geochemical change. Because of their small size, they have a very large surface-to-volume ratio that permits rapid interchange of materials between their cells and the environment. Equally important is their extremely rapid rate of reproduction, generation times in bacteria being measured in minutes and hours. In addition, they are ubiquitous in distribution, being found in every conceivable habitat on the surface of the Earth.

Regulation in ecosystems

A mature or climax ecosystem may be regarded as an open system in a steady state, that is a condition independent of time in which production and consumption of each component are equally balanced, the concentration of all components within the system remaining constant even though there is continual change. It is true that over short periods of time ecosystems appear to show considerable change, but if cognisance is taken of the time factor the steady state condition is seen to apply. Thus in a deciduous forest where leaf shed occurs in autumn, there are large fluctuations in the amount of leaf litter on the forest floor during the course of a single season. However, since there is no net

TABLE 1.2 Energy-yielding oxidations in microbial metabolism*

Reductant	Oxidant	Products	Organism
Sugars	O_2	CO_2, H_2O	Protozoa, fungi, many bacteria
Ethyl alcohol	O_2	Acetic acid, H_2O	Acetic acid bacteria
H_2	O_2	H_2O	Hydrogen bacteria
NH_4^+	O_2	NO_2^-, H_2O	Nitrifying bacteria
NO_2^-	O_2	NO_3^-	Nitrifying bacteria
H_2S	O_2	S, H_2O	Thiobacilli
S, $S_2O_3^{2-}$	O_2	SO_4^{2-}	Thiobacilli
Fe^{2+}	O_2	Fe^{3+}, H_2O	Iron bacteria
Sugars and other organic substrates	NO_3^-	NO_2^-, H_2O	Denitrifying bacteria
Sugars and other organic substrates	NO_2^-	N_2, N_2O, H_2O	Denitrifying bacteria
Sugars and other organic substrates	SO_4^{2-}, SO_3^{2-}	S^{2-}, H_2O	Desulphovibrio
Sugars and other organic substrates	$S_2O_3^{2-}$	SII^-, H_2O	Desulphovibrio
H_2, CO, organic acids, alcohols	CO_2	CH_4, H_2O	Methane bacteria
Sugars and related compounds†		Lactic acid, ethyl alcohol, CO_2	Lactic acid bacteria
Sugars		Ethyl alcohol, CO_2	Yeasts
Sugars		Acetic, succinic and lactic acids, formic acid or H_2 and CO_2, ethyl alcohol	Escherichia
Sugars		Butanediol, lactic acid, formic acid or H_2 and CO_2, ethyl alcohol	Aerobacter
Sugars, organic acids		Propionic, succinic and acetic acids, CO_2	Propionibacterium, Veillonella
Sugars, starch, pectin		Butyric and acetic acids, CO_2, H_2	Clostridium
Amino acids		Acetic acid, NH_3, CO_2	Clostridium

* Only those organisms using organic compounds as reductants (H-donors) are decomposers.
† In this and subsequent oxidations, the oxidant is an organic compound, but for the sake of simplicity the individual compounds are not listed. In any event, because of the complexity of the reactions and the variety of end products, it is not always possible to quote specific H-acceptors (oxidants).

accumulation over a period of years, production (leaf fall) being equal to consumption (leaf decomposition), the litter layer may be regarded as a steady state system.

Ecosystems, being open systems, do not strictly speaking obey the second law of thermodynamics, which states that systems in isolation spontaneously tend towards states of greater disorder, i.e. their entropy increases. In contrast to closed (isolated) systems, ecosystems increase in order as they mature towards a climax or steady state, i.e. their entropy decreases. A system in steady state is a stable system, and its stability is maintained by regulatory processes which act in such a way as to minimize entropy. This tendency for a mature ecosystem to resist change, and to return to a steady state if disturbed, is termed **homeostasis**. Homeostatic controls sometimes involve outside factors (organism x environment interactions), but in many instances self-regulating processes (organism x organism interactions) are responsible. A major purpose of this book is to demonstrate the role of plant–microbe interactions in the functioning of terrestrial ecosystems.

Ecosystem models

An ecosystem may be illustrated graphically as a series of compartments or storages linked by flows of energy and materials. Figure 1.2 is a generalized diagram of a hypothetical ecosystem in the steady state

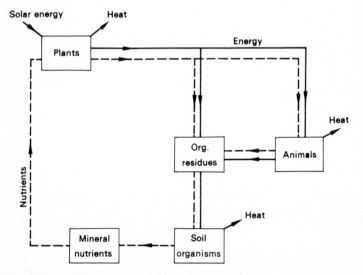

FIG. 1.2 Generalized picture of an ecosystem, showing the major pathways of energy and nutrients.

condition, with a closed nutrient cycle (i.e. no gains from weathering, rainfall, etc., nor losses by leaching, gaseous diffusion, etc.). Storages are represented by boxes, flows by arrows. The potential energy available for metabolic work is indicated by the storage of organic matter in plant and animal residues, while low energy compounds resulting from respiration (mineral nutrients, CO_2) are shown as an inorganic pool.

The **energy network diagram**, introduced by H. T. Odum, describes energy flow throughout the ecosystem in more rigorous fashion (Fig. 1.3). Each compartment or module represents a particular structure and function with certain inputs and related outputs (see Appendix I for greater detail). Pathways of energy flow are shown as lines, and potential energy sources by a tank symbol. Energy may flow from sources

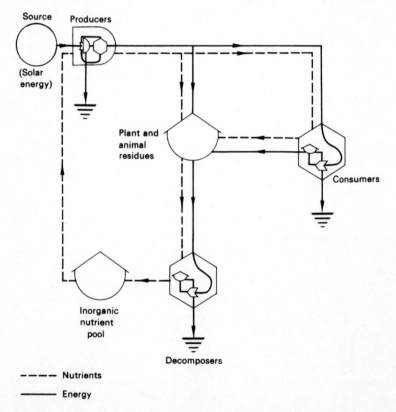

FIG. 1.3 Energy circuit diagram of a hypothetical ecosystem in the steady state condition with a closed nutrient cycle. Major energy flows are depicted as solid lines, while the pathways of low energy compounds (inorganic nutrients) are shown as broken lines. (Based on the notation of Odum, H. T. (1971) *Environment, Power and Society*, Wiley.)

either alone (e.g. as heat or light) or in association with a flow of materials such as inorganic nutrients or organic matter. The hexagonal symbol represents a self-maintaining subsystem and is a combination of two modules in which potential energy stored in one part of the subsystem is fed back to control the work done within the whole; the process is autocatalytic provided the flow of energy from an outside source is maintained. The bullet-shaped symbol depicts a green plant, and is also a complex module, made up of a cycling receptor unit which captures solar energy and uses a small part of this energy through a self-maintaining feedback control subsystem to keep the receptor machinery (photosynthetic apparatus) working.

The 'control valve', or regulatory mechanism, in both the foregoing complex modules is the work gate, symbolized as a pointed block (sometimes truncated), and representing the multiplicative effect of two interacting energy flows. When the two input flows are maintained at the work gate in constant concentrations, the output is a function of their product. When the supply of one of the reactants is limited, increases in the concentration of the other will lead to progressively diminishing increments in output, producing a response curve which is characteristically a rectangular hyperbola. Limiting plant nutrients act in this fashion, controlling the flow of solar energy, and thus the productivity of the ecosystem, by means of the work gate. The remaining symbol, an arrow directed into the ground, indicates the dispersion of potential energy into heat which occurs during every spontaneous process, according to the second law of thermodynamics.

The physiological processes basic to ecosystem function are photosynthesis, respiration and nutrient absorption. The solar energy captured by photosynthesis (gross primary production) is normally the total amount of energy available for all the energy requiring reactions of the system, although some ecosystems have important auxiliary energy sources as well. Energy fixed by photosynthesis does biologically useful work through the process of respiration. This work includes that needed to maintain the structure and organization of the ecosystem as well as that needed for the more obvious processes of biosynthesis, growth and nutrient uptake.

Figure 1.3 is greatly simplified, and shows only the major energy pathways. To understand how the system functions, we need to identify and measure as many of the individual storages and flows as possible. Lack of knowledge of all the individual processes involved may prevent us from doing this, but the energy network diagram is still useful because it enables us to direct attention to the energy flows which are of particular interest, even if others remain unidentified as miscellaneous respiration. Throughout this book, much use will be made of such graphic models. Illustrating structure and function in this way has a profound and unifying influence on ecological thought, since the most diverse ecosystems can be depicted in the same fashion.

Soil as an ecosystem

As pointed out previously, the mineral and organic matter fractions of the soil are part of the abiotic environment of most terrestrial ecosystems. In other words, soil constitutes a subsystem of a larger system. We can, however, regard the soil as an ecosystem in its own right, and study the relationships between its structure and function as we would the larger system. One point of difference immediately emerges, however: the producer component is relatively insignificant in the soil, algae being the only photosynthetic organisms present. The soil ecosystem does not therefore have the capacity to capture a substantial amount of solar energy, and so depends on energy-rich substances brought in from outside. These materials are in the form of plant and animal residues, especially the former. Such a situation fits the concept of ecosystem even though the soil system is not self-contained. All ecosystems derive their energy from beyond their boundaries: some are directly dependent on solar energy, while others depend on energy derived from another, usually larger, system. Furthermore, as will be seen later, there are subsystems in the soil which derive their energy from neither sun nor organic detritus, but from inorganic compounds. While such subsystems contribute only insignificant amounts to the energy budget of the soil ecosystem, they nevertheless play a vital role in the geochemical cycles of the elements; their activities in this regard form the subject matter of much of Chapter 6.

If there are few producers among soil organisms, the other major components, viz. consumers, decomposers and non-living materials, are readily discernible. A great variety of animals is found in the soil, with representatives of nearly all the animal phyla except those that are restricted to marine environments (Fig. 1.4). There are those, such as earthworms, nematodes, some mites and springtails, which spend their entire life-cycle in the soil whereas others, no less important, are present for only part of their existence. The soil fauna is usually taken to include all animals that pass one or more active stages wholly or largely in the soil or surface litter, and to exclude those species which occur there only in passive stages, e.g. as eggs, cysts or pupae, or which use the soil during periods of dormancy or for temporary shelter. The most numerous and widespread soil animals are described in Chapter 2.

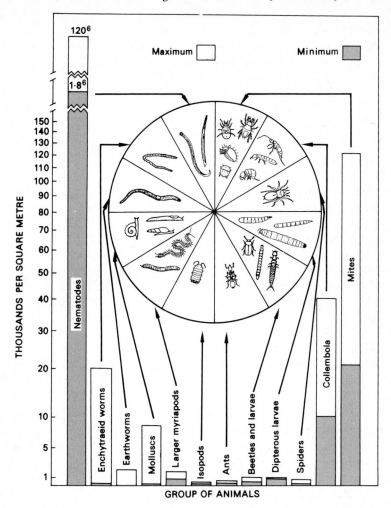

FIG. 1.4 The major kinds of animals found in the soil, showing the range of population densities likely to be encountered in a cool temperate grassland ecosystem. (From Kevan, D. K. McE. (1965) in *Ecology of Soil-borne Plant Pathogens*, eds. K. F. Baker and W. C. Snyder, University of California Press.)

Environmental components of the soil system

The abiotic or environmental portion of the soil ecosystem has several recognizable components: the mineral fraction, organic matter, soil water and the soil atmosphere.

The mineral fraction

Examination of the physical nature of soil reveals that it consists of particles, which are named according to their size, as follows:

Diameter (mm)	Fraction
> 2	gravel
$2\ \ -0.2$	coarse sand
$0.2\ -0.02$	fine sand
$0.02-0.002$	silt
< 0.002	clay

The relative proportions of the various sized particles in a soil determine its texture. Thus we may speak of a sand ($> 90\%$ sand), a loam (approx. 70% sand, 15% clay, 15% silt), or various combinations of these terms, such as sandy clay, silty clay loam, and so on. Gravel consists of relatively unweathered fragments of the parent rock, whereas sand nearly always comprises grains of single minerals, mainly quartz, derived from rock weathering. Clay, however, is made up of minerals which are different from those found in unweathered rocks. Silicates of calcium, magnesium and potassium make up the majority of primary rock minerals, and when these break down, releasing the metal ions, the silicate fraction remains to be converted into secondary clay minerals.

It is the chemical composition of the mineral fraction of soil which largely determines its fertility. In a strongly leached soil, developed on highly weathered acidic rocks, some 90–95 per cent of the sand may be quartz, while in a soil arising from a moderately weathered basic rock, quartz may comprise only 60 per cent of the sand fraction, and minerals such as felspars, augite and olivine make up the rest.

The **cation exchange capacity** of the soil is determined primarily by the density of the negative charges on the surfaces of clay minerals and amorphous organic matter, and the cations adsorbed by these colloidal particles constitute the exchange phase of the soil. Most soil reactions take place in this thin layer of ionized solution which is tightly held on the solid soil particles. The adsorbed ions can be exchanged for others brought near the colloid surface by moving water, or produced there by biological activity. The carbon dioxide evolved during respiration of soil organisms dissolves in water to form carbonic acid, which dissociates to produce hydrogen ions that may exchange with calcium, potassium or other ions of the exchange phase. The ions so released into the soil solution are available for uptake by plants and microorganisms.

Soil organic matter

Rock weathering will not produce a soil in the absence of organisms. The residues of dead plants and animals sooner or later find their way into the soil. Some of these residues decay on the surface, and only the end-products enter the soil, but some are incorporated by the action of earthworms and other animals before decomposition begins. The final stage of organic matter breakdown is the more or less amorphous material known as **humus**.

Soils vary greatly in the amount of organic matter they contain, from less than 1 per cent in some sands to over 80 per cent in some peats. The Danish worker, P. E. Müller, was the first to recognize that there were two broad classes of organic matter, mull and mor. In a **mull** soil, such as a krasnozem associated with subtropical rainforest in Eastern Australia, or a brown earth with deciduous broad-leaved forest in Europe, plant remains are decomposed and well incorporated in the surface layers of soil. There is no sharply demarcated organic horizon, and the organic matter decreases gradually with depth. Mull soils are often rich in mesofauna, earthworms being especially abundant, and the upper part of the profile is loose textured and shows a good crumb structure (Fig. 1.5). **Mor** humus contrasts strongly with mull, and develops typically in podzol soils. The leaf litter forms a thick layer clearly disjunct from the mineral soil below, and although the uppermost leaves may be loosely scattered, the underlying ones are more or less decomposed and matted together with fungal hyphae. The lower part of the organic horizon is amorphous and dark coloured, and the upper layer of mineral soil below is usually sandy and stained dark with organic matter. Animal life is not abundant (earthworms are characteristically absent) and mor soils show no signs of being aggregated into crumbs. The organic matter on the surface of mor soils is sometimes separated into distinct layers. Three such layers may be recognized: the litter or **L-layer** which is uppermost and consists mainly of freshly fallen plant debris; the fermentation or **F-layer** where active decomposition is taking place; and the lowermost humification or **H-layer** which comprises more or less amorphous organic material. Mor humus is best seen on acid podzols in the cool temperate coniferous forests of the northern hemisphere. Although occurring on the surface of the mineral soil, it is just as much an integral part of the soil ecosystem as is the humus fraction of mull soils.

Agricultural scientists do not find Müller's classification of humus into mull and mor very useful, but ecologists and foresters have found the terms valuable and use them widely. Grassland soils, such as cherno-zems and black earths, resemble mull soils in the sense that organic matter is well distributed throughout the profile. Compared to trees, however, grasses translocate a greater proportion of their photosynthate into roots, which are extensive and fine and decompose *in situ* to add to the soil organic fraction at considerable depth.

Soil water

Water is held within the structural components, i.e. the soil matrix, by a variety of forces, the net effect of which is to lower the free energy of the water; in other words, the matrix forces lower the chemical poten-tial of the water, or the **water potential**. The presence of solutes also decreases the water potential. For an unsaturated soil, the water poten-tial equals the sum of the matrix and solute potentials, and is always less than the energy of pure, free water at the same temperature and pressure in the same location. Relative to a free water surface, there-fore, water in unsaturated soil is under negative pressure, i.e. tension or suction. This pressure deficiency may be expressed in a number of different units, e.g. as centimetres of water (h), as atmospheres ($h/1\,035$), or as bars (atmospheres × 0.99). A common practice in soil science is to express suction as $\log_{10}h$ and to call the derived quantity 'pF'.

As weathering progressively produces smaller and smaller particles, both the pore volume of the soil and the proportion of small pores increases. This leads not only to an increase in the total amount of water that can be held in the interstices between the soil particles, but also results in a greater fraction of the stored water being influenced by close proximity to adsorption surfaces, and therefore a reduction in the average energy status of the water molecules, i.e. an increase in matrix potential. The amount of water in soil therefore depends on its texture, but in addition another property, known as **structure**, is important. Structure expresses the way in which the individual soil particles are aggregated into units of differing size, such as crumbs and clods. Con-versely, it reflects the size class distribution of the pore spaces between the aggregates. Prevailing weather conditions also influence the water content of soil. During or immediately after heavy rain, all the pore spaces may be filled with water, but if the soil is allowed to drain freely under the influence of gravity, the larger pores empty of water and become filled with air. Following this initial drainage, the soil moisture content stabilizes at a level where gravitational forces are more or less balanced by matrix forces, and the soil is said to be at **field capacity**. As the soil dries out still further, organisms have increasing difficulty in extracting water from it, since they must exert a suction large enough to overcome the retentive forces of the matrix before water will move into them. Finally a stage is reached when plants can no longer remove water and the soil is then said to be at the **permanent wilting point**. Soils vary a great deal in the amount of water available to organisms between field capacity and wilting point, and in the strength with which it is held. Furthermore, some microorganisms have the capacity to extract water from soils too dry to support the growth of plants.

The soil atmosphere

The composition of the soil atmosphere is the resultant of a number of processes which are proceeding concurrently. Respiration of plant roots and soil organisms utilizes oxygen and produces carbon dioxide, and the concentration gradients so formed cause oxygen to diffuse in from the soil surface and carbon dioxide to diffuse out into the air above. In dry soils, and in litter, the carbon dioxide concentration seldom exceeds 0.5 per cent (cf. the average concentration of the earth's atmosphere, 0.03 per cent) but in wet soils where diffusion is hindered and microbiological activity is stimulated, it increases several fold and may even reach 10 per cent for short periods.

Soil aeration depends to a large extent on the arrangement of the soil particles with respect to one another, i.e. on structure. Mull soils are characteristically well structured with many soil aggregates exceeding 0.25 mm in diameter, so that these soils contain many pores larger than 50 μm. It is the proportion of such large pores, which will not hold water by capillarity and which are therefore normally filled with air, that determines how well aerated is a soil.

The soil profile

As already indicated, the transformation of rock into soil involves not only the comminution of rocks into smaller particles as a result of physical and chemical weathering, but also requires the incorporation of organic matter derived from the activities of plants, animals and microorganisms. The continual interaction of all these processes usually leads to the differentiation in soil of more or less distinct horizontal layers, termed **horizons**, which collectively constitute the **soil profile** (Fig. 1.5).

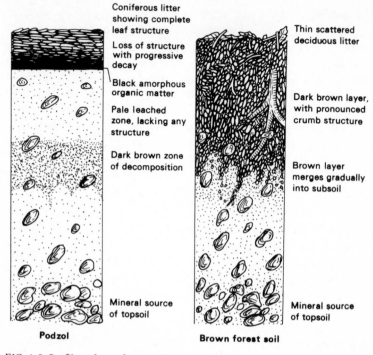

Podzol

Coniferous litter
showing complete
leaf structure

Loss of structure
with progressive
decay

Black amorphous
organic matter

Pale leached
zone, lacking any
structure

Dark brown zone
of decomposition

Mineral source
of topsoil

Brown forest soil

Thin scattered
deciduous litter

Dark brown layer,
with pronounced
crumb structure

Brown layer
merges gradually
into subsoil

Mineral source
of topsoil

FIG. 1.5 Profiles of two forest soils, showing the contrast between mull and mor humus developing, respectively, in deciduous broadleaved and coniferous forest ecosystems respectively. (From Fenton, G. R. (1947) *J. Anim. Ecol.*, 16, 76–93.)

In cool, humid, forested regions with abundant rainfall, iron and aluminium compounds are leached from the surface soil (A horizon) and accumulate, along with clays, in the subsoil (B horizon), which grades gradually into comminuted but otherwise unaltered parent material (C horizon). Soils of this kind, which are usually acidic, and grey or brown in colour, are called podzols and podzolics. They develop typically on sandy, glacial tills or on sandstones, and characteristically have mor humus.

In the wet tropics and subtropics, intense leaching removes all the iron and aluminium oxides from the surface horizon and results in their accumulation either as gravel or cemented masses on the underlying clay horizons. Such lateritic soils, as they are called, are red or yellow in colour. In the temperate humid zone of Eastern Australia there occur red or brown soils, mainly developed on basalt and typically associated with rain forest, and which are known as krasnozems. They are friable clay loams with a deep and uniform profile, usually without any marked differentiation into horizons other than the presence of organic matter in the surface soil. Morphologically, krasnozems resemble the typical mull soils of the broadleaved forests of cool temperature regions of the northern hemisphere, the brown earths.

In areas of low rainfall, associated with shrubs and sparse grasses, soluble salts accumulate in the upper part of the profile as a result of water rising to within a few feet of the surface by capillarity. Sulphates and chlorides of calcium and sodium are the most common salts, and these may on occasion accumulate in amounts sufficient to form a crust on the soil surface. These soils are called saline soils. If an appreciable amount of sodium carbonate is present, the pH becomes high enough to disperse the humic matter, imparting a black colour to the surface horizon; such soils are known as alkali soils. In intermediate, sub-humid climates, permanent grasslands are found along with deep, black clays known as black earths or chernozems, in which subsoil accumulations of calcium carbonate occur.

Further details on soils and soil formation may be found in the works of G. W. Leeper and E. W. Russell, while the development of the soil ecosystem is discussed in Chapter 4.

Selected references

Brock, T. D. (1966) *Principles of Microbial Ecology.* Prentice-Hall.

Garrett, S. D. (1963) *Soil Fungi and Soil Fertility.* Pergamon Press.

Leeper, G. W. (1964) *Introduction to Soil Science,* 4th edn. Melbourne University Press.

Macfadyen, A. (1963) *Animal Ecology: Aims and Methods.* Pitman.

Odum, E. P. (1971) *Fundamentals of Ecology,* 3rd edn. W. B. Saunders.

Odum, H. T. (1967) 'Work circuits and systems stress' in *Primary Productivity and Mineral Cycling in Natural Ecosystems.* University of Maine Press.

Odum, H. T. (1971) *Environment, Power, and Society.* Wiley.

Russell, E. W. (1961) *Soil Conditions and Plant Growth,* 9th edn. Longman.

Whittaker, R. H. (1970) *Communities and Ecosystems.* Macmillan.

2 The soil biota

Soil organisms may be conveniently classified on the basis of size into the microbiota (algae, protozoa, fungi and bacteria), the mesobiota (nematodes, springtails, small arthropods and enchytraeid worms), and the macrobiota (earthworms, molluscs, and the larger enchytraeids and arthropods). The macrobiota might also be taken to include the roots of plants, burrowing rodents, reptiles and amphibia. However, plants can hardly be regarded solely as soil organisms, while vertebrates, together with many insects, are only temporary soil inhabitants. Plant roots, none the less, are important components of the soil ecosystem by virtue of their interrelationships with microorganisms. Other members of the macrobiota are not however within its province, but a brief outline of the major groups which are included is given below.

Soil microorganisms: the microbiota

Detailed descriptions of the different kinds of microorganisms found in the soil are beyond the scope of this book. The generalized account which follows is meant to provide some background in microbiology for those readers with little or no exposure to this field. It may be supplemented by reference to the reading list at the end of the chapter. Most attention is given to the bacteria and fungi, since these two groups of microbes are those most intimately concerned with energy flow and nutrient transfer in terrestrial ecosystems.

The boundary line between plants and animals becomes blurred when one considers organisms of microscopic dimensions. Some microbiologists use this as a rationale for proposing a third kingdom of organisms to include all those creatures which can be distinguished from typical plants and animals by virtue of their simpler level of biological organization. The members of this group (the **Protista**) are either unicellular or coenocytic,* or if multicellular then they lack the

* Coenocytic organisms are multinucleate but not multicellular, although at some stage of their life-cycle they may exhibit cellular structure.

extensive differentiation into distinctive tissues which is a characteristic of plants and animals in the adult state. The Protista as thus defined comprises two quite distinct groups of organisms, the bacteria and blue-green algae on the one hand, and the fungi, protozoa and remainder of the algae on the other. Since the advent of the electron microscope, it has been possible to relate this division of protists into two groups to differences in cellular organization. There are two quite different kinds of cells among existing organisms, viz. the **eucaryotic** cell, which is the structural unit of all plants and animals, and of the fungi, protozoa and most algae, and the **procaryotic** cell, found in all bacteria and blue-green algae. Apart from being generally smaller, the procaryotic cell differs from the eucaryotic in several important respects, the most outstanding differences being its lack of a proper nucleus and the absence of membrane-bound organelles such as mitochondria. For the sake of convenience, protists possessing eucaryotic cells are often called **higher protists**, while those having procaryotic cells are referred to as **lower protists**.

Classification of protists

The higher protists are differentiated on the basis of energy source, feeding habit and structure (Table 2.1). The boundaries between the various groups are not well defined: there is much overlapping between categories. For example, many unicellular protozoa are similar in morphological detail to the unicellular algae but they lack chloroplasts or photosynthetic pigments. The lower protists are classified according to their energy source and structure, and whether or not they possess organs of locomotion.

Higher protists: algae, protozoa and fungi

The presence or absence of chloroplasts is the primary basis of classification in the higher protists, separating the photosynthetic algae from the protozoa and fungi in terms of both cell structure and physiology. The fungi and protozoa are chemotrophic organisms, i.e. they depend on chemical sources of energy for their life processes (see Chapter 3), and it is not easy to make a clear separation between them. Certainly, typical members of either group are quite distinctive, but there are transitional forms, classified as slime moulds, which have some of the features of both groups. Most of the protozoa are, however, unicellular

TABLE 2.1 Characteristics of the major groups of protists

Group	Energy source	Feeding habit	Structure	Flagella
Higher Protists				
Algae	Photosynthetic	Absorb dissolved nutrients (except carbon)	Unicellular, or multi-cellular filaments or colonies	Mainly present
Protozoa	Chemosynthetic	Ingest solid particles, or absorb dissolved nutrients (including carbon)	Unicellular without cell walls	Mainly present
Fungi	Chemosynthetic	Absorb dissolved nutrients (including carbon)	Mainly filamentous and coenocytic	Mainly absent
Lower Protists				
Blue-green algae	Photosynthetic	Absorb dissolved nutrients (except carbon)	Unicellular or filamentous	Absent
Bacteria	Chemosynthetic *	Absorb dissolved nutrients (including carbon)	Mainly unicellular, also filamentous	Present or absent

* Green and purple bacteria can photosynthesize but — unlike algae and blue-green algae — without evolution of oxygen.

(or acellular) and motile, whereas fungi are generally filamentous and non-motile. Furthermore, while all fungi absorb their nutrients from solution, many protozoans can ingest solid particles.

The eucaryotic algae

The algae are predominantly aquatic organisms, occurring in lakes, rivers and swamps, and in the oceans. Some however occur in terrestrial habitats especially if these are moist. Free swimming and free floating algae, together with protozoa and small animals, make up the **plankton** of seas and lakes. As the primary source of energy and food for fish and other aquatic animals, the algae (phytoplankton) are of great significance in marine and lacustrine ecosystems. Seven divisions of eucaryotic algae are recognized but only one, the **Chlorophyta**, or green algae, occurs in soil to any great extent. Many soils, however, also contain diatoms (**Chrysophyta**), a group that is better known as the main component of marine phytoplankton. Algae are frequently unicellular, the cells occurring singly or in association as colonies, though in some species the cells are arranged in filaments. Some representative green algae are illustrated in Fig. 2.1.

Protozoa

The majority of protozoa are parasitic on or in animals, some causing serious diseases such as malaria. Other protozoans live in mutualistic relationships (see Chapter 4) with higher organisms. Certain flagellates, for example, live in the gut of termites and play an essential role in the digestion of wood by these insects. Free living protozoa are abundant in the soil, in fresh water and in the sea.

Four main groups of protozoa are recognized. Amoeboid forms, many of which move by extending finger-like projections of cytoplasm, or pseudopodia (Fig. 2.2), are placed in the **Sarcodina**. Those which have as organs of locomotion numerous, short, hairlike cytoplasmic extensions known as cilia, are classified as **Ciliophora** (Infusoria). Members of the **Mastigophora** are motile by means of one or more longer, whiplike appendages, called flagella.* Amoebae, flagellates and ciliates are all common in soil, where they feed on bacteria. The fourth group is the **Sporozoa** representatives of which are all parasitic; their mechanism of locomotion is in many cases not yet clearly understood.

---

* Structurally, flagella and cilia are homologous; they differ only on the basis of relative length.

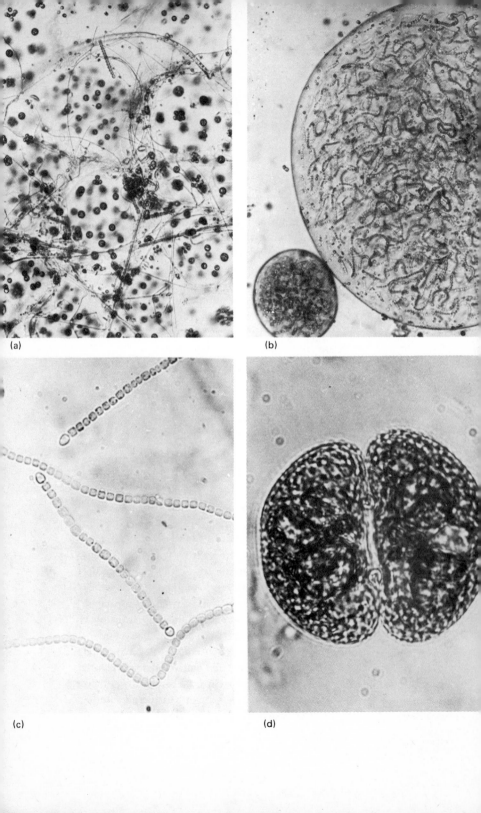

(a)

(b)

(c)

(d)

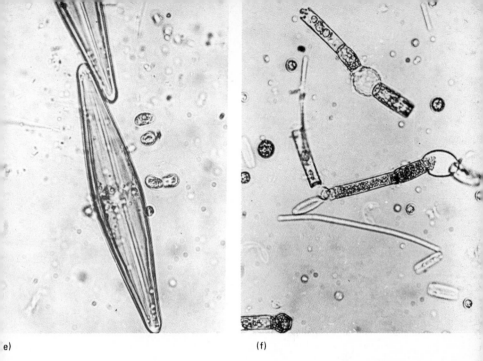

(e)   (f)

FIG. 2.1 Some representative soil algae. *(a)* Mixed green and blue-green algae, as they appear in a smear of soil on a microscope slide. *(b)* Colonies of *Nostoc*, a blue-green alga (Cyanophyta), each embedded in a mucilaginous matrix. *(c)* *Anabaena*, a filamentous blue-green alga. *(d)* *Cosmarium*, a unicellular green alga (Chlorophyta) belonging to the group known as desmids. *(e)* Spindle shaped yellow-green algae (Chrysophyta) of the type known as diatoms, together with some smaller, unidentified forms. *(f)* *Oedegonium*, a filamentous green alga, together with some diatoms and various other types. (Photos by I. H. Parbery.)

Fungi

Like the protozoa, the fungi are chemosynthetic higher protists. Although their most common habitat is the soil, many of the less advanced species such as the water moulds are entirely aquatic. While some of the more primitive forms closely resemble the flagellates, the typical fungus possesses a very distinctive and characteristic form. Its vegetative body usually consists of microscopic branched filaments, $3-8$ μm in diameter,* known as **hyphae** (Fig. 2.3). Collectively this system of branching hyphae is known as a **mycelium**. At certain stages in the life-cycle, the mycelium bears minute propagules called **spores**, which germinate to produce new hyphae. Not all fungi have a mycelium, however. The yeasts, for example, are a group of fungi that have globose or ellipsoidal cells which reproduce by budding.

* μm = micrometre = 1/1 000 mm. Also known as a micron (μ).

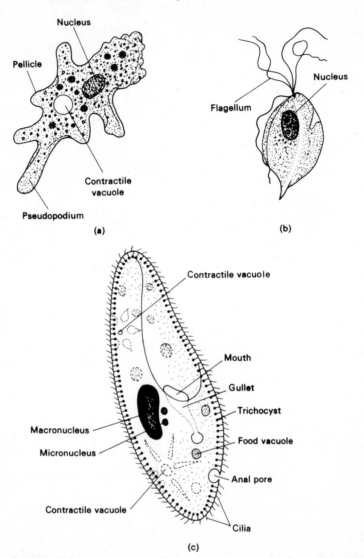

FIG. 2.2 Diagrammatic representation of some common protozoa. *(a)* Amoeba. *(b)* Flagellate. *(c)* Ciliate. (*(a)* and *(b)* from Stanier, R. Y. *et al.* (1970) *The Microbial World*, 3rd edn. Prentice-Hall © 1970. By permission of Prentice-Hall, Inc., Englewood Cliffs, New Jersey, USA; *(c)* from Brock, T. D. (1970) *Biology of Microorganisms*, Prentice-Hall © 1970. By permission of Prentice-Hall, Inc., Englewood Cliffs, New Jersey, USA.)

A fungus colonizing a fresh substrate grows vegetatively for a short time, and then may produce one or more kinds of asexual spore, i.e. a spore which does not result from nuclear fusion. Later, as the mycelium

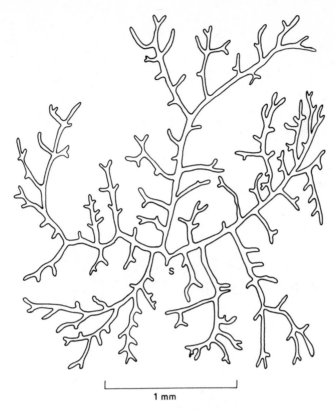

1 mm

FIG. 2.3 Fungal mycelium developed from a germinated spore (s) after one day's growth on malt agar at 20°C. (Redrawn from Ingold, C. T. (1961) *The Biology of Fungi*, Hutchinson.)

ages or when environmental conditions become unfavourable for further vegetative growth or when sufficient reserves have been amassed, many fungi reproduce sexually, forming distinctive spores following the fusion of two nuclei. In some species sexual reproduction is the only form of sporulation; others have no known sexual stages and produce only asexual spores. The life-cycle of a common fungus is shown diagrammatically in Fig. 2.4.

A common method of asexual reproduction among filamentous fungi is by fragmentation of hyphae: any fragment of a vigorously growing mycelium is capable of developing into a new individual if the environment is favourable, and this is the method most commonly used for propagating fungi in the laboratory. One form of hyphal fragmentation, which occurs in some fungi in response to an unfavourable environment, is the rounding-off and separation of parts of the hyphae to

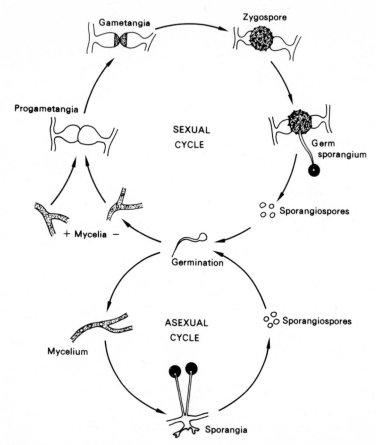

FIG. 2.4 Life-cycle of *Rhizopus stolonifer*, a zygomycete. Sporangiospores produced from somatic hyphae are released when the wall of the sporangium disintegrates, and germinate to produce an aerial mycelium on which further sporangia
develop, thus completing the asexual phase of the life cycle. Sexual reproduction
requires the conjugation of two different but compatible mycelia, designated + and −, with the formation of gametangia from which, following nuclear
fusion, a thick-walled zygospore arises. Meiosis occurs during the germination of
the zygospore, so that the vegetative phase of the fungus is haploid.

form spore-like bodies known as **arthrospores** or **oidia** (Fig. 2.5).

The most important method of asexual reproduction in fungi is
however, by spores. Basically, there are only two ways in which asexual
spores can be formed, viz. in sac-like structures called sporangia, or
directly on the mycelium. Spores borne in sporangia are designated
sporangiospores while those borne directly on hyphae are known as
conidia (Fig. 2.6). Conidia are never motile. Sporangiospores of some
species are however flagellated and resemble the zoospores of algae.

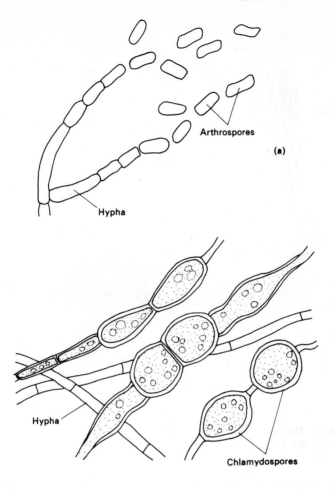

FIG. 2.5 Asexual reproduction in fungi. *(a)* Arthrospores or oidia, produced by hyphal fragmentation. *(b)* Chlamydospores, organs of survival each formed by developing a thick, protective wall around a hyphal cell.

Such motile sporangiospores are in fact called zoospores; they differ from other kinds of asexual spore in another important respect, in that they do not possess cell walls. Zoospores occur only in the most primitive aquatic families; conidia are characteristic of more advanced groups.

In addition to asexual spores, which are usually relatively short lived and not well adapted for survival, a mycelium may produce resistant structures which can survive adverse conditions for long periods of

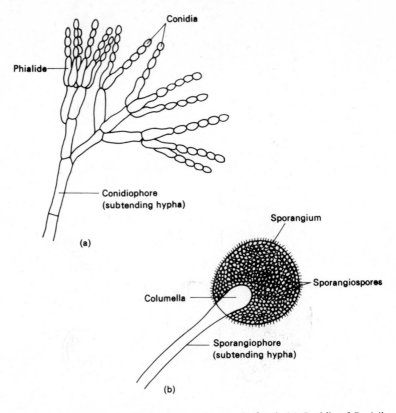

FIG. 2.6 The two basic kinds of asexual spores in fungi. *(a)* Conidia of *Penicillium*, spores borne directly on the hyphae. *(b)* Sporangiospores of *Rhizopus*, produced in sac-like structures known as sporangia.

time, and which recommence growth when the environment again becomes favourable. The two most common survival organs are chlamydospores and sclerotia. **Chlamydospores** are formed by the laying down of a thick wall around hyphal cells or spores. They may develop from intercalary or terminal cells, and differ from conidia and sporangiospores not only by virtue of their thick protective wall but also because they are generally not deciduous (Fig. 2.5). A **sclerotium** is a firm, more or less globose, mass of hyphae which upon germination gives rise to a sexual fruiting body or to asexual spores or to a mycelium. Another vegetative structure produced by some fungi is the **rhizomorph**, an organ of spread which also has some survival value. Rhizomorphs are cord-like bodies formed by the aggregation of numerous hyphae, structurally resembling elongated sclerotia; both structures are illustrated in Fig. 2.7.

Classification of fungi

Owing to their number and wide range of form, there is no general agreement as to the best method of classifying fungi. Until recently, three classes and one 'form-class' were recognized, viz. the classes Phycomycetes, Ascomycetes and Basidiomycetes, and the form-class Deuteromycetes (Fungi Imperfecti). Most authorities now contend that the Phycomycetes does not represent a natural unit and so subdivide this group into several classes based on motility. It contains all the unicellular forms (except the yeasts) together with those whose vegetative mycelium is aseptate, that is, not normally divided into compartments by cross walls or septa.

Two of the most widespread classes of Phycomycetes or lower fungi are the Oomycetes and Zygomycetes. The **Oomycetes** make up a fairly large and important group of fungi. The most primitive forms are entirely aquatic, but the class as a whole shows evidence of adaptation to terrestrial habitats. The most advanced species are terrestrial obligate parasites of plants, passing almost their entire life-cycles within the tissues of their hosts. The **Zygomycetes** are terrestrial fungi which have lost the ability to form motile cells of any kind, the typical spore being known as a **zygospore** (Fig. 2.4). The group includes many common moulds, some of which are responsible for the spoilage of foodstuffs. Other species play an important part in the breakdown of organic matter in the soil. Members of the genus *Endogone* infect the roots of higher plants to form dual absorbing organs known as mycorrhizas; these are discussed in Chapter 8.

The higher fungi are distinguished from the Phycomycetes by the regularly septate nature of their hyphae. In addition, there is a marked tendency towards aggregation of the hyphae into large, complex structures in which the identity of the component parts is lost. Two classes are recognized, the Ascomycetes and the Basidiomycetes.

The **Ascomycetes** is a large group, occurring in a wide variety of habitats. Many are saprophytic (saprophagous) soil inhabitants while others are important agents of plant disease. The yeasts, which are unicellular ascomycetes, form the basis of the baking, brewing and wine-making industries. The primary characteristic of the class is the **ascus** (Fig. 2.8), a sac-like structure containing typically eight ascospores, the product of sexual fusion. The typical asexual spores of filamentous ascomycetes are conidia. These are borne on special hyphae known as conidiophores and are sometimes contained in fruiting bodies.

The family Eurotiaceae (Aspergillaceae) contains some of the most common and widely distributed of fungi. The conidial or imperfect

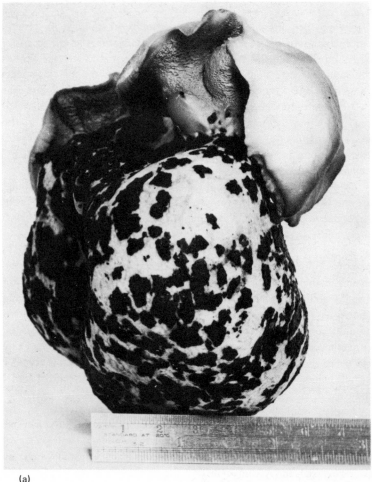

(a)

stage dominates the life-cycle. *Aspergillus* and *Penicillium* are two genera of great economic significance as spoilage organisms and as commercial sources of antibiotics and enzymes. Their conidia are very numerous and readily dispersed by air. The protoplasm of some aspergilli and penicillia develops a high osmotic pressure and consequently they are able to grow in very dry environments and in concentrated solutions of sugars or salts; this enables them to exploit habitats unavailable to most other fungi and to bacteria. A different group contains the genus *Chaetomium*, which includes some common soil fungi having an important role in the breakdown of cellulosic plant remains, especially in acid soils where bacterial activity is at a minimum.

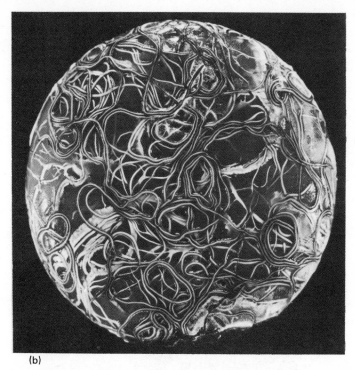

(b)

FIG. 2.7 Vegetative structures of fungi. (*a*) sclerotium of *Polyporus mylittae* showing fruiting bodies (basidiocarps) produced on germination (*on facing page*). The upper edge of the scale is marked in centimetres, the lower in inches; this species produces some of the largest sclerotia known. (Photo by V. A. Raszewski.) (*b*) Rhizomorphs of *Armillariella mellea* on potato dextrose agar $x^2/_3$ (Photo by A. M. Smith, Biological and Chemical Research Institute, Rydalmere, NSW.)

Another widespread ascomycete is *Sordaria fimicola*, a coprophilous species occurring on the dung of various animals and in the soil.

There are many fungi which have septate hyphae and which, so far as is known, reproduce only by asexual means. Since these fungi apparently lack a sexual stage, they are commonly referred to as imperfect fungi and are placed in the 'form-class' **Deuteromycetes** or **Fungi Imperfecti**. This form-class is a heterogeneous assemblage of species which bear no phylogenetic relationship to one another. Their conidial stages are generally very similar to the conidial stages of some well known Ascomycetes, and it is assumed that with relatively few exceptions the imperfect fungi represent the conidial (asexual) stages of Ascomycetes whose sexual stages either rarely occur in nature and have not yet been found, or have disappeared from the life-cycle during the course of evolution. A few species, which produce only vegetative structures,

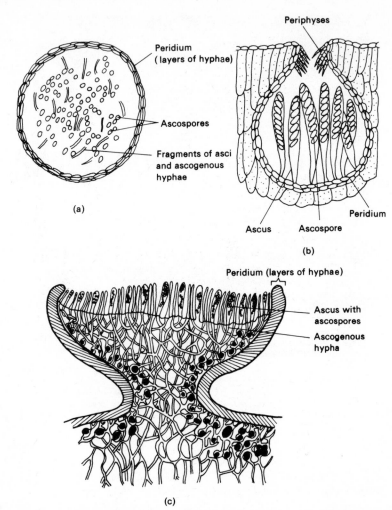

(a)

(b)

(c)

FIG. 2.8 Three kinds of ascocarp or fruiting body found among Ascomycetes. (a) Cleistothecium, in which the asci are completely enclosed and from which ascospores are released by distintegration of the cleistothecial wall. (b) Perithecium, a flask shaped structure from which the ascospores escape through a pore or ostiole. (c) Apothecium, a cup-shaped ascocarp which is completely open. (From Poindexter, J. S. (1971) *Microbiology, an Introduction to Protists*, Fig. 14.23 (p. 238), Macmillan. Reprinted with permission of Macmillan Publishing Co., Inc. Copyright © 1971 by Jerome Stene Poindexter.)

represent imperfect stages of Basidiomycetes. The conidial stages of many Ascomycetes (e.g. *Penicillium* and *Aspergillus*) are, for the sake of convenience, also classified as Deuteromycetes. The group contains many fungi of economic importance, including most of the fungal

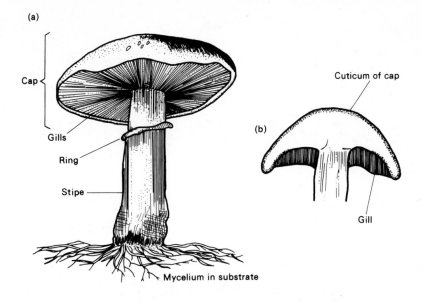

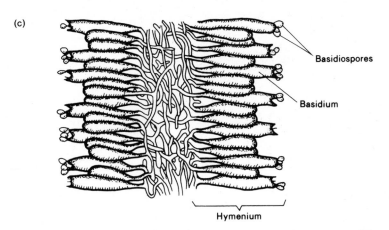

FIG. 2.9 Fruiting body or basidiocarp of the common mushroom, a Basidiomycete. *(a)* Diagram of a mature mushroom. *(b)* Vertical section through cap. *(c)* Vertical section through a gill, showing the characteristic feature of the group, the basidium. (From Poindexter, J. S. (1971) *Microbiology, an Introduction to Protists*, Fig. 14.37 (p. 257), Macmillan. Reprinted with permission of Macmillan Publishing Co., Inc. Copyright ©1971 by Jerome Stene Poindexter.)

pathogens of man, many serious plant pathogens, many industrially important fungi, and many common soil saprophytes.

The large class known as **Basidiomycetes** has such common fungi as mushrooms, puffballs, bracket fungi and rusts. The distinguishing

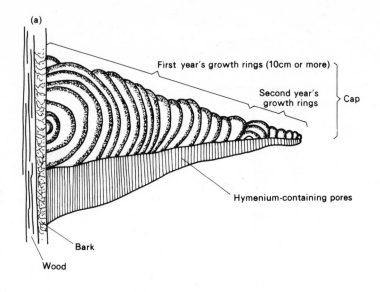

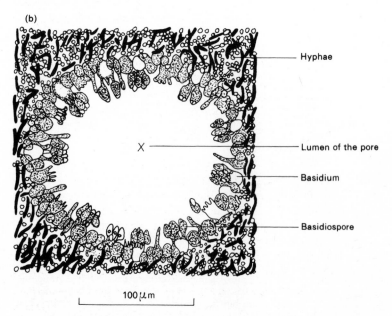

FIG. 2.10 Basidiocarp of a bracket or shelf fungus. *(a)* Vertical section of the fruiting body. *(b)* Cross-section of a pore. (From Poindexter, J. S. (1971) *Microbiology, an Introduction to Protists*, Fig. 14.38 (p. 258), Macmillan. Reprinted with permission of Macmillan Publishing Co., Inc. Copyright © 1971 by Jerome Stene Poindexter.)

feature of the group is the basidium, normally a club-shaped structure which bears four exogenous basidiospores (Fig. 2.9), and which is usually produced within a complex fruiting body called a basidiocarp. The Basidiomycetes are a diverse group of fungi occupying a wide range of habitats. Many species form mycorrhizas with the roots of forest trees (see Chapter 8). Some play an important part in the breakdown of leaf-litter and woody debris in forests; others are characteristic of grassland soils. The large and important family Polyporaceae includes the majority of the wood destroying fungi, many of which cause heart rot of living trees, while others are saprophytic on woody residues in the forest. The basidiocarps of most species in this family are bracket-like, hence the common name bracket fungi or shelf fungi (Fig. 2.10). The family Agaricaceae includes the majority of mushrooms, the best known being the edible field mushroom, *Agaricus campestris.*

Slime moulds

This is a group of fungus-like organisms some of which also have close affinities with the protozoa. They resemble fungi in forming spores surrounded by a definite wall, although the manner of spore formation is often very different from that found in the true fungi. During part of their life-cycle they exist in amoeboid form, unbounded by cell walls. One group, the **Myxomycetes**, is widespread in moist leaf litter and beneath the bark of decaying logs.

Lower protists: bacteria and blue-green algae

The lower protists are conveniently subdivided into five more or less distinct groups on the basis of photosynthetic ability, means of locomotion and nature of the cell wall. The blue-green algae are photosynthetic organisms which, if motile, exhibit gliding motility.* The filamentous gliding bacteria are similar but non-photosynthetic. The myxobacteria and spirochaetes are two groups of non-photosynthetic bacteria having thin and flexible cell walls; the myxobacteria show gliding motility, the spirochaetes have their own peculiar means of movement. The final group is the true bacteria or eubacteria, which have rigid cell walls and, if motile, move by means of flagella (see below). Among the eubacteria there exists great versatility in metabolism, and this gives them singular importance in the functional processes of ecosystems, such as the

---

* Gliding is a peculiar means of movement which occurs only when cells are in contact with a solid substratum; its mechanism is obscure.

decomposition of organic matter and the cycling of nutrient elements. For this reason, the eubacteria will be treated in more detail than the other groups.

Blue-green algae (Cyanophyta)

The blue-green algae (Fig. 2.1) include both aquatic and terrestrial forms. Although the majority are filamentous, unicellular and colonial forms are known. They have an extremely wide distribution in soils, freshwater lakes and streams, and in the oceans. Some species can fix* atmospheric nitrogen, either as free living organisms or in association with certain fungi as lichens (see Chapter 9).

Myxobacteria

Some myxobacteria are able to lyse and digest bacteria, while others are saprophytic. The genus *Cytophaga* is particularly active in the aerobic decomposition of cellulose; there are species which decompose chitin also. The myxobacteria are widely distributed in soil, and are especially common in decaying vegetation, rotting wood, dung and composts.

Eubacteria

Three basic cell shapes occur among the true bacteria, viz. cocci, rods and spirals (Fig. 2.11). **Cocci** are roughly spherical cells, and may occur singly, or in pairs, tetrads or other groupings; the particular way in which the cells are arranged is a useful taxonomic feature. **Rods** are straight or slightly curved cylinders, which are found singly or in chains of varying length. **Spirilla** are curved rods in the shape of a helix; the shorter forms, which appear comma-shaped under the microscope, are termed **vibrios**.

Bacteria which are motile are provided with one or more **flagella**,

* The 'fixation' of gaseous nitrogen, i.e. its reduction to ammonia which is then used for biosynthesis and growth, is the province of relatively few micro-organisms, yet is the ultimate source of nitrogen for all organisms.

FIG. 2.11 Bacterial morphology. (*a*) The three basic cells shapes among eubacteria: left to right, cocci, rods, spirilla ×1 000. (*b*) Preparations specially stained to show flagella: left, *Spirillum volutans* with polar flagella; right, *Salmonella typhosa* with peritrichous flagella ×1 000. (*c*) Endospores in cells of *Clostridium* sp. ×1 000. (*a*) from Stanier, R. Y. *et al.*, (1970), *The Microbial World*, 3rd edn., Prentice-Hall Inc. © 1970. By permission of Prentice-Hall, Inc., Englewood Cliffs, New Jersey, USA. (*b*) and (*c*), photographed by Webster, W. J. E. from material supplied by Donelan, M. J.

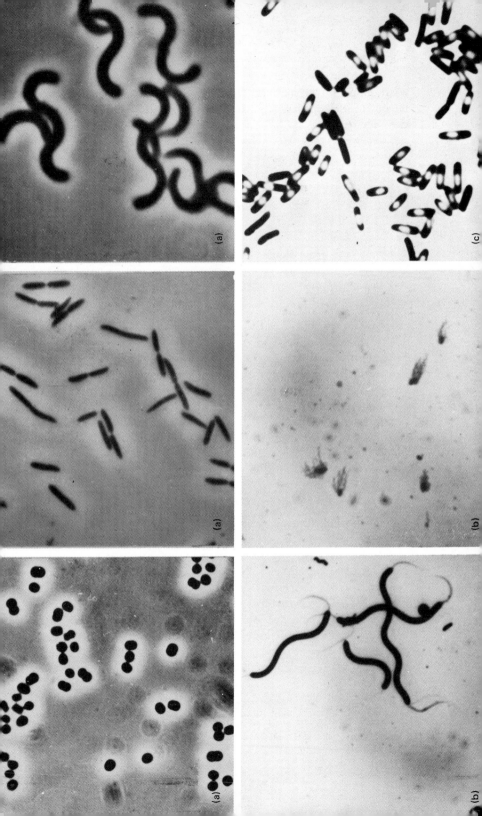

which propel the organism through a liquid medium by their rhythmic movement. Flagella may arise from the ends of the cells, in which case they are termed **polar**, or they may be distributed all over the cell surface, when they are known as **peritrichous** (Fig. 2.11). Many bacterial cells are surrounded by **capsules** or slime layers, consisting of polysaccharides or, less frequently, polypeptides. A few genera of bacteria, e.g. *Bacillus* and *Clostridium*, have the capacity to form **endospores**, which are structures highly resistant to heat and desiccation (Fig. 2.11). Certain other genera, e.g. *Azotobacter*, produce a different kind of resting cell known as a cyst, which is less distinctive than an endospore and is not as resistant to adverse environmental conditions. The majority of bacteria, however, possess no specialized resting cells, and survive by their vegetative cells persisting in a state of reduced vitality.

The gram stain

An important differentiating characteristic of bacteria is their reaction to the gram stain,* which correlates well with certain morphological and physiological features of bacteria. Most cocci, nearly all the spore forming rods, and all actinomycetes are gram-positive. Gram-negative forms include the spirilla, all the polarly flagellated non-spore forming rods, and most of the peritrichously flagellated non-spore forming rods.

Reproduction and colony formation in bacteria

The true bacteria normally reproduce by transverse binary fission, resulting in the formation of two equal daughter cells. On the surface of a solid medium, the progeny of a single cell remain together as a discrete aggregate known as a **colony**, the type of colony being frequently characteristic of the species (Fig. 2.12). The close proximity of a large number of cells in a bacterial colony results in a condition known as physiological crowding, in which individual cells compete with each other for available nutrients and inhibit each other by the localized accumulation of toxic waste products. The rate of breakdown of a solid medium by bacteria is determined by the rate at which enzymes diffuse

---

* Named for the Danish physician who devised it in 1884, this consists essentially of staining with crystal violet in weakly alkaline solution, adding iodine as a mordant, then washing with alcohol. Bacteria which are decolorized by the alcohol are termed gram-negative, and those which retain the stain gram-positive.

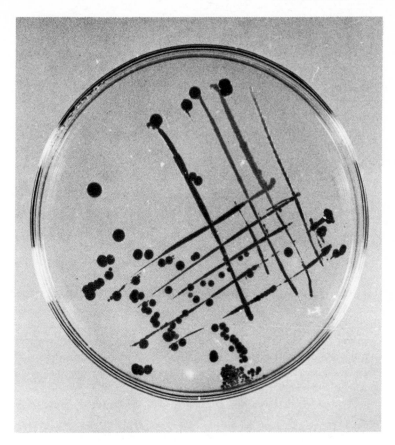

FIG. 2.12 Colony formation in bacteria. Characteristic, pigmented colonies of *Serratia marcescens* streaked on nutrient agar. The petri dish is 9 cm in diameter. (Photo by G. Wray and V. A. Raszewski.)

out from the periphery of the colony and bring fresh substrates into solution. This contrasts markedly with the behaviour of a fungal colony, which grows by hyphal extension, the hyphae at the colony margin continually exploiting fresh substrates, and conducting nutrients to the older parts of the mycelium. The component hyphae of a fungal colony are thus less affected by physiological crowding than are the individual cells of a bacterial colony. Bacteria rapidly colonize and decompose soft animal tissues, which are high in protein content, but are less well adapted than fungi for the decomposition of plant residues which generally have a lower nitrogen status than animal matter. The development of mechanical pressure by fungal hyphae further enhances their ability to penetrate tough plant tissues, as indicated on p. 6.

Classification of eubacteria

The problem of classifying bacteria is made difficult because their range of form is sufficient to establish only very broad groups, and is inadequate for the definition of species, genera or even families. Physiological properties are needed to define the lower taxa, and even some of the higher ones. In other words, bacteria (unlike fungi and other organisms) are classified not so much by how they look as by what they do. For this reason, various physiological groups of bacteria are discussed, in later chapters, in the context of their contributions to functional processes in ecosystems. For the moment, it suffices to give a brief description of some of the groups which may be recognized on mainly morphological grounds.

The gram-negative straight rods with polar flagella are typified by the genus *Pseudomonas*. The pseudomonads are aerobic* or facultatively anaerobic bacteria which decompose organic compounds, and are widely distributed in soil and water. The morphologically similar nitrifying bacteria are obligate aerobes found in soil and fresh water, where they oxidize inorganic nitrogen compounds; *Nitrosomonas* converts ammonium to nitrite, *Nitrobacter* nitrite to nitrate. The sulphur-oxidizing bacteria include those forms capable of oxidizing reduced sulphur compounds; all such polarly flagellated rods are assigned to the genus *Thiobacillus*, which has a wide occurrence in soil and water.

The spirilla and vibrios are gram-negative curved rods with polar flagella. The genus *Cellvibrio* occurs in soil and can decompose cellulose.

Representing the gram-negative rods with peritrichous flagella (and related immotile forms) are two common soil bacteria, *Achromobacter* and *Aerobacter*; the former is mainly aerobic but has a limited ability to ferment sugars, while the latter is facultatively anaerobic and actively ferments sugars. The nitrogen fixing bacteria, *Azotobacter* and *Beijerinckia*, are members of this morphological group; they are free-living obligate aerobes occurring in soil and water. The rod shaped bacteria which fix nitrogen in symbiosis with legumes are assigned to the genus *Rhizobium* (see Chapter 9).

With the exception of one spore-forming coccus, all the spore-forming gram-positive bacteria are rods. They are widely distributed in soil, the aerobic forms being placed in the genus *Bacillus*, the anaerobic forms in *Clostridium*. Both genera include species able to fix atmospheric nitrogen.

The corynebacteria are gram-positive immotile rods of irregular

---

* The oxygen relationships of bacteria are discussed in Chapter 3.

shape, and are mainly aerobic oxidizers of organic matter. In *Coryne-bacterium* a peculiar mode of cell division, known as 'snapping fission', results in aggregations of cells taking on the appearance of a palisade. The genus *Arthrobacter* contains a number of common soil saprophytes. *Cellulomonas* also occurs in soil, where it decomposes cellulose.

The actinomycetes are gram-positive eubacteria with a mycelial habit, closely related to the corynebacteria. In the genus *Mycobacter-ium* the mycelium is rudimentary, soon breaking into irregular, some-times branched rods. The mycelial habit is more pronounced in *Nocardia* and *Actinomyces*, but after growth ceases the mycelium frag-ments into rods or cocci which are indistinguishable from unicellular eubacteria. In *Streptomyces* and *Micromonospora* the mycelium is permanent, and reproduction takes place by means of conidia; both these genera are commonly found in soil.

The micrococci are gram-positive, aerobic spherical cells widely dis-tributed in nature. In the genus *Sarcina* the cells are arranged in cubical packets, in *Micrococcus* they occur in irregular groups.

Soil fauna: the meso- and macrobiota

The soil fauna proper is generally considered to include only those animals which are a permanent component of the soil ecosystem, to-gether with those that regularly pass one or more active phases of their life-cycle in the soil or surface litter. Other animals make casual, irre-gular visits to the soil; such animals may have a marked effect on the soil but these effects are localized and temporary so these occasional visitors are not usually considered to be members of the soil fauna proper.

Classification of the soil fauna

The soil fauna has been classified in a number of different ways, using different criteria as the basis of subdivision. The criteria which are the most widely used are: *(a)* the amount of time which the animals spend in the soil; *(b)* the habitat preference of the animals; *(c)* the method of feeding; *(d)* the means of locomotion; and *(e)* the size of the animals. None of these criteria is entirely satisfactory but together, at least, they form a basis for dealing with the very diverse assemblage of soil animals in manageable categories.

The time which different animals spend in the soil varies from permanent residency to transitory visitation. There are two main micro-habitats for soil animals, aquatic (water-filled pores and the surface moisture film surrounding soil particles) and terrestrial (the soil atmosphere); animals will show a preference for one or other of these. In terms of feeding, animals may be biophagous or saprophagous. The former include carnivorous, phytophagous or microbivorous forms (see Chapter 5). Where locomotory activity is considered, a distinction is usually made between the 'burrowers', i.e. those animals which actively dig their own tunnels, and the 'non-burrowers' which move through existing channels.

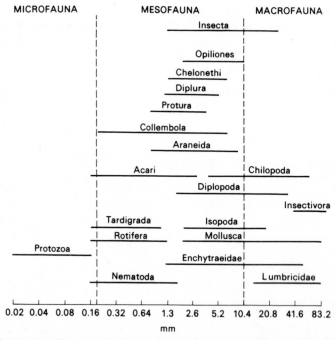

FIG. 2.13 Classification of soil animals according to size. (From Wallwork, J. A. (1970) *Ecology of Soil Animals*, McGraw-Hill. © 1970 McGraw-Hill Book Company (UK) Ltd. Used with permission.)

A subdivision of the soil fauna on the basis of body size is probably the most widely used classification system, perhaps because the size classes chosen correspond quite closely with the various kinds of sampling apparatus that have been devised. Using the criterion of size the soil fauna may be divided into three categories (Fig. 2.13). Animals less than 200 μm long comprise the **microfauna**;* all the soil protozoa

* 200 μm is the limit of comfortable visibility with the naked eye.

are in this category. In addition to protozoa (which have already been considered under the microbiota, p. 23) some nematodes, rotifers and mites are just small enough to be classified as microfauna. The **macrofauna** consists of those animals whose length is measured in centimetres, viz. vertebrates, earthworms and the larger members of the enchytraeid, mollusc and arthropod groups. Animals of intermediate size (200 μm–1 cm) constitute the **mesofauna** (sometimes called the meiofauna). Thus defined, the mesofauna includes most of the nematodes, rotifers, springtails and mites together with various small enchytraeids, molluscs and arthropods.

TABLE 2.2   Common groups of invertebrate soil and litter fauna

Phylum	Class	Sub-class or order	Common name
Platyhelminthes	Turbellaria		Flatworms
Aschelminthes	Nematoda		Nematodes (roundworms)
	Rotifera		Wheel animalcules
Mollusca	Gastropoda	Pulmonata	Snails and slugs
Annelida	Oligochaeta		Earthworms and potworms
Arthropoda	Crustacea	Isopoda	Woodlice
	Myriapoda	Diplopoda	Millipedes
		Chilopoda	Centipedes
	Insecta (Apterygota)	Collembola	Springtails
	Insecta (Pterygota)	Isoptera	Termites
		Coleoptera	Beetles
		Diptera	Flies
		Lepidoptera	Moths and butterflies
		Hymenoptera	Ants, etc.
	Arachnida	Scorpionidea	Scorpions
		Araneida	Spiders
		Acarina (Acari)	Mites

Although some vertebrates may be classified as soil animals (e.g. moles, root-feeding rodents, some lizards and frogs), the greater part of the soil fauna consists of invertebrates (Table 2.2). After the protozoa, nematodes are by far the most numerous of the soil animals but the group showing the greatest diversity, that is the largest number of species, is the Arthropoda. The most commonly occurring arthropods are mites and springtails; others which are found in the soil fairly frequently are the millipedes, termites, ants, and the larvae of flies and beetles. Annelid worms, though few in species, make a significant contribution to biomass in some soils. Brief descriptions of the better known groups of soil invertebrates follow.

Invertebrates other than arthropods

Flatworms

The phylum Platyhelminthes contains not only the well known parasitic forms, the flukes and tapeworms, but also the free-living flatworms (**Turbellaria**). Some Turbellaria inhabit the soil: they are always found in damp situations, e.g. under logs, in decaying leaf litter of moist fertile soils. Perhaps the best known soil Turbellaria are the 'land planaria'; these are not usually numerous although a fairly rich fauna may be found in the warm moist litter of subtropical and tropical rainforests. Other turbellarians which are microscopic and which live in the water film have occasionally been recorded in large numbers in certain fertile soils. Many of the larger soil Turbellaria are carnivorous; other much smaller ones may be microbivorous while still others are carrion feeders.

Nematodes and rotifers

Both nematodes and rotifers are aquatic animals; those forms which occur in the soil are only active when there is sufficient water. Most rotifers have some protective device which operates when desiccating conditions prevail: some secrete shells but many of them enter a state of 'anabiosis' in which a great deal of water is lost and their metabolism slows down considerably. It is thought that certain of the soil nematodes can survive repeated desiccations.

Rotifers are quite abundant in the litter and humus layers of forest soils, their population density reaching $10^5/m^2$. About 100 soil inhabiting species have been recorded. They rarely exceed 2 mm in length and the soil forms are usually much smaller than this. Most of the commonly occurring soil rotifers are creeping forms, many of which consume plant or animal debris although some feed on protozoa or algae.

Most of the 10 000 or so known species of **nematodes** are either free living in the sea or parasitic; of the 2 000 or so fresh-water forms about 1 000 are true soil inhabitants. Most soil nematodes are microscopic, transparent, threadlike animals (Fig. 2.14). They are usually found in the upper 10 cm of the profile, where population densities of the order of $10^6/m^2$ are not uncommon. They are usually more numerous in mull and grassland soils than in acid podzols; however relatively few nematode species are restricted to one particular soil type. Nematode numbers are generally higher in the vicinity of plant roots than elsewhere in the soil. Most nematodes have a high reproductive capacity:

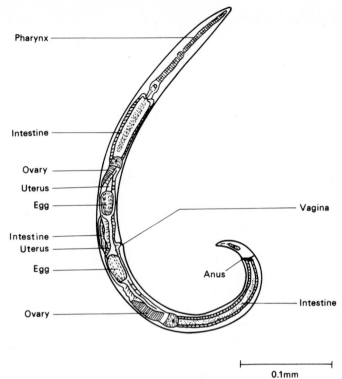

FIG. 2.14 Diagrammatic view of a female soil nematode, *Plectus granulosus.* (From Wallwork, J. A. (1970) *Ecology of Soil Animals*, McGraw-Hill. © 1970 McGraw-Hill Book Company (UK) Ltd. Used with permission.)

they produce large numbers of young and there are usually at least five or six generations a year.

All nematodes appear to feed on living material, the dead organic matter in the soil not forming part of their diet. Soil nematodes have varied food requirements. Some ('eelworms') extract plant sap by piercing roots, others prey on rotifers or other nematodes, while others consume bacteria, algae, fungi or protozoa. Most workers agree that nematodes cannot participate directly in the decomposition of organic matter in the soil but they may be significant ecologically as regulators of microbial populations, and as a food source for other members of the soil biota.

Snails and slugs

The **Mollusca** is predominantly a group of marine animals: there are many terrestrial forms but their diversity is small compared with that shown by marine species. Truly terrestrial molluscs belong to the Pulmonata. There are two main groups of land pulmonates, the slugs and the snails; many of these live in well defined habitats. Slugs and snails are very sensitive to micro-environmental changes and therefore are not distributed uniformly throughout the soil nor over its surface but instead aggregate in favourable situations. Population densities of $10-25/m^2$ are not uncommon, and they may exceed $50/m^2$.

The food of terrestrial molluscs is extremely varied; many feed on living plant material while others prefer dead or decaying vegetation. Many snails and slugs browse on fungi whilst others eat algae and lichens; some are carnivorous and prey on earthworms, and on other slugs or snails. A few species are omnivorous. Many of those which consume surface vegetation move down into the soil after feeding: it seems likely therefore that they have a role in incorporating organic matter in the soil. A number of slugs and snails appear to produce cellulases (see Chapter 3); in addition they may also contain cellulase-producing bacteria in their guts. The part played by molluscs in the degradation of plant material in the soil may thus be considerable. Molluscs also produce mucoproteins (as do earthworms, see the section which follows) and these products may help in the formation of water-stable soil aggregates; thus molluscs may contribute to the improvement of soil structure.

Earthworms and potworms

The phylum Annelida comprises the segmented worms. Several families which belong to the class Oligochaeta are soil dwellers. The soil oligochaetes of Europe belong to two families, the **Lumbricidae** or 'true' earthworms and the **Enchytraeidae** — the smaller, less well known, potworms. Lumbricids are less abundant outside the Palaearctic realm where earthworms of other families, e.g. the **Megascolecidae**, are more common. The Megascolecidae are chiefly southern hemisphere forms: the giant earthworms of Australia belong to this family.

Earthworms

In grassland soils and woodland mulls of the northern hemisphere earthworms number hundreds per square metre, but in acid podzols they are numbered in tens. Earthworms are not generally as widespread throughout the tropics and subtropics as they are in temperate climates. Furthermore, while northern temperate species are most abundant in neutral and alkaline soils, many tropical and southern hemisphere earthworms are well adapted to acid conditions. Earthworms can only exist in an active state under moist conditions: they require copious water for excretion, a moist skin for respiration and a fairly turgid body cavity (to act as a hydrostatic skeleton) for locomotion. Yet most earthworms have a remarkable ability to withstand desiccation and can survive several months of drought in a quiescent state. In soils where earthworms are abundant they dominate the invertebrate biomass and since they are relatively large animals their effects on the physical structure of the soil may be considerable.

The Lumbricidae fall into two main groups, those that live in surface organic horizons and ingest little mineral material, and those that live predominantly in the mineral soil. Members of the latter group ingest mineral matter when burrowing or feeding, and most of this is voided through the anus when the associated nutrients have been utilized. Some lumbricids, however, both feed on the surface and ingest mineral soil. The common European earthworm *Lumbricus terrestris* may burrow to a depth of several metres to escape unfavourable surface conditions, but most lumbricids do not tunnel more than a few centimetres below ground level, and only rarely collect food from the surface. *L. terrestris* however emerges, at night, to feed on leaf fragments and other plant debris at the soil surface.

Earthworms ingest both decaying plant material and mineral soil, some being quite selective in the type of plant material they eat. Perhaps the most important effect of earthworms in the soil is the fragmentation of litter and the mixing of the small fragments of plant material with the soil. These fine particles pass out of the worm's gut bound together in crumbs which form the familiar worm casts. These casts are more water-stable than the original soil, and because of this it has been suggested that earthworms are important in promoting a more stable soil structure. It should be pointed out however, that worm casts on the surface of the soil are only stable for a short time. The mucus which worms secrete, and which binds the walls of their burrows, may also be important in promoting the structural stability of soil.

The microbial population of worm casts is generally higher than in the surrounding soil. Fresh earthworm faeces have a paste-like consistency, are poorly aerated but rich in ammonia and organic matter which is partially digested; these faeces may well act as a substrate conducive to microbial growth.

Earthworms are of special significance in the soil since both cellulases and chitinases are present in their alimentary canals: these worms thus take a direct part in the decomposition of litter in the soil. This is in addition to their indirect effects as comminutors of litter and promoters of microbial activity.

Enchytraeids

The potworms are small (1–5 mm in length), white oligochaete worms which are often present in the soil in very large numbers; they are not distributed uniformly but usually occur in groups. Enchytraeids are very sensitive to drought, and soil forms are most abundant in moist temperate climates. Maximum numbers are found in acid soils of high organic matter content, where populations of $10^5/m^2$ may be found.

Enchytraeids do not possess enzymes which would enable them to digest complex plant polysaccharides and there is no evidence that any of the organic material they ingest is chemically decomposed. They probably feed mainly on bacteria and fungi. Plant fragments, fungi, bacteria and silica grains have been found in their guts and it is possible that the enchytraeids produce water-stable crumbs in the soil. As with earthworms, the faecal material produced by enchytraeids may serve to stimulate the activities of the soil microflora.

Arthropods

The phylum Arthropoda contains more species than any other animal phylum. Arthropods often dominate all other groups of the meso- and macrofauna in the soil, both in terms of the number of individuals and the number of species present. They reach their greatest diversity and abundance in undisturbed habitats such as forests, woodlands or permanent grasslands. The most common soil arthropods are the centipedes and millipedes together with certain insects. The more important insect groups are the springtails, termites and ants and also the adults and/or young stages of beetles and flies.

Myriapods (Myriapoda)

Centipedes (Chilopoda) are found in moist habitats in the temperate and tropical parts of the world. The larger ones live under stones and logs or in cracks or crevices in the soil; the smaller forms are truly subterranean and many can burrow. Centipedes are found mainly in woodland and forest, to a lesser extent in grassland and arable soils. They are mainly carnivorous but some species also feed on decaying plant material.

Millipedes (Diplopoda) prefer calcareous soils and are more common in woodland than in grassland or cultivated soils (Fig. 2.15). Some are restricted to the loose litter layer while others burrow in the soil. Some species feed on living plants, others on fungi, others on fresh litter but

FIG. 2.15 Typical members of the soil fauna, natural size. (From Russell, E. W. (1961) *Soil Conditions and Plant Growth*, 9th edn. Longman.)

Key: *Chilopoda:* Centipedes 4, 5, 28, 40; *Diplopoda:* Millipedes 19, 22, 41; *Arachnida:* (*a*) Araneida: Spiders 31, 33; (*b*) Acarina: Mites 2, 14, 36: Gamasidae 24, 32, 37, 45: Oribatidae 42: Tyroglyphidae; *Insecta:* (*a*) Collembola: Springtails 3, 6, 10, 13, 16, 20, 50; (*b*) Lepidoptera 8: Larva; (*c*) Coleoptera 7, 9, 17, 30, 35, 38, 44: Staphylinoidea (adults) 15, 23, 27, 29, 34, 41: Staphylinoidea (larvae) 25: Carabidae (adult (small species)) 12: Carabidae (larva (large species)) 21, 26, 39, 45: Elateridae (larvae) Wireworms; (*d*) Diptera 1, 43, 48, 49: Bibionidae (larvae) 11: Cyclorrhapha (larva) 18: Anthomyiidae (adult).

most millipedes prefer decaying plant material as food. There is little evidence to suggest that any chemical breakdown of plant material occurs in the guts of millipedes; their main role in the soil seems to be the fragmentation of litter which is thus more susceptible to rapid microbiological decay.

Insects (Insecta)

Springtails

The Collembola are small, primitive insects. The group is one of the most numerous and widely distributed of the soil arthropods, numerous with regard to both numbers and species diversity. Springtail populations in the soil commonly reach a density of 10^4/m² but these insects contribute little to the soil biomass because of their small size. They are usually less than 1 mm long and rarely exceed 3 mm (Fig. 2.15).

Collembola exist only in moist situations but some of them can resist desiccation to a certain extent. In the soil some springtails live in the surface layers while others are commonly found deeper in the soil. The surface dwellers are usually larger, have a spring-like appendage and simple eyes; the spring and the eye-spots are usually reduced or absent in the smaller species which live deeper in the soil. Populations of springtails are largest in the surface layers of the soil, especially where the macropore space is greatest. Soil-dwelling springtails, like other soil microarthropods, tend to aggregate; the reason for this is not known for certain.

The feeding habits of soil Collembola are very varied: their food may be bacteria, fungal hyphae and spores, decomposing organic material, faeces, living plants or animals. It seems that the detritus feeders consume decaying plant material for the fungi and other microbes it contains rather than for the nutritive value of the detritus itself. Thus Collembola do not appear to play a direct part in the turnover of soil nutrients but they are active in fragmenting plant litter and in this respect they may be a significant factor in certain soils.

Termites

The Isoptera are mainly tropical or subtropical in distribution. They have a highly developed social organization and build up complex colonies which may take several years to become properly established. They may be divided into three groups on the basis of food preference, i.e. those which feed exclusively on wood, those which consume humus or decaying litter and those which cultivate fungi for food. Cellulose is the main carbohydrate in the diet of all termites which consume wood or other relatively undecomposed plant tissue. Such termites do not produce their own cellulases but rely on the activities of a rich gut fauna of cellulose-producing flagellates (p. 23). Those termites which feed on humus or on fungi lack the flagellate gut fauna.

In the tropics and subtropics termites play an important part in the decomposition of cellulosic residues and in transporting and mixing organic matter with mineral soil from different horizons. In other words, their role in the soil is similar to that of earthworms in more temperate climates. Some termites erect earth mounds of varying degrees of complexity, these being constructed of sand and clay

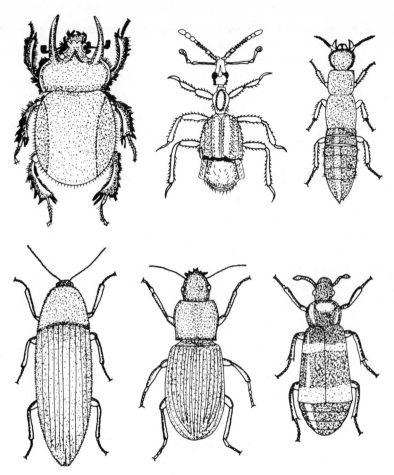

FIG. 2.16 Representatives of some common families of beetles found in the soil. Left to right, top row, Scarabeidae, Pselaphidae, Staphylinidae; bottom row, Elateridae, Carabidae, Silphidae. (From Wallwork, J. A. (1970) *Ecology of Soil Animals* McGraw-Hill. © 1970 McGraw-Hill Book Company (UK) Ltd. Used with permission.)

particles cemented with saliva or faeces. Not all species build mounds: many humus feeders are entirely subterranean and some wood feeders live in galleries excavated in rotting logs or trees.

Beetles

The Coleoptera (Figs. 2.15, 2.16) is the largest of the insect orders, and contains a number of forms which live in the soil as larvae and/or adults. Soil Coleoptera are not particularly numerous, rarely exceeding

$100/m^2$ in number or $1 g/m^2$ in biomass; most of them live on the surface of the soil or in the upper layers.

Some soil Coleoptera are predators of other soil animals, others are phytophagous; included in the latter group are the well known larvae of certain scarabs and chafers which feed upon plant roots. Other soil Coleoptera are saprophagous, feeding on decaying plant or animal matter while still others feed on dung. Some beetles consume the more refractory plant materials such as cellulose and this may involve the intermediate activity of cellulase-producing gut microbes. The main role of Coleoptera in the soil seems to be that of assisting in the breakdown and incorporation of organic matter.

Flies

Many soil and litter inhabiting insects belong to the order Diptera or two-winged flies (Fig. 2.15). Their larvae rival the Coleoptera in the number of species and in the range of feeding habits, but relatively few adults are true soil dwellers. Diptera as a whole are less well adapted to dry soil conditions than Coleoptera. Dipteran larvae are generally found in damp situations especially in the L- and F-layers of soils, where these are present. Very few of them are able to burrow; the majority move through existing crevices in the soil. The more familiar dipteran larvae are carrion feeders, but many species consume plant residues or living roots, others such as the fungus-gnats eat fungal hyphae. Still others are coprophilous, while a number are predacious, preying upon a variety of other soil animals.

There is no evidence that plant material undergoes humification as it passes through the gut of dipteran larvae but these larvae, like many other arthropods, are important in the fragmentation of organic debris; their faeces may also provide favourable habitats for microorganisms.

Ants, bees and wasps

A few species of bees and wasps are permanent members of the soil fauna and their burrowing activity may help to aerate the soil. The most important soil inhabiting Hymenoptera, however, are ants. These well known social insects forage on the surface and make extensive subterranean excavations; some also build large earth mounds above ground level. They are often the first animals to become established in newly exposed habitats such as riverine deposits.

The food of ants is extremely varied. Many species are predatory on the larger arthropods of the soil; many take plant food, leaves, woody tissues or seeds; others feed on the hyphae of fungi which they cultivate in underground galleries. The mound building activities of ants, as in the case of termites, may involve the transfer of large quantities of mineral matter from below ground to the soil surface; this is believed to promote the development of crumb structure in the soil. Their activities may also bring about local increases in the organic matter content of the soil.

Arachnids (Arachnida)

Mites

The Acari (Acarina) are the most numerous of all soil animals. Several hundred families are represented in the soil; they fall into four orders, viz. Prostigmata, Mesostigmata, Astigmata and Cryptostigmata (Fig. 2.17). Members of the first two orders are usually active forms which range freely through the soil, and many are predatory. Most Crypostigmata are smaller, slower moving mites, which are mainly detritus feeders. The Astigmata are not usually common in soils.

The predatory Mesostigmata prey upon nematodes, small enchytraeid worms, insects or other mites; other members of the order are saprophagous, while some are fungivorous or coprophagous. The Prostigmata is a large diverse group of mites. Many are predators and their prey is similar to that of the Mesostigmata; some species are phytophagous but little is known about the feeding habits of many of the smaller forms.

The group Cryptostigmata contains most of the typical soil mites. They are found in greatest numbers in mor soils under forest, and are most abundant in the F-layer. The distribution of Cryptostigmata, like that of the Collembola, is governed by the need for habitats with a saturated atmosphere. Many Cryptostigmata are relatively unspecialized feeders not restricted to any one type of food, ingesting organic matter in various stages of decomposition. Many of them however prefer soil fungi and bacteria, while others eat woody tissues and some are coprophagous.

Mites probably contribute very little to the chemical decomposition of plant litter although many of them are associated with the later stages of decay. They do however have a significant role in the fragmentation of litter; this is especially true of the Cryptostigmata. The small litter fragments expose a large surface area to microbial activity. Evidence suggests that the faeces of detritivorous mites are particularly

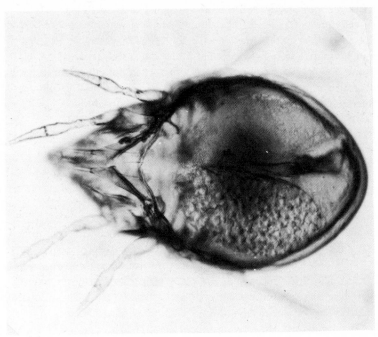

(a)

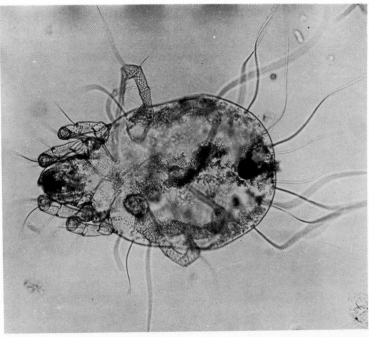

(b)

(c)

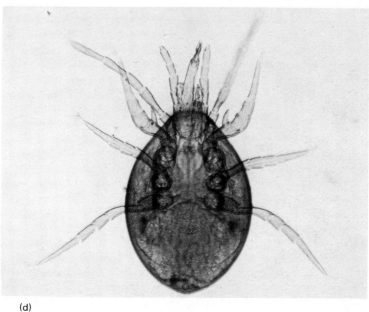

(d)

FIG. 2.17 Representatives of four common orders of soil-inhabiting mites. *(a)* Cryptostigmata. *(b)* Astigmata. *(c)* Prostigmata. *(d)* Mesostigmata. (From Wallwork, J. A. (1970) *Ecology of Soil Animals*, McGraw-Hill. © 1970 McGraw-Hill Book Company (UK) Ltd. Used with permission.)

susceptible to invasion by microbes. Mites are also important trans-
porters: they may disseminate fungal spores and many of them (especially the Cryptostigmata) carry decomposing organic matter from the
surface to the deeper soil layers.

Selected references

Alexopoulos, C. J. and Bold, H. C. (1967) *Algae and Fungi.* Macmillan.

Brock, T. D. (1970) *Biology of Microorganisms.* Prentice-Hall.

Burges, A. and Raw, F., eds. (1967) *Soil Biology.* Academic Press.

Gray, T. R. G. and Williams, S. T. (1971) *Soil Microorganisms.* Oliver
and Boyd.

Kevan, D. K. McE. (1962) *Soil Animals.* Witherby.

Stanier, R. Y., Doudoroff, M. and Adelberg, E. A. (1970) *The Microbial
World,* 3rd edn. Prentice-Hall.

Talbot, P. H. B. (1971) *Principles of Fungal Taxonomy.* Macmillan.

Whittaker, R. H. (1959) 'On the broad classification of organisms', *Q.
Rev. Biol.* 34, 210–26.

3 The sources of energy and nutrients for soil organisms

In order to comprehend the role of soil organisms in such aspects of ecosystem function as energy flow and nutrient cycling, it is necessary to have an understanding of the manner in which the organisms themselves satisfy their demands for energy and nutrients. These considerations are taken up in the present chapter.

Nutritional categories and energy-yielding processes

The concept of living organisms falling into one of two nutritional categories, autotrophic or heterotrophic, is a long standing one in biology. It was originally based on the belief that autotrophs were entirely independent of the presence of organic matter in their environment, but this is not strictly accurate since many such organisms are now known to require specific organic growth factors, such as vitamins, even though their principal nutrients are inorganic. The classification retains its value, however, provided the use of the terms is restricted to indicating the nature of an organism's **principal carbon source**, i.e. whether organic (heterotrophic) or inorganic (autotrophic). The nature of the **energy source** forms the basis of another fundamental division of organisms, those using radiant (solar) energy being called phototrophic (or photosynthetic), and those dependent on the energy released during chemical oxidations being termed chemotrophic.

Combining these two basic criteria leads to the recognition of four major nutritional categories* (Fig. 3.1(a)):

1 **Photoautotrophs**, utilizing light as an energy source and CO_2 as the principal source of carbon. Examples are higher plants, eucaryotic algae, blue-green algae, and certain photosynthetic bacteria (purple and green sulphur bacteria).

* The prefixes 'litho-' and 'organo-' are sometimes substituted for 'auto-' and 'hetero-', respectively.

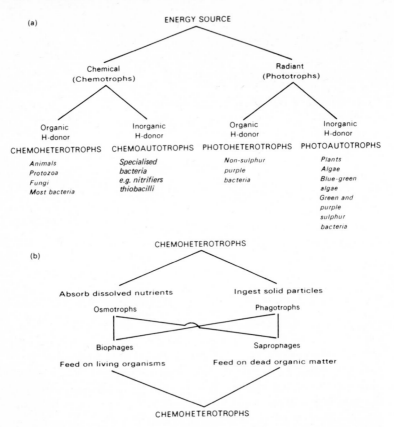

FIG. 3.1 Functional categories of organisms. *(a)* Classification of organisms based on the nature of their energy and principal carbon sources. *(b)* Classifications of chemoheterotrophs based on the nature of their food source and the manner of acquiring it.

2 **Photoheterotrophs**, dependent on light as a source of energy and deriving much of their carbon from organic compounds. This category is represented by a specialized group of photosynthetic bacteria known as non-sulphur purple bacteria.

3 **Chemoautotrophs**, deriving energy from the oxidation of inorganic compounds and using CO_2 as the principal carbon source. This category comprises several groups of specialized bacteria, including the nitrifying bacteria and the thiobacilli.

4 **Chemoheterotrophs**, utilizing organic compounds as both energy and carbon source. Included here are animals, protozoa, fungi and most bacteria.

Chemoheterotrophs may be further subdivided according to the manner in which they obtain their carbon and energy requirements, being called **osmotrophs** if, like bacteria and fungi, they absorb organic substances in solution, and **phagotrophs** if, like many animals and protozoans, they ingest them as solid particles. Alternatively, subdivision of chemoheterotrophs may be made on the basis of whether they satisfy their needs by feeding upon other living organisms, in which case they are called **biophages**, or on dead organic matter, when they are known as **saprophages**† (Fig. 3.1(*b*)).

Energy-yielding processes of chemotrophic organisms

Any substance which is oxidized by an organism to provide energy for metabolic processes is termed a **substrate**. By definition, substrates of chemoautotrophs are inorganic, while those of chemoheterotrophs are organic. Many biological oxidations take the following form:

$$AH_2 + B \rightarrow BH_2 + A$$

Such a reaction is representative of the type known as dehydrogenation, and involves the transfer of hydrogen atoms (and electrons) from one substance AH_2, called the **hydrogen-donor** to another substance B, called the **hydrogen-acceptor**. Hydrogen-donor is merely another name for substrate, and while its composition will clearly influence the kinds of end products, it is the nature of the hydrogen-acceptor which characterizes the energy-yielding reactions of chemotrophic organisms. According to their specific hydrogen-acceptors, three kinds of energy-yielding metabolism may be recognized (Table 3.1), but it is emphasized that the categories listed in the table do not provide a basis for dividing the living world into mutually exclusive groups. For example, many microorganisms respire aerobically in the presence of oxygen, but turn to anaerobic respiration or fermentation as an energy source when

TABLE 3.1 The energy-yielding reactions of chemotrophic microbes

Energy-yielding process	Hydrogen-acceptor
Aerobic respiration *	Molecular oxygen
Anaerobic respiration	Inorganic substance other than oxygen
Fermentation	Organic compound

* Aerobic respiration is usually referred to simply as respiration.

† The second of the two classifications is the more useful from the ecological viewpoint, but it should be noted that it cuts across the first, since phagotrophs may be either biophagous or saprophagous while the same is true of osmotrophs.

the oxygen supply is depleted. Nevertheless, since an organism's prime requirement is for energy, a classification based on the four major energy-yielding processes — **aerobic respiration, anaerobic respiration, fermentation** and **photosynthesis** — provides a useful framework for examining the ecological role of soil organisms (see, for example, Chapter 6).

Oxygen relationships

So far as microorganisms are concerned, access to oxygen may or may not be beneficial, and four categories can be distinguished on the basis of their reactions to molecular oxygen: *(a)* **aerobes**, which grow only in the presence of oxygen and are completely dependent on respiration as a source of energy; *(b)* **anaerobes**, which are inhibited or killed on access to oxygen, and so depend on fermentation or anaerobic respiration as energy sources; *(c)* **micraerophiles** which are obligate aerobes but which develop best at low oxygen tensions; and *(d)* **facultative anaerobes**, which are active under either aerobic or anaerobic conditions. The four types of oxygen relationships are not found in all taxonomic groups of microbes. Most of these, like plants and animals, are aerobes, but yeasts and a few other fungi are facultative anaerobes, while among the bacteria all degrees of sensitivity to oxygen exist. In passing, it should be noted that while most photosynthetic organisms (plants, algae and blue-green algae) are aerobes, the photosynthetic bacteria are anaerobes.

Sources of nutrients

An organism requires not only a source of energy, but must also find in its environment all the materials needed to build and maintain its cellular organization, that is to say, it must have available a supply of **nutrients**. Phagotrophs obtain all their nutrients from ingested materials, but many of the nutrients absorbed by osmotrophs enter the organisms more or less independently from the ambient solution. Two factors determine whether or not a given compound can be used as a nutrient by an osmotroph: first, the ability of the compound to penetrate the cytoplasmic membrane and enter the cell, and second, the ability of the organism to metabolize the substance once it enters. Molecules too large to penetrate the plasma membrane may however be utilized as nutrient sources if the organism can hydrolyse them to their constituent moieties by enzymatic action outside the cell (see p. 69). The compounds which are taken up and metabolized by microorganisms in order to satisfy their requirements for various nutrients are discussed below.

Carbon, hydrogen and oxygen

These elements are considered together because a single compound often provides all three. Hydrogen and oxygen are also supplied as water, which is an essential requirement for all organisms because their metabolic reactions take place in aqueous solution.

Carbon is the element required by organisms in greatest amount. All photosynthetic forms can reduce atmospheric CO_2, but not all can use CO_2 as the sole source of carbon. In the photoheterotrophic non-sulphur purple bacteria, organic substances such as acetate and succinate act as H-donors for CO_2 reduction. Chemoautotrophic microbes such as the nitrifying bacteria utilize inorganic substances exclusively, and must therefore use atmospheric CO_2 as their sole carbon source. Most chemotrophic forms however, oxidize organic compounds which serve not only as substrates in energy-yielding reactions, but also as sources of carbon for nutrition. The range of organic compounds from which carbon is extracted by chemoheterotrophic organisms is extremely wide. Microorganisms, as a group, are especially versatile in this respect: in fact, for every naturally occurring organic material there are presumed to be microbes capable of decomposing it. This is the reason why microorganisms play such a vital role in the geochemical cycling of the elements, especially carbon and nitrogen.

Carbohydrates are among the more readily available sources of carbon for microorganisms. Monosaccharides, especially hexoses, are widely used, but polyhydric alcohols such as mannitol and glycerol are often good carbon sources too, especially for actinomycetes. Organic acids of the tricarboxylic acid cycle cannot usually penetrate the cytoplasmic membrane, but amino acids are readily used as carbon sources by most microorganisms, and fatty acids can also be utilized by some. Hydrocarbons can serve as a carbon source for a few bacteria of the genera *Corynebacterium*, *Mycobacterium* and *Pseudomonas*. Utilization of aromatic compounds such as lignin is quite extensive under aerobic conditions, but when oxygen is limiting such compounds are not decomposed and therefore accumulate, e.g. as peat and coal. The major lignin decomposers are fungi, notably some of the higher basidiomycetes, while among bacteria the ability to use aromatic compounds is often found in the pseudomonads and actinomycetes. A discussion of several important naturally occurring organic substrates will be found in Chapter 5.

Although the range of organic materials which can be metabolized by microorganisms in general is very great, some species have narrow preferences, others wide. Furthermore, there are certain synthetic carbon compounds which are relatively resistant to decomposition by microbes. These 'recalcitrant molecules', to use the phraseology of Martin Alexander, usually derive from insecticides, herbicides or detergents, and constitute one of the major pollution problems of technological society (see p. 131).

Nitrogen

Relatively large amounts of this element are required for the synthesis of amino acids and proteins, purine and pyrimidine nucleotides, and certain vitamins. The nitrogen atom occurs in nature in a variety of oxidation states, each of which can be utilized by different microorganisms. The preferred state seems to be the ammonium ion, which is not surprising since it is in this form (NH_4^+) that nitrogen is incorporated into organic compounds. However, nitrate (NO_3^-) can be used by many algae and fungi, though not so extensively by bacteria. Certain bacteria and blue-green algae can use molecular nitrogen (N_2); these will be discussed in Chapter 9. Organic nitrogen compounds are used as sources of nitrogen by those organisms that decompose them to produce ammonia. Many microorganisms have a particular capacity to do this, a single amino acid often serving as their sole source of nitrogen.

Phosphorus and sulphur

Phosphorus occurs in living organisms chiefly as sugar phosphates in nucleotides and nucleic acids, hence phosphorus, usually as inorganic phosphate, needs to be provided in considerable amount if an organism is to grow.

Sulphur is present in organisms as the sulphydryl (−SH) group of the amino acid cysteine, and most other sulphur compounds in the cell, such as the amino acid methionine and the vitamins biotin and thiamine, derive from cysteine. Most microorganisms, like plants, absorb sulphur as sulphate (SO_4^{2-}) and must reduce it to sulphydryl. Thiosulphate ($S_2O_3^{2-}$) can also serve as the sole source of sulphur for many microorganisms. A few microbes are unable to reduce sulphate or thiosulphate, however, and require reduced sulphur compounds as nutrients, such as hydrogen sulphide or cysteine.

Other mineral elements

Unlike animals and plants, which have additional requirements for certain minerals to build or repair structural tissues, microbes require the remaining elements mainly as activators of various enzymes. The macronutrient elements potassium, magnesium and calcium are required in concentrations of about 10^{-3} to 10^{-4}M. Micronutrients are needed in much lower concentrations (10^{-6} to 10^{-8}M). Because of the technical difficulties involved, it is extremely difficult to demonstrate a micronutrient deficiency in microorganisms, though the need has been shown for manganese, iron, zinc and copper. The micronutrient requirements of most microbes are in fact so low that it is considered unnecessary to incorporate these elements in microbiological media used for cultivating microorganisms in the laboratory; they are normally present in adequate concentration as impurities in other constituents of the media. Notwithstanding this generality, some fungi are sufficiently sensitive to the concentration of micronutrients in the environment to enable them to be used as indicators in the bio-assay of micronutrient deficiencies in soils. For example, copper is needed for the production of the brownish-black melanin pigments found in the conidia of *Aspergillus niger*, so that if soil samples are added to copper-free nutrient media which are inoculated with this fungus, the copper content of the soil can be determined by assessing the degree of pigmentation of these spores.

Growth factors

Many organisms require certain organic compounds in addition to those needed as carbon and energy sources. Such nutrients are called **growth factors**, and include amino acids, purines, pyrimidines and vitamins. These are specific nutrients only in the sense that the organisms which require them lack the ability to produce them; an organism which requires a particular growth factor is said to be auxotrophic for that substance. Those organisms which have no requirement for growth factors must of necessity possess all the enzyme systems needed to synthesize, during the normal course of metabolism, all of the organic compounds they require for biosynthesis and growth. Some microorganisms are more demanding than others for growth factors: lactic acid bacteria and protozoa are among the most fastidious. A growth factor may be essential or stimulatory, depending on whether the organism requiring it is completely unable to synthesize it or is able to synthesize small amounts but not enough to satisfy all its metabolic needs.

Any of the twenty or so amino acids found in proteins may be required as a growth factor by microorganisms; one strain of the bacterium *Leuconostoc mesenteroides* requires no fewer than seventeen amino acids for growth. Purine and pyrimidine requirements are most commonly encountered among protozoa and in certain bacteria, especially lactobacilli. Protozoa and the lactic acid bacteria are also the most exacting microbes for vitamins, and may require up to five or six separate vitamins for growth. Some root infecting fungi, including the mycorrhizal basidiomycetes, have a requirement for thiamine (vitamin B_1) and biotin, while among the algae and phytoflagellates a requirement for vitamin B_{12} is not uncommon.

Nutrient uptake

All cells constantly exchange materials with their environment yet cell composition remains relatively constant. Osmotrophs absorb nutrients from the surrounding medium and release excretory products. These exchanges are specific in that only certain substances move in and certain ones out. The reason for this selectivity lies in the nature of the plasma membranes. In bacteria, it is primarily the cytoplasmic membrane that is involved, but eucaryotic cells have intracellular selective membranes in addition to that bounding the cytoplasm. Cell membranes are principally lipoprotein, and have both hydrophilic and lipophilic properties. They have the important property of being semipermeable, i.e. they are able to keep out solute molecules except in certain circumstances.

There is no evidence that pores exist in the membrane, other than those small enough to permit water and a few other molecules of like size to pass, hence some mechanism of penetration other than simple diffusion must exist. In this regard the membrane contrasts sharply with the cell wall itself, which is relatively porous and does not appreciably restrict the entry of materials. This is not to say that the cell walls of plants and microbes are freely permeable to all solutes, but their permeability is greater, and their selectivity is much less, than that of the plasma membrane. Because water can pass freely through the cytoplasmic membrane, it is taken up by osmosis. In organisms with rigid cell walls it is the rigidity of the wall itself which eventually prevents further entry of water. Organisms which lack rigid cell walls are restricted to a limited osmotic environment, unless they possess some mechanism for removal of excess water, such as the contractile vacuoles found in some protozoa. For the uptake of solutes, the plasma membrane is not only a semipermeable barrier but a vectorial one, the direction of flow of solutes being as important as their nature. Thus cells can take up K^+ faster than the rate at which it can leak out, resulting in the internal concentration of potassium ions being greatly in excess of their concentration in the external medium. In other words, the vectorial property of the membrane permits movement of ions against an electric potential gradient, or of non-electrolytes against a concentration gradient, giving rise to the phenomenon known as **accumulation**, i.e. the accumulation of solutes within cells at concentrations greatly in excess of their concentration in the surrounding medium.

Not all materials accumulate against a gradient. Some, like urea and glycerol, pass in by simple diffusion, the rate of transport being proportional to the concentration gradient, the size of the molecules and their solubility in lipids. However, only a very small proportion of the total solutes enter thus. A few others enter by facilitated diffusion, a process which involves the operation of a carrier system. Facilitated diffusion permits the entry of some molecules which cannot enter by simple diffusion because of their large size and low solubility. Both kinds of diffusion are **passive uptake** processes, the energy for transport being derived from thermal agitation of the solute molecules. Through the expenditure of metabolic energy, many substances which could not penetrate the plasma membrane by passive mechanisms are taken up by a process known as **active transport**. This is defined as net movement of solutes or ions independent of any chemical or electric potential gradient. Most inorganic ions enter the cell this way. Transport of monosaccharides and disaccharides is also usually an active process, and active transport of amino acids has been demonstrated in a number of microorganisms. Active transport mechanisms are usually highly specific, resulting in the selective uptake of one or more compounds from a mixture of closely related substances.

Nature of the uptake process

Most recent hypotheses advanced to explain active transport involve the reversible binding of solutes to a proteinaceous constituent of the cytoplasmic membrane known as a **permease**. Thus β-galactoside permease mediates the entry of lactose into *Escherichia coli*, whilst other permeases are believed to be responsible for the active transport of amino acids, and possibly inorganic ions as well. Although they are proteins, permeases are quite distinct from enzymes.

The mechanism by which solute molecules are transported from one side of the plasma membrane to the other (a distance of $7.5-10$ nm) is

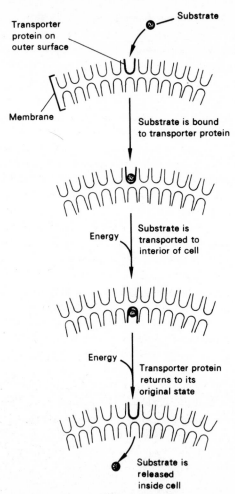

FIG. 3.2 A diagrammatic representation of the active transport of solutes across the plasma membrane. (From Brock, T. D. (1970) *Biology of Microorganisms*, Prentice-Hall ©1970. By permission of Prentice-Hall, Inc., Englewood Cliffs, New Jersey, USA.)

not known for certain, but it is thought to involve the binding of solute molecules to certain sites on one or more permease molecules. Once bound, the transfer across the membrane seems to involve the metabolizing of the solute, or of membrane lipids, and may be effected by some change in the configuration of the permease protein. Whatever the actual mechanism, it requires the expenditure of metabolic energy in the form of adenosine triphosphate (ATP). A diagrammatic representation of the process of active transport is shown in Fig. 3.2.

Molecules too large to enter microbial cells directly by diffusion or permease action may be digested extracellularly by enzymes secreted into the medium (Fig. 3.3). These are known as extracellular enzymes or **exoenzymes**. They are mostly hydrolases, i.e. they catalyse the hydrolysis of high molecular weight molecules such as polysaccharides, proteins and lipids into their constituent sub-units, which are then absorbed into the cell by passive or active processes. Thus a-amylase hydrolyses the polysaccharides starch and glycogen into smaller glucose polymers known as dextrins and eventually into the disaccharide maltose, while cellulase digests cellulose to produce the disaccharide cellobiose; both these exoenzymes are commonly produced by saprophytic fungi. The disaccharides may be further hydrolysed extracellularly to their constituent monosaccharides by the enzymes maltase and cellobiase, respectively. Extracellular proteases and peptidases, which promote the hydrolysis of proteins (proteolysis), are typical of bacteria such as *Proteus, Clostridium* and *Pseudomonas*, and fungi such as *Aspergillus* and *Penicillium*. The decomposition of complex organic residues in soil is considered in more detail in Chapter 5.

Not all exoenzymes diffuse into the environment, some remaining bound to the surface of the plasma membrane or held in the cell wall. Many are inducible, in other words they are often synthesized only in

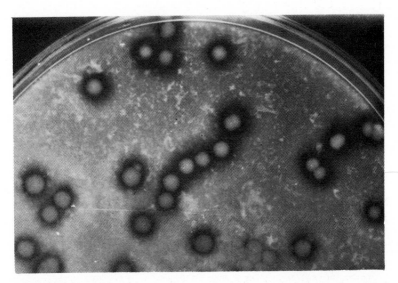

FIG. 3.3 Hydrolysis of macromolecules by exoenzymes. Milk agar plate inoculated with *Bacillus subtilis*, the clear zones around the colonies indicating hydrolysis of the milk protein, casein.

the presence of an inducer which is usually (though not necessarily) the substrate for the particular enzyme involved.

Ingestion

Ingestion is the usual means of food intake among the higher animals. It also occurs in amoebae, which are thereby able to transport solutes, and even solid particles such as bacteria, into the interior of their cells. In these protists, the process involves the pinching off of small vesicles from the end of a deep invagination in the plasma membrane. The contents of the vesicle are subsequently digested by intracellular enzymes, the mechanism being known as **pinocytosis** when solutions only are taken in, and **phagocytosis** when solid particles enter. It is not known whether these processes occur in other microorganisms, but they have been detected in mammalian cells. Pinocytosis may be regarded as active uptake since presumably metabolic energy is expended in the process of invagination. However, it is a relatively non-selective mechanism for effecting the entry of solutes.

Selected references

Alexander, M. (1971) *Microbial Ecology.* Wiley.
Brock, T. D. (1970) *Biology of Microorganisms.* Prentice-Hall.
Rose, A. H. (1968) *Chemical Microbiology,* 2nd edn. Butterworths.
Stanier, R. Y., Doudoroff, M. and Adelberg, E. A. (1970) *The Microbial World,* 3rd edn. Prentice-Hall.
Thimann, K. V. (1963) *The Life of Bacteria.* Macmillan.

4 Development of the soil ecosystem

Soil organisms occur in a bewildering array of habitats, the diversity in habitat being brought about by variation in such soil properties as moisture, aeration, temperature, pH, and nutrient or food supply. No one species of organism is able to grow in every kind of habitat. For every environmental factor, there is a minimum level below which the organism will not grow at all, an optimum level at which growth is best, and a maximum level above which again no growth occurs. The limits between which the species makes good growth define the **ecological tolerance** of the species for that factor, and any factor which tends to slow down the growth of the organism is referred to as a **limiting factor**.

The concept of limiting factors was first formulated in 1840 by the German chemist Justus von Liebig, who observed that the growth of crops was restricted by whatever essential nutrient was in short supply. Liebig's 'law of the minimum', as it became known, was later extended by ecologists to include the limiting effect of the maximum, that is to say, an excess of any particular factor can limit growth as well as a deficiency. Since to make good growth, an organism requires a source of energy together with a supply of nutrients and an appropriate physical environment, any of these things is a potential limiting factor. It should also be recognized that the factors which control growth may interact, in other words one factor in short supply may affect the requirement for another which is not itself limiting. E. P. Odum has therefore restated Liebig's concept of limiting factors as follows: the success of a population or community depends on a complex of inter-acting factors; any factor which approaches or exceeds the limits of tolerance for the organism or group concerned may be regarded as a limiting factor.

Figure 4.1 illustrates the interaction of two limiting nutrients on the growth of a coniferous tree. Yield, which is represented by the surface of the three-dimensional figure, depends on an optimum combination of the two nutrients: when either is grossly limiting, increases in the other have little or no effect. One could, in theory, depict the effect of

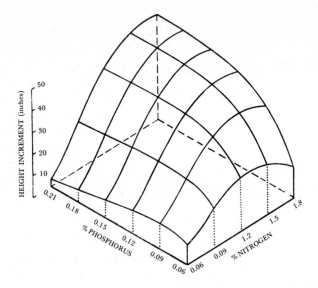

FIG. 4.1 The interaction of limiting factors, illustrated by the effect of nitrogen and phosphorus on the growth of *Araucaria cunninghamii*. Note how the response to increasing foliar concentrations of either nutrient depends on the level of the other. (From Richards, B. N. and Bevege, D. I. (1969) *Plant Soil*, **31**, 328–36.)

all limiting factors as a multi-dimensional figure, the several factors varying along horizontal axes radiating from a common origin, and the yield (or some other parameter of productivity) along a vertical axis. The surface of this figure would be a gently sloping plateau representing an optimum combination of all factors, and falling increasingly steeply in every direction as the various factors become more and more limiting.

Limiting factors in relation to ecosystem development

One way of analysing ecosystems, and of studying their evolution and development, is the state factor approach of Hans Jenny, which has its origins in the work of the Russian pedologist, V. V. Dokuchaev, and which is based on the principle of interacting limiting factors. According to this viewpoint, the state of the system at any point in time is defined by a certain number of variables, or **state factors**. Thus any measurable properly, l, of the system is a function of (*a*) the amount of that property or material present at time zero, l_0, i.e. when system development begins; (*b*) the external flux potentials, P_x, which determine gains from and losses to the environment of energy and matter; and *(c)* the time, *t*, or the age of the system from time zero. Thus we may write:

$$l = f(l_0, P_x, t) \tag{1}$$

To be of use in ecosystem analysis, the state factors l_0 and P_x must be partitioned into more specific components. The factor l_0 is made up of soil parent material, *p*, and topography or relief, *r*. External potentials, P_x, are environmental properties, such as the regional climate, *cl*, and the biotic factor, *o*, the latter consisting of all the organisms which were available for colonization of the site, or already present, at time zero. Having partitioned the state factors we can re-write eq. (1) as follows:

$$l = f(cl, o, r, p, t) \tag{2}$$

Equation (2) is the general **state factor equation**, and it applies not only to the total system but to various subsystems as well. Thus we may regard *l* as a composite entity being the product of three interacting subsystems, viz. the soil, *s*, vegetation, *v*, and animal, *z*, subsystems. These three components of the total system are mutually interdependent, so that a particular property of the soil subsystem, for example, is determined not only by its own external potentials but also indirectly by many others which directly affect the vegetation or animal subsystems. We may therefore extend the general state factor equation as follows:

$$l, v, z, s = f(cl, o, r, p, t) \tag{3}$$

The influence of an individual state factor on ecosystem development may be studied by examining situations in nature where that factor varies while all other factors remain relatively constant. For example, Jenny was able to show that soil nitrogen content was a function of climate by studying 'climofunctions', that is, a range of climates in situations where parent material, topography and the biotic factor were similar. In this instance, eq. (3) becomes $s = f(cl)_{o,r,p,t}$. In the same way, we could determine the effect of parent material on any soil property by studying a 'lithofunction' such that $s = f(p)_{cl,o,r,t}$, or the effect of relief by examining a 'topofunction', i.e. $s = f(r)_{cl,o,p,t}$.

One conceptual difficulty inherent in state factor analysis is the fact that a term for organisms appears on both sides of eq. (3). This difficulty may be resolved by regarding those biotic factors which existed prior to time zero as independent components, while those which have developed since are considered to be dependent variables. In practice, the regional biota is taken to be independent, since segregation into regional flora and fauna is assumed to have preceded time zero. For a further treatment of the organism factor in state factor analysis, the reader is referred to a paper by R. L. Crocker (see under 'Selected References').

Some ecologists question the validity of this 'functional, factorial' approach to ecosystem analysis, arguing that it is impossible to distinguish between dependent and independent variables when most, if not all, are in any event interrelated. It is further argued that the response of an ecosystem to variations in environmental factors is difficult, if not impossible, to interpret since the environment itself is part of the ecosystem. Such argument fails to take account of the fact that some environmental factors, viz. those within the system boundaries, can be clearly recognized as dependent variables, as distinct from those which operate at or beyond the boundary and which are therefore independent. It also fails to recognize the full extent of the potential contribution which the general systems approach can make to the study of ecosystems. The techniques of systems analysis will permit the identification of those variables which are important in ecosystem function, and lead to the building of models which may be subjected to rigorous mathematical testing. This approach has been concisely stated by A. M. Shultz as follows:

> The state of a system is describable uniquely by a finite set of state factors which, when quantified, yields a set of n numbers. The set of all points in the n-dimension hyperspace determines all possible states of the system. Then the functional relationships can be solved by means of a set of simultaneous differential equations.

This statement should not be interpreted as the only approach to the modelling of ecosystems. It is not essential, for example, that relationships between the variables be expressed as mathematical equations, since it is possible to represent in a computer any relationship that can be plotted graphically, even if the shape of the graph is such that it cannot be explicitly defined in mathematical form.

The biotic factor

The development of ecosystems involves the phenomenon of **ecological succession**, which is an orderly process of community change that results from modification of the physical environment by organisms, and culminates in the system attaining a steady state, or **climax**. It is important to realize that succession is controlled by the biological attributes of the developing community, and not primarily by physical factors. Certainly the physical environment sets limits of how far development may proceed, and also influences the pattern and rate of change, but it is the biotic factor which is generally of overriding significance.

Although autogenic (within-system) processes predominate in succession, the interplay between biotic and environmental factors is such that external (allogenic) processes sometimes become dominant. In the soil ecosystem, allogenic succession of soil microbes may be observed as occurring in close association with the early developmental stages of autogenic plant succession. In this situation, external factors (plant roots) control the pattern of microbial succession. Nevertheless, successions involving chemoheterotrophic soil organisms are in general autogenic.

Succession in the soil subsystem differs in one important respect from that in the vegetation subsystem. In autogenic plant succession, there is a progressive increase in the organic matter and the amount of energy stored in the system as it matures from the pioneer stages towards the climax. In contrast, the succession of heterotrophic microbes in the soil ecosystem leads to a progressive depletion of energy sources (plant and animal residues and exudates), so that as S. D. Garrett has expressed it, 'the end-point of the microbial succession is not a climax association, but zero'. In so far as the final product of organic matter decomposition in soil, viz. humus, is a more or less permanent constituent of the soil ecosystem (see Chapter 5), the theoretical zero endpoint will never be reached. Rather, the climax microbial community in the soil is represented by what is termed the 'autochthonous microflora'; this is discussed later (p. 104) in the context of organic matter decomposition.

Heterotrophic succession may also be differentiated from autotrophic succession on the basis of system energetics. In the developmental stages of an autogenic succession, the gross production/community respiration (P/R) ratio exceeds one, whereas in a heterotrophic succession the P/R ratio is much less than one initially. Note however that in both kinds of succession the P/R ratio approaches unity as the systems mature.

Microbial succession in soils

Succession in the soil ecosystem is epitomized in a schema proposed by S. D. Garrett for the colonization of plant tissues by soil fungi (Table 4.1). According to this hypothetical sequence, moribund tissues of

TABLE 4.1 Hypothetical fungal succession on plant tissue*

Stage	State of tissue	Substrate group
1a	Senescent	Weak parasites
1	Dead	Primary saprophytic sugar fungi
2	Dead	Cellulose decomposers and secondary sugar fungi
3	Dead	Lignin decomposers

* After Garrett, S. D. (1963) *Soil Fungi and Soil Fertility*, Pergamon Press.

plants are normally colonized by weak parasites before they fall to the ground. Upon reaching the ground, they are invaded first by saprophytic 'sugar fungi' which utilize sugars and other carbon compounds simpler than cellulose. These fungi, typically certain phycomycetes and imperfect fungi, are characterized by the ability for rapid spore germination and a high mycelial growth rate, which give them a competitive advantage over slower growing species. This advantage is further enhanced by the fact that some of them produce metabolic waste products which have an inhibitory effect on other fungi. Following on after the primary sugar fungi are the cellulose decomposers together with associated secondary sugar fungi. The cellulose decomposers, mainly ascomycetes, imperfect fungi and some basidiomycetes, are quite capable of utilizing simpler carbon compounds such as sugars, but are usually denied the opportunity of developing in nature until such substrates have been exhausted. The secondary sugar fungi likewise cannot compete successfully with the primary colonizers for the sugars present in recently fallen leaves, and must therefore share the breakdown products of cellulose hydrolysis with the cellulose decomposers. The final stage of Garrett's hypothetical fungal succession is represented by the lignin decomposing basidiomycetes.

A somewhat similar succession has been postulated by W. A. Kreutzer for the reinfestation of soil which has been 'partially sterilized' by treatment with a strong chemical fumigant, such as chloropicrin. Four seral stages are visualized: *Stage 1* — Fast growing fungi (phycomycetes and imperfect species) invade the treated zone from without, while actinomycetes and various bacteria arise from resistant residues (conidia, endospores) within the treated zone. These initial invaders utilize simple substrates such as sugars and amino acids. *Stage 2* — With the simpler substrates largely exhausted, microorganisms capable of hydrolysing complex carbohydrates make their appearance. Imperfect fungi still dominate, but ascomycetes and basidiomycetes also develop, together with other cellulose degrading organisms such as actinomycetes, bacteria and myxobacteria. *Stage 3* – When the only remaining energy sources in non-rhizosphere soil are lignin and other complex materials of biological origin, basidiomycetes begin to dominate together with a few autochthonous bacteria. Most of the simple 'sugar-organisms' and cellulose decomposers are now limited to the rhizospheres of developing plants. *Stage 4* – After most of the potential energy sources originally available have been depleted, the microorganisms in non-rhizosphere soil either grow very slowly, utilizing humic materials, attacking and parasitizing one another, or else enter a dormant phase. The fumigated soil is now ecologically indistinct from the surrounding untreated soil. The only regions of available free energy left are in the rhizospheres of young plants, in sloughed-off root cells, or in decaying rootlets.

Experimental studies of heterotrophic succession

Attractive as they may be, these hypothetical microbial successions are far too simple and generalized, and fail to take account of the fact that successional development is influenced not only by the kind of energy source or substrate, but also by the nature of the microflora and mesofauna (the organism factor), and by environmental factors as well. Two experimental approaches have been used to study microbial succession. One is to follow the colonization of specific, chemically defined substrates introduced into the soil, the other is to follow succession during the breakdown of complex natural substrates such as leaf litter. Using the former approach, the primary colonizers of cellulose film buried in English soils were found by H. T. Tribe to be fungi, the actual species present varying from soil to soil. The imperfect genera *Botryotrichum* and *Humicola*, and the ascomycete *Chaetomium*, were dominant in neutral to alkaline arable soils, whereas the imperfect fungus *Oidiodendron* was common in acid soil under coniferous forest. The absence of phycomycetes among the primary colonizers is explained by the complexity of the substrate. After several weeks, bacteria grew profusely around the fungal mycelium and over the cellulose film, but they were not usually prominent before fungal growth occurred. The bacteria invariably supported a population of nematodes and sometimes colonies of amoebae, and the nematodes were often parasitized by predacious fungi. Frequently the microbial tissue and cellulose were consumed by soil animals: in acid sand, mites dominated the fauna but in neutral to alkaline soils, springtails and enchytraeid worms were more common. These observations demonstrate clearly that decomposition of substrates in soil is a complex process in which many members of the mesofauna participate along with microbes.

A similar study was made by D. M. Griffin of fungal succession on sterile human hair in three soils from the environs of Sydney, Eastern Australia; the particular substrate of interest here was keratin, the major protein of hair, wool, horn and feathers. Aqueous extracts of hair however are known to contain, in addition to keratin, appreciable quantities of readily available nitrogen and energy sources including pentoses and amino acids, so that many fungi that are not keratinolytic can develop. The first colonizers were the imperfect genera *Fusarium* and *Penicillium*, and various phycomycetes. These overlapped with or were followed by a second group, of which the imperfect genera *Gliocladium* and *Humicola*, and the ascomycete *Chaetomium*, were characteristic; other *Penicillium* spp. were also common at this stage. The third and final group were typified by the slow-growing keratinolytic fungi, *Keratinomyces* and *Microsporium*. The pattern of succession was broadly similar on all three soils, but there were differences in detail which reflected initial differences in the native microflora.

The second approach to the experimental study of microbial succession in the soil ecosystem is illustrated by the data of W. B. Kendrick and A. Burges in Fig. 4.2, which shows the temporal and spatial changes that take place in the fungal populations colonizing pine needles in the litter layers of a Scots pine forest in England. In this forest, needle fall occurs towards the end of summer but the needles were found to be infected by parasites, such as the 'leaf-cast' ascomycete *Lophodermium*, several months before they were shed. *Lophodermium* remained active in the fallen needles of the L-layer throughout the autumn and winter, sporulating in late winter and spring to provide an inoculum for reinfecting living needles. Shortly before leaf fall, the saprophytic fungi imperfecti, *Aureobasidium* and *Fusicoccum*, invaded senescent needles, and remained prominent on the fallen needles while these were in the L-layer. In this layer, the needles were invaded by rather uncommon species, some of which, e.g. the imperfect fungi *Sympodiella* and *Helicoma*, formed a network of hyphae on the needle surface while others, such as the ascomycete *Desmazierella* attacked the internal tissues. The needles remained in the L-layer for about six months, on the average, and as they passed into the F_1-layer, the saprophytic fungi sporulated. During the ensuing summer, many of the spores and much of the superficial mycelium were eaten by mites and springtails. A year after the first sporulation, a second one occurred and was again followed by renewed grazing by the mesofauna. As more needles fell they compressed the older needles, and the microenvironment became much

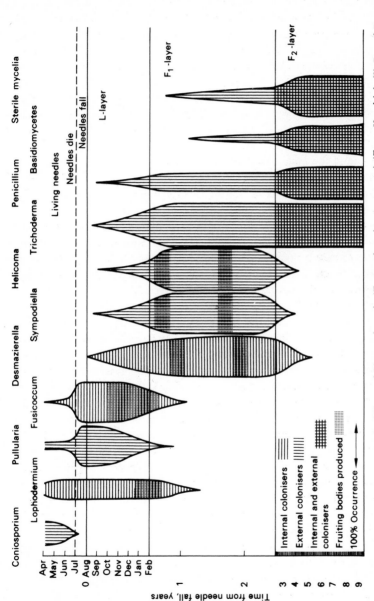

FIG. 4.2 Fungal succession in the leaf-litter of *Pinus sylvestris*. (For explanation, see text.) (From Kendrick, W. B. and Burges, A. (1962) *Nova Hedwig.*, **IV**, 3 + 4.)

moister. During this phase much of the mesophyll was destroyed, leaving the outer shell of the needle with its thick cuticle and the vascular strands plus associated lignified tissues. About 2½ years after being shed, the needles had entered the F_2-layer, and this is the stage when basidiomycetes, which first gained entry in the F_1-layer, caused active decomposition of cellulose and lignin. Also prominent in all but the earliest stages of the succession were the common soil saprophytes, *Trichoderma viride* and *Penicillium* spp. Basidiomycete activity was terminated by a considerable increase in the activity of the soil fauna, and the remains of the needles and the fungi were converted to a dark mass of faecal pellets which became part of the H-layer at the junction of the litter and the mineral soil. In this zone, chitin decomposing fungi were active. Needles took about seven years to progress through the F_2-layer, after which they passed into the H-layer where biological activity was reduced to a low level.

In this succession on pine needle litter the dominant organisms were fungi and small animals; bacteria played relatively little part. This is perhaps because the pH of the litter is low (3–4), and perhaps because some of the phenolic compounds released during decomposition of pine needles are bacteriostatic. A few actinomycetes were present, but their role in the succession is unknown. In other successions, for example in straw composts with a pH of six or higher, bacteria play a very active part and large populations develop. Nor is the decomposition of fungal mycelium always restricted to the activity of other fungi or to small animals, since many bacteria are chitin decomposers and have been shown to lyse fungal hyphae.

Another study of fungal succession on leaves was carried out by B. J. Macauley' and L. B. Thrower in the *Eucalyptus regnans* forests of South-Eastern Australia. As with pines in England, some of the early colonizers of leaf litter were imperfect fungi which invaded the leaves before they were shed, e.g. *Protostegia* and *Raederiella*, while others such as *Piggotia* and *Hormiscium* became established as saprophytes on freshly fallen leaves. None of these genera is particularly widespread in soils, but well known soil fungi such as *Mucor* and *Penicillium* were prominent later in the succession.

Several other studies have confirmed that the fungal colonizers of freshly fallen leaves are often not typical soil saprophytes, but are rather common airborne ascomycetes and imperfect fungi. As noted previously, some of these primary colonizers are weak parasites, and others infect senescent leaf tissues, but still others may be a part of the normal surface microflora of leaves. Members of the latter group possibly have some affinities with the sugar fungi, living as they do on the relatively simple organic compounds found in leaf exudates. Many of those fungi which invade mature or senescent leaves, however, are not considered to be sugar fungi, and the same is true of many of the species which colonize freshly fallen leaves. Perhaps this is not so surprising when one considers that leaves may be already largely depleted of simple carbohydrates before abscission, or become so very rapidly after reaching the ground. The extent to which the processes of autolysis and translocation within the leaf influence primary colonization is an unknown factor, but both leaf physiology and anatomy are certain to have some effect on the pattern of succession in decomposing leaf litter. In a steady state ecosystem, one might speculate that the whole decomposition process is 'programmed' by the leaf in such a way as to regulate the release of nutrients to the producers, and so govern the rates of nutrient recycling.

It would seem that the 'nutritional hypothesis' of fungal succession, inherent in the sequences proposed by Garrett and Kreutzer, is not fully substantiated by the results of experimental studies such as those just described. The hypothesis was derived in part from observations of the sequential development of fruiting bodies of coprophilous fungi. When fresh herbivore dung is incubated in a moist chamber in the laboratory, a succession of fruiting bodies occurs, with phycomycetes such as *Mucor* and *Pilobolus* appearing first, followed by the ascomycetes *Ascobolus* and *Sordaria*, basidiomycetes such as *Coprinus* developing last; various imperfect fungi are found in all seral stages. Few if any terrestrial phycomycetes have the ability to utilize cellulose and lignin, whereas cellulose decomposers are common in the ascomycetes and fungi imperfecti, and many basidiomycetes can decompose both cellulose and lignin. Furthermore, at least some ascomycetes and basidiomycetes are known to germinate and grow more slowly than many phycomycetes. Thus the physiology and nutrition of these major taxonomic groups, combined with evidence that, as manures and composts decompose, sugars, starches and proteins disappear first, followed by hemicelluloses, cellulose and lignin, in that order, provided a basis for the interpretation of fungal successions as nutritional sequences. Further research has shown, however, that many ascomycetes and imperfect fungi in soil successions germinate and grow as rapidly as phycomycetes. Again, there is no doubt a differential depletion of other nutrients, e.g. nitrogenous compounds, concomitantly with the progressive utilization of more and more complex carbohydrates. Hence fungal successions might perhaps be interpreted as readily in terms of nitrogen availability as on the basis of carbohydrate nutrition. It must be concluded that while the nutritional hypothesis explains many of the observed facts, it does not account for all. Not only this, but all of the stages postulated by Garrett and Kreutzer will not be found in every microbial succession in the soil—litter system. In particular, the stage of dominance by the so-called primary saprophytic sugar fungi, and typified by the phycomycetes, may be greatly foreshortened or even omitted altogether.

Reproduction, dispersal and survival of soil microbes

Availability of substrates is the most important single limiting factor for the heterotrophic microflora, and furthermore, these substrates are discontinuous in space and time (see Chapter 5). It follows that soil microorganisms must have a mechanism for reaching new substrates once existing ones are depleted. Dispersal is thus a key factor in the continuity of the microflora. Soil microbes can move to new substrates, or fresh substrates can be brought to them by mechanisms such as leaf fall and root decay of plants, and by death or defaecation of soil animals. In other words, they can disperse either in space or time. Dispersal in space is linked to reproduction, while dispersal in time requires the existence of survival structures or organs; all three processes are interrelated, however (Fig. 4.3).

Dispersal in space involves both active and passive mechanisms. Motility and growth are active means of dispersal. Motile structures such as the zoospores of lower fungi may be important in aquatic habitats but their efficacy in the soil environment is limited. Likewise it is doubtful whether motile bacteria move very far in soil, though in

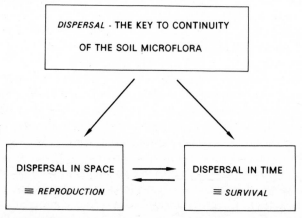

FIG. 4.3 The interrelationships of reproduction, survival and dispersal of soil microorganisms.

relation to the size of their habitat even small distances could be significant. Of all soil microbes, only fungi and perhaps actinomycetes can disperse by growing towards new substrates. The usefulness of growth as a means of dispersal is difficult to evaluate because it is hard to follow hyphal extension through soil. Occasionally it becomes evident however, as in the familiar 'fairy rings' of mushrooms or by the presence of macroscopic aggregations of hyphae into strands or rhizomorphs. Passive dispersal embraces transport by air, water and animal vectors. Dispersal on dust particles is one of the most important means available to bacteria. These organisms may also provide the solid phase of aerosols, as too may fungal spores. Basidiospores can be effective in dispersing root disease fungi such as *Fomes annosus* and some mycorrhizal fungi.

Where no means exist for dispersal of soil microbes in space, survival mechanisms become of paramount importance. Various structures are implicated in survival. Many of them, especially those of fungi, are often bulky. Possibly great bulk is necessary to provide sufficient energy reserves for the colonization of fresh substrates. Certainly survival structures cannot be effective in the dispersal of soil microbes unless their activation is followed by successful establishment on a new substrate. Sclerotia, the largest of fungal resting structures, are frequently regarded as storage organs but they undoubtedly have considerable survival value also. Chlamydospores are well adapted for long term survival, and many other reproductive structures of fungi can be converted into chlamydospores, for example conidia. The phycomycetes which form endotrophic mycorrhizas with plants (see Chapter 8) seem to persist in soil as thick-walled resting cells resembling chlamydospores. Even unmodified conidia have some survival value. In addition, viable mycelium is not uncommon in soil and some of it appears to occur in a resting condition. Hyphal strands and rhizomorphs are believed to function in part as survival structures too.

Actinomycetes seem to survive in soil as spores rather than as mycelium or mycelial fragments. Some species of bacteria persist as active cells. A few genera produce endospores that are extremely resistant to adverse conditions, but this is thought to be an adaptation to aerial dispersal rather than to survival. Resting cells, rather than endospores, seem to be the main agents of bacterial survival. Furthermore, bacteria rarely occur in soil as single cells but survive as microcolonies each of which may be surrounded by mucilage (possibly originating as extracellular capsules or slime layers) and embedded in humic materials.

The concept of soil as a matrix of discrete and transient microhabitats provides a rationale for the growth pattern of heterotrophic

microorganisms, which is one of successive cycles or substrate colonization, exploitation and exhaustion, separated by periods of migration or
quiescence. The frequency or brevity of the cycles does not diminish
the significance of the dispersal process, although it may disguise it.

Microbial interactions

Organisms respond to the factors of the environment in such a way that
overall homeostasis of the ecosystem is achieved. In other words, the
conditions of existence (physical state factors) act as regulatory agents.
As indicated previously, however (p. 9), homeostatic controls may be
self-regulatory processes not involving the physical state factors at all.
As the functional—factorial approach to ecosystem development illustrates, the concept of limiting factors is not confined to physical parameters, since biological interactions may be equally or even more
important in controlling the development of ecosystems. These interactions frequently prevent some organisms from taking full advantage
of optimum physical conditions, and at times may completely prevent
an organism from developing even though all physical factors are well
within its range of tolerance. In other instances, biological interactions
may result in better utilization of the conditions of existence than
would otherwise have been the case.

Interactions between plants and microorganisms, and their regulatory function in terrestrial ecosystems, are the subject matter of the last
three chapters of this book. Microbe x microbe interactions in the soil
also have such a regulatory role in the total system, albeit indirectly.
The existence of purely microbial interactions provides the rationale for
the biological control of plant pathogens, that is the control of pathogenic microbes through encouraging the growth of non-pathogenic
species which inhibit the development of the pathogens.

Interactions between individuals or between populations may be
either positive of negative, according as to whether one or both parties
are stimulated or inhibited. Most negative interactions can be described
as examples of either competition or antagonism, while positive interactions comprise commensalism, protocooperation and mutualism.*
Other more specific terms can be used when describing particular interactions, but this simplified scheme is satisfactory for the present
purpose.

* The term 'symbiosis' is often used by botanists as a synonym for mutualism.
Since its literal meaning is 'living together' it is perhaps best used in that general
sense, without regard to the effect of the symbiosis on either partner.

Competition and antagonism

Competition

Broadly speaking, competition involves active demand by two or more organisms for a material or condition in short supply. Botanists began to study competition many years before microbiologists. The classical botanical concept is that plants compete for light, water, nutrients, and possibly space. Soil microbiologists have frequently assumed that, with the exception of light, these same factors are involved in competition among heterotrophic microorganisms, but many now subscribe to the view that microbes compete basically for substrate, i.e. energy supply, and that competition for water, nutrients and space is insignificant or non-existent. There is no doubt that water is essential for microbial activity, but it appears that the metabolic reactions of microbes frequently produce water rather than consume it: provided sufficient water is available to initiate decomposition of a substrate, the process becomes autocatalytic in that metabolic water is produced. This does not mean that microorganisms do not have a water requirement nor does it imply that they are not influenced by changes in the soil water potential; indeed there is evidence that the composition of the fungal flora of the soil is affected by the differential response of different fungi to changes in the availability of soil water.

How intensively do microbes compete for substrates? The answer to this question depends on whether one is considering intraspecific competition — that which occurs between individuals or groups within a species — or interspecific competition — that which takes place between different species. A close spatial association is undoubtedly important in determining the degree of intraspecific competition: two individuals will compete more strongly if contiguous than if separated. This does not necessarily hold for interspecific competition, however, because of the operation of a concept known as **Gause's principle**. This states that as a general rule only one species may occupy any specific niche in a habitat. A corollary to this is that no two species in a stable community are in direct competition: they must have different niche requirements or they could not continue to coexist in the same habitat (Fig. 4.4). Because one species would be excluded as a result of competition, Gause's principle is also referred to as the **competitive exclusion principle**. To understand it fully, it is necessary to know what is meant by the terms 'habitat' and 'niche'.

Habitat is a word in common usage outside the field of ecology, and is generally understood to mean simply the place where an organism

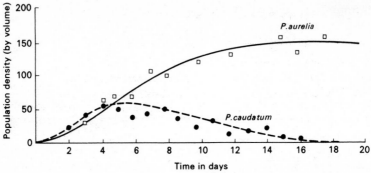

FIG. 4.4 The competitive exclusion principle, illustrated by the experiments of G. F. Gause. When grown separately in controlled cultures with constant food supply, both *Paramecium caudatum* and *P. aurelia* exhibit normal sigmoid growth curves. The diagram illustrates that, when in competition, *P. caudatum* is eliminated while *P. aurelia* maintains its usual growth pattern. (From Whittaker, R. H. (1970) *Communities and Ecosystems*, Macmillan. © Robert H. Whittaker 1970.)

lives. The concept of **ecological niche** is more recent and has a wider connotation, embracing not only the physical space occupied by an organism but also its activities, i.e. its contribution to ecosystem processes such as energy flow and nutrient cycling. Put briefly, the basic difference between the two terms is that niche is used to suggest an organism's functional role in the community or ecosystem, while habitat indicates the kind of physico-chemical environment in which it occurs. Like many broad concepts, the idea of niche is difficult to define and quantify, but it is none the less useful for that. A more detailed explanation may be found in E. P. Odum's *Fundamentals of Ecology*.

Soil organic matter contains a great many different chemical compounds which act as substrates for soil microorganisms, and the species involved in organic matter decomposition are often in separate ecological niches and not in direct competition. In many instances these niches are complementary, as for example in the nitrifying bacteria, where nitrite produced by *Nitrosomonas* forms the substrate for *Nitrobacter*. A close spatial association does not therefore increase competition between these two genera and in fact *Nitrobacter* benefits from it. The degree of physiological and biochemical specialization among microorganisms, combined with the complexity and variety of organic substrates, makes possible the existence of a large number of ecological niches in a given habitat. In spite of the overwhelming significance of energy source in determining the tempo of microbial activity in soil we should not jump to the conclusion that soil contains a teeming mass of microorganisms that are fiercely competitive for common substrates. In many situations, soil microbes are as likely to be cooperative as competitive.

Antagonism

Competition as described above is competition for a scarce, common resource. Another form of competition involves the antagonism of one species towards another which results in the inhibition of the second.* The growth-regulating properties of metabolites excreted into the environment by microorganisms exert an important influence on the composition of the soil microflora. Some microbial excretions are stimulatory because they contain substances which may be used by other organisms as energy substrates, nutrients or growth factors, others are inhibitory or antagonistic even in very low concentration; the latter are called **antibiotics**. Often one substance acts in two capacities, depending *inter alia* on its concentration and the identity of the species affected. Antagonism may be readily demonstrated in the laboratory (Fig. 4.5).

The production of antibiotics is considered by some microbiologists to be one of the most important mechanisms operative in competition. Not all antagonistic effects seen in soil can be attributed to antibiosis, however. Soil contains many substances of biological origin which when present in sufficiently high concentrations are toxic to certain microorganisms. Thus organic acids liberated during microbial metabolism can inhibit the growth of fungi, especially in acid soils. Carbon dioxide produced by the respiration of one group of microorganisms may restrict the growth of others. Ammonia formed by mineralization markedly inhibits *Nitrobacter* in alkaline soils (p. 145), and the consequent high level of nitrite may adversely affect other microbes, and even plants. Decomposition products of certain plant constituents, e.g. resins, tannins and phenolic compounds, may also prove toxic to microorganisms. All of these products or by-products of microbial metabolism differ from antibiotics in that they must be present in relatively high concentrations to be effective.

Many microorganisms isolated from soil exhibit antibiotic effects on laboratory media. Actinomycetes are particularly active, especially *Streptomyces* isolates. In fact many actinomycetes are utilized for the commercial production of antibiotics including streptomycin, chloramphenicol, and the tetracyclines aureomycin and terramycin. Many fungi

---

* The term 'amensalism' is sometimes used to describe a situation in which one species of an interacting pair is inhibited while the other is not, the use of the word 'competition' being then restricted to cases of mutual inhibition.

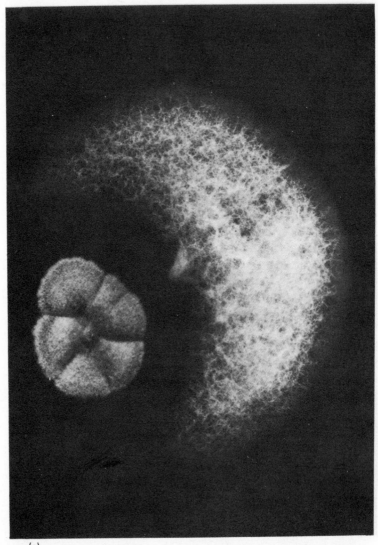

(a)

imperfecti are prominent antibiotic producers, for example *Penicillium* (the commercial source of penicillin), *Trichoderma, Aspergillus* and *Fusarium*. Aerobic spore formers (*Bacillus* spp.) and some pseudomonads (*Pseudomonas* spp.) are among the more common bacterial antibiotic producers. Antibiosis has also been recorded in algae and protozoa.

While antibiosis is easy to demonstrate in the laboratory, there has been a great deal of argument and much speculation about its possible

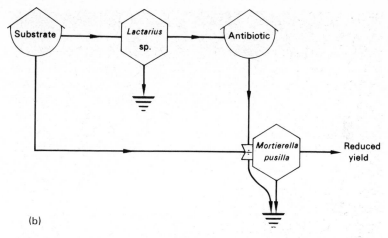

(b)

FIG. 4.5 (*a*) Microbial antagonism, illustrated by the inhibition of the saprophytic fungus *Mortierella pusilla* (right) by *Lactarius* sp. (left), a fungus isolated from ectomycorrhizas of *Tilia americana*. (From Park, J. Y. (1970) *Can. J. Microbiol.*, **16**, 798–800.) Photograph kindly supplied by Mr Douglas C. Anderson. (*b*) Action of the antibiotic, illustrated diagrammatically in energy circuit language. The work gate symbol, which is normally used for multiplicative effects, is shown containing a division sign, indicating that the output is some fraction of the interacting inputs.

regulatory role in microbial ecosystems in the soil. There is no doubt that substances with antibiotic properties are produced in soil under appropriate conditions, and microorganisms which are known from laboratory studies to produce antibiotics have been observed to antagonise root pathogens in the soil. However, unequivocal proof of their regulatory function is lacking.

Fungistasis

The phenomenon of antibiosis operates on a microscopic scale and is of limited duration, many antibiotics being rapidly deactivated in soil by adsorption on colloidal surfaces or degradation by the soil biota. There is, however, a long term and widespread inhibitory phenomenon in soils which is known as fungistasis or mycostasis. It was first demonstrated by C. G. Dobbs and W. H. Hinson, who placed spores of *Penicillium frequentans* in folds of cellophane, buried them in the soil, and found spore germination to be inhibited; the inhibitory principle is water soluble and diffusible.

Not all fungi are susceptible to fungistasis, and where it occurs the effect can be overcome by adding an appropriate energy and carbon source such as glucose. It can also be eliminated by 'partial sterilization' of the soil by steam or chemical fumigants, and reinstated by inoculating with a suspension of non-sterile soil. All this evidence points to fungistasis as being microbial in origin, and it was formerly thought to be due to the accumulation of antibiotics in sufficient quantities to give the soil as a whole antibiotic properties. If this were so, one would not expect fungistasis to be overcome by the addition of sugars. In any event, it is improbable that antibiotics could produce such a persistent and widespread effect. It is now generally believed that the primary causative factor is microbial competition for energy and nutrients in the immediate environment of the spore.

Predation and parasitism

In these cases of antagonism one organism is actually consumed by the other as a source of energy and materials for biosynthesis. A parasite lives either in or on its host, which is therefore both substrate and habitat to it whereas a predator tends to be free-living and uses its prey as a source of energy and nutrients but not as a habitat. There is, however, no clear line of demarcation between the two and they have a similar role in ecosystem regulation.

While predation is of common occurrence among biophagous soil animals, in the microbial world it is restricted to phagotrophic organisms like protozoa, which are built in such a way that they can engulf particles or even whole organisms. Microorganisms with cell walls, such as bacteria, fungi and algae, are not usually regarded as predators because the cell wall prevents entry of solid particles. Nevertheless the fungi which trap and digest nematodes are commonly referred to as predacious fungi. Bacteria form the staple food of soil protozoans and it is conceivable that the protozoa have a role in soil as regulators of the bacterial population.

While perhaps not so dramatic in its effects as predation, parasitism is also seen among soil microbes. Fungi may parasitize other fungi and this phenomenon is known as mycoparasitism. It is however difficult to distinguish this from the colonization and lysis of hyphae which have died from other causes. Nor is there conclusive evidence that bacteria can parasitize fungi, that is by actually penetrating fungal hyphae and destroying them from within. However, lytic enzymes produced by bacteria on the surface of fungi can digest living hyphae, and this can be seen to happen in soil using appropriate microscopic techniques. Lysis of fungi by extracellular enzymes is clearly a form of antagonism yet it cannot properly be described as parasitism. The infection and lysis of bacteria by phages is however clearly parasitism, although it is not known to what extent bacteriophages regulate bacterial populations in the soil. A little studied but apparently widespread soil organism is *Bdellovibrio*, a very small vibrio-like bacterium with a single polar flagellum which is highly motile and which attaches to the surface of bacteria, in particular gram-negative forms, causing them to lyse. It too may be of significance in the regulation of microbial ecosystems, although at the population densities so far reported (*ca.* 50 cells per gram) its effects are probably slight.

Commensalism and mutualism

Commensalism

Two broad groups of beneficial interactions may be recognized: one is termed commensalism, the other mutualism. In commensalistic relationships one organism benefits while the other is unaffected. Microbial succession provides numerous examples of commensalism. Among the pioneer organisms colonizing plant remains are some which decompose complex organic compounds and in so doing release simpler substances which serve as substrates for secondary colonizers. The relationship between cellulose decomposing fungi and secondary sugar fungi (p. 76) is a case in point. Again, there are many soil bacteria which will not grow in pure culture unless the medium is supplemented with water-soluble B-vitamins and amino acids. In nature, they are of necessity dependent on exudates of other microorganisms or plant roots for a supply of these growth substances. The widespread occurrence of such bacteria in soil is evidence that commensalism is among the major biological determinants of the composition of the soil microflora.

It has already been pointed out (p. 86) that two or more kinds of microbe are frequently associated in complementary niches and so are cooperative rather than competitive with respect to substrate. Complementarity of ecological niches is a form of commensalism and many examples can be cited. The provision of nitrite as a substrate for *Nitrobacter* by *Nitrosomonas* is one, as previously indicated, so too is the release of ammonium ions by bacterial deamination of amino acids to serve as a source of energy for *Nitrosomonas*. In fact, most of the transformations of sulphur, carbon and nitrogen in soil involve the production by some microbes of substances which can be used by others as sources of energy and materials.

Other examples of commensalism involve a change wrought by one organism in the physical environment which makes it favourable for the growth of another. Aerobes frequently reduce the redox potential of the environment to the point where anaerobes can grow, thus explaining why it is possible for obligate anaerobes such as clostridia to persist and grow in an essentially aerobic environment like soil. Similarly, osmophilic yeasts can grow in concentrated sugar solutions, and by utilizing the sugar they reduce the osmotic concentration to the point where less tolerant organisms can grow. Again, T. D. Brock has observed that hyphae of the zygomycete *Rhizopus nigricans* (syn. *R. stolonifer*) grow rapidly across the surface of an agar plate and provide a transportation route along which motile bacilli are able to travel, whereas the bacteria are unable to move across the surface of agar in the absence of the fungus. He has speculated that filamentous fungi might perform a similar function for motile bacteria in soil.

Mutualism

When an interaction between two organisms confers benefit on both, but is not obligatory for either, it is spoken of as protocooperation. Where the association is so close as to be obligatory for one or both partners it is referred to as mutualism. It is however often difficult to distinguish between the two. Among the best known cases of mutualism are those involving microorganisms and green plants, for example mycorrhizas and root nodules, and these will be discussed in subsequent chapters.

Bacteria of the genus *Azotobacter* assimilate molecular nitrogen but only simple organic compounds are suitable substrates for these bacteria in pure culture. H. L. Jensen and R. J. Swaby have shown, however, that N_2 could be fixed by *Azotobacter* using cellulose as an energy source provided a cellulose decomposer was present to convert the polysaccharide into simple sugars or organic acids. The cellulose decomposer benefited in turn from an increased supply of nitrogen. Since the association is not obligatory for either partner, the relationship is one of protocooperation.

Mutualistic associations between two microbes also exist, permitting the two organisms to grow together where neither could grow alone. Thus in a medium deficient in phenylalanine and folic acid neither *Streptococcus faecalis* nor *Lactobacillus arabinosis* can develop, since the former requires folic acid as a growth factor and the latter phenylalanine. Nevertheless, if the same medium is inoculated with a mixed culture, both organisms will grow because *Streptococcus* synthesizes and excretes phenylalanine, and *Lactobacillus* synthesizes and excretes folic acid.

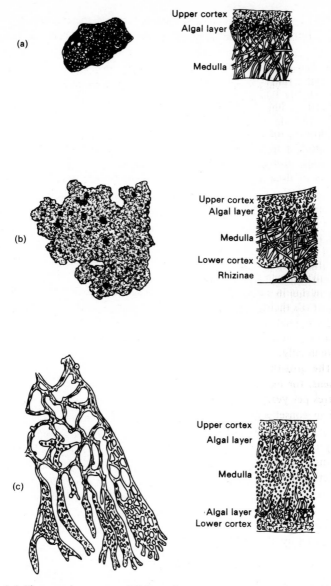

FIG. 4.6 Three major types of lichen. *(a)* Crustose lichen, which is closely appressed to the substratum. *(b)* Foliose lichen, which is leafy in form and loosely attached to the substratum. *(c)* Fructicose lichen, which may consist of pendulous or upright stalks. Vertical sections of crustose and foliose lichens, and a horizontal section of a fructicose lichen, are shown beside the corresponding diagrams. (From Stanier, R. Y. *et al.* (1970) *The Microbial World*, 3rd edn. Prentice-Hall © 1970. By permission of Prentice-Hall, Inc., Englewood Cliffs, New Jersey, USA. From V. Ahmadjian.)

A widespread mutualistic symbiosis is the association between an alga and a fungus which is known as a **lichen** (Fig. 4.6). The interaction between the two organisms results in a wide range of morphological adaptations but the functional relationship remains more or less constant, the alga providing carbon compounds as energy sources and vitamins for the fungus and the fungus apparently aiding the alga by the provision of mineral nutrients and water; the fungus also affords the alga some protection from the elements, especially from the deleterious effects of desiccation and high light intensity. Some lichens contain a blue-green alga that fixes atmospheric nitrogen and presumably some of this nitrogen is eventually passed on to the fungus (see Chapter 9). Of the 17 000 known species of lichen, only a few contain more than one alga and one fungus. The algae are generally greens or blue-greens, the fungi nearly all ascomycetes. Lichen fungi rarely if ever occur free-living in nature; the lichen algae may do so, but not usually under the exacting environmental conditions where lichens occur. In most lichens, the alga occurs in a narrow, clearly demarcated zone just beneath the surface of the thallus, with a thin, tough fungal cortex above and a thicker, looser hyphal medulla below. The symbionts are in intimate contact with each other, the algal cells being penetrated by fungal haustoria or, more usually, surrounded by closely appressed, modified hyphae.

The growth of lichens in nature is extremely slow, and crustose lichens, for example, increase in diameter at the rate of a few millimetres per year, at most. They are extremely sensitive to air pollutants and in consequence are rarely found in urban areas. Their great sensitivity to a polluted atmosphere is thought to be due to the fact that they absorb and concentrate nutrients from rainwater and possess no means of excreting them, so that toxic substances may rapidly build up to lethal levels. Many lichens live in habitats exposed to direct sunlight where they are subject to intense variations in environmental factors such as moisture and temperature. Under these conditions, organic compounds dissolved in rainwater may supplement the carbohydrates produced by algal photosynthesis although it is generally believed that net photosynthetic assimilation of carbon dioxide occurs in lichens, despite the adverse physical environment.

The algal component of the lichen excretes carbohydrate when in symbiosis with the fungus, but loses the ability to do so when grown in pure culture; it may also lose the capacity to synthesize the excreted carbohydrate altogether. In those lichens which contain blue-green algae the carbohydrate is transferred to the fungus as glucose, while those containing green algae transfer polyols (sugar alcohols). In both cases the lichen fungi convert the excreted carbohydrate into mannitol and thus maintain a concentration gradient from autotroph to heterotroph.

Biotic interactions in microbial succession

According to E. P. Odum, 'in the evolution and development of ecosystems negative interactions tend to be minimized in favour of positive symbiosis that enhances the survival of the interacting species'. Whether this statement applies to the soil—litter subsystem is not entirely clear. While many of the early colonizers of organic substrates are involved in negative interactions such as inhibition by antibiosis, e.g. penicillia and actinomycetes, these organisms are by no means confined to the pioneer stages of the sere. Nor is the production of antibiotics the sole province of those species which do not enter into mutualistic symbioses. D. H. Marx has shown, for example, that the mycorrhizal fungus *Leucopaxillus cerealis* var. *piceina* inhibits the root pathogen *Phytophthora cinnamomi* by producing the antibiotic diatretyne nitrile (see also Fig. 4.5). Furthermore, other positive symbioses such as commensalism seem also to occur at all stages of microbial succession.

The complexity, diversity and ephemeral nature of organic substrates, combined with the microscopic scale on which succession occurs in the soil ecosystem, make generalization difficult. At one and the same time, adjacent microhabitats may exhibit the two extremes of a successional series. Such a situation is not however incompatible with the achievement of overall homeostasis, by dominance of positive over negative interactions, in the total system of which the soil—litter subsystem is a part.

Selected references

Alexander, M. (1971) *Microbial Ecology.* Wiley.

Brock, T. D. (1966) *Principles of Microbial Ecology.* Prentice-Hall.

Gray, T. R. G. and Williams, S. T. (1971) *Soil Microorganisms.* Oliver and Boyd.

Garrett, S. D. (1970) *Pathogenic Root-infecting Fungi.* Cambridge University Press.

Odum, E. P. (1971) *Fundamentals of Ecology,* 3rd edn. Saunders.

Brian, P. W. (1957) 'The ecological significance of antibiotic production' in *Microbial Ecology* (Soc. Gen. Microbiol. 7th Symp.), eds. C. C. Spicer and R. E. O. Williams, pp. 168—88. Cambridge University Press.

Burges, N. A. (1960) 'Dynamic equilibria in the soil' in *The Ecology of Soil Fungi*, eds. D. Parkinson and J. S. Waid, pp. 185–91. Liverpool University Press.

Burges, A. (1965) 'The soil microflora – its nature and biology' in *Ecology of Soil-borne Plant Pathogens*, eds. K. F. Baker and W. C. Snyder, pp. 21–31. University of California Press.

Burges, A. (1967) 'The decomposition of organic matter in the soil' in *Soil Biology*, eds. A. Burges and F. Raw, pp. 479–92. Academic Press.

Clark, F. E. (1965) 'The concept of competition in microbial ecology' in *Ecology of Soil-borne Plant Pathogens*, eds. K. F. Baker and W. C. Snyder, pp. 339–45. University of California Press.

Clark, F. E. (1967) 'Bacteria in soil' in *Soil Biology*, eds. A. Burges and F. Raw, pp. 15–49. Academic Press.

Crocker, R. L. (1952) 'Soil genesis and the pedogenic factors', *Q. Rev. Biol.* **27**, 139–68.

Dobbs, C. G. and Hinson, W. H. (1953) 'A widespread fungistasis in the soil'. *Nature, Lond.*, **172**, 197.

Garrett, S. D. (1951) 'Ecological groups of soil fungi: a survey of substrate relationships'. *New Phytol.*, **50**, 149–66.

Griffin, D. M. (1960) 'Fungal colonization of sterile hair in contact with soil'. *Trans. Br. mycol. Soc.*, **43**, 583–96.

Griffin, D. M. (1969) 'Soil water in the ecology of fungi'. *A. Rev. Phytopath.*, **7**, 289–310.

Hirst, J. M. (1965) 'Dispersal of soil microorganisms' in *Ecology of Soil-borne Plant Pathogens*, eds. K. F. Baker and W. C. Snyder, pp. 69–81. University of California Press.

Hudson, H. J. (1968) 'The ecology of fungi on plant remains above the soil'. *New Phytol.*, **67**, 837–74.

Jackson, R. M. (1965) 'Antibiosis and fungistasis of soil microorganisms' in *Ecology of Soil-borne Plant Pathogens*, eds. K. F. Baker and W. C. Snyder, pp. 363–69. University of California Press.

Jenny, H. (1958) 'Role of the plant factor in the pedogenic functions'. *Ecology*, **39**, 5–16.

Jenny, H. (1961) 'Derivation of state factor equations of soils and ecosystems. *Soil Sci. Soc. Am. Proc.*, **25**, 385–88.

Jensen, H. L. and Swaby, R. J. (1941) 'Association between nitrogen-fixing and cellulose-decomposing micro-organisms'. *Nature, Lond.*, **147**, 147–8.

Kendrick, W. B. and Burges, A. (1962) 'Biological aspects of the decay of *Pinus sylvestris* leaf litter. *Nova Hedwig*, **4**, 313–42.

Kreutzer, W. A. (1965) 'The reinfestation of treated soil' in *Ecology of*

Soil-borne Plant Pathogens, eds. K. F. Baker and W. C. Snyder, pp. 495–507. University of California Press.

Lockwood, J. L. (1964) 'Soil fungistasis', *A. Rev. Phytopath.,* 2, 341–62.

Macauley, B. J. and Thrower, L. B. (1966) 'Succession of fungi in leaf litter of *Eucalyptus regnans'. Trans. Br. mycol. Soc.,* 49, 509–20.

Macfadyen, A. (1967) 'The animal habitat of soil bacteria' in *The Ecology of Soil Bacteria,* eds. T. R. G. Gray and D. Parkinson, pp. 66–76. Liverpool University Press.

Major, J. (1951) 'A functional, factorial approach to plant ecology'. *Ecology,* 32, 392–412.

Marx, D. H. (1969) 'The influence of ectotrophic mycorrhizal fungi on the resistance of pine roots to pathogenic infections. II. Production, identification, and biological activity of antibiotics produced by *Leucopaxillus cerealis* var. *piceina'. Phytopathology,* 59, 411–17.

Odum, E. P. (1969) 'The strategy of ecosystem development'. *Science,* 164, 262–70.

Park, D. (1965) 'Survival of microorganisms in soil' in *Ecology of Soil-borne Plant Pathogens,* eds. K. F. Baker and W. C. Snyder, pp. 82–97. University of California Press.

Park, D. (1967) 'The importance of antibiotics and inhibiting substances' in *Soil Biology,* eds. A. Burges and F. Raw, pp. 435–47. Academic Press.

Schultz, A. M. (1967) 'The ecosystem as a conceptual tool in the management of natural resources' in *Natural Resources: Quality and Quantity,* eds. S. V. Ciriacy-Wantrup and J. J. Parsons, pp. 139–61. University of California Press.

Smith, D., Muscatine, L. and Lewis, D. (1969) 'Carbohydrate movement from autotrophs to heterotrophs in parasitic and mutualistic symbiosis'. *Biol. Rev.,* 44, 17–90.

Stanier, R. Y. (1953) 'Adaptation, evolutionary and physiological: or Darwinism among the microorganisms' in *Adaptation in Microorganisms* (Soc. Gen. Microbiol. 3rd Symp.), eds. R. Davies and E. F. Gale, pp. 1–14. Cambridge University Press.

Tribe, H. T. (1957) 'Ecology of microorganisms in soils as observed during their development upon buried cellulose film' in *Microbial Ecology* (Soc. Gen. Microbiol. 7th Symp.), eds. C. C. Spicer and R. E. O. Williams, pp. 287–98. Cambridge University Press.

Waid, J. S. (1960) 'The growth of fungi in soil' in *The Ecology of Soil Fungi,* eds. D. Parkinson and J. S. Waid, pp. 55–75. Liverpool University Press.

Warcup, J. H. (1965) 'Growth and reproduction of soil microorganisms in relation to substrate' in *Ecology of Soil-borne Plant Pathogens*, eds. K. F. Baker and W. C. Snyder, pp. 52–67. University of California Press.

Warcup, J. H. (1967) 'Fungi in soil' in *Soil Biology*, eds. A. Burges and F. Raw, pp. 51–110. Academic Press.

Webley, D. M., Eastwood, D. J. and Gimmingham, C. H. (1952) 'Development of a soil microflora in relation to plant succession in sand dunes including rhizosphere flora associated with colonizing species'. *J. Ecol.*, **40**, 168–78.

Webster, J. (1970) 'Coprophilous fungi'. *Trans. Br. mycol. Soc.*, **54**, 161–80.

Wright, J. M. (1956) 'The production of antibiotics in soil. III. Production of gliotoxin in wheatstraw buried in soil'. *Ann. appl. Biol.*, **44**, 461–6.

5 Organic matter decomposition and energy flow

The flow of energy through the soil subsystem is bound up with the process of organic matter decomposition or carbon mineralization, both occurring concurrently and both being the province of the decomposer group of soil organisms, in particular the chemoheterotrophic microorganisms. Since for these microbes, the supply of substrates is a major limiting factor, a knowledge of the manner in which their activities are influenced by substrate availability is essential to an understanding of ecosystem function. There are other microbial groups, the phototrophs and chemoautotrophs, which are producer organisms but, as has already been noted (Chapter 1), their role in terrestrial ecosystems as organic matter accumulators is insignificant beside that of the vascular plants. Furthermore, when compared with the chemoheterotrophs, their part in energy and carbon transfers in such systems is slight also, so that they need not be considered further in this context.

Distribution of chemoheterotrophic microbes in relation to substrate

Chemoheterotrophic microorganisms are not distributed uniformly throughout the soil: on a microscopic scale there are large volumes of soil which appear to be unoccupied even though available for colonization (Fig. 5.1). Knowledge of the actual extent of microbial habitats is very slight, but it must be emphasized that the scale is minute. As R. Y. Stanier has pointed out, 'a single cellulose fibre provides a specialized environment with its own characteristic microflora, yet may occupy a volume of not more than a cubic millimetre'. While it is difficult to determine the individual factors that control the distribution of microorganisms, there seems little doubt that the primary limiting factor for chemoheterotrophs is the availability of substrate. Substrates for these organisms have been defined by S. D. Garrett as 'living or dead, virgin or partially decomposed plant or animal tissues lying in or

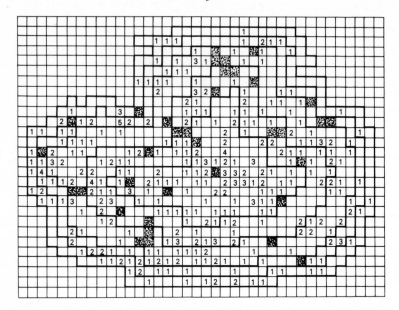

FIG. 5.1 Distribution of microorganisms in soil. Plan of a section through a soil crumb, with figures indicating the number of bacterial colonies per 70 μm square; shaded squares are empty or obscured by debris. (From Jones, D. and Griffiths, E. (1964) *Plant Soil*, **20**, 232–40.)

upon the soil, or soluble products diffusing therefrom'. The addition to soil of carbonaceous materials such as these greatly increases the number and activity of chemoheterotrophs, and in particular it activates the so-called zymogenous fraction of the population, i.e. those organisms that depend upon an external source of energy and nutrients, in the absence of which they remain quiescent (see p. 104). Among the fungi, for example, genera such as *Penicillium, Aspergillus, Trichoderma, Fusarium* and *Mucor* become dominant.

Within the soil, chemoheterotrophs are characteristically concentrated in the upper part of the profile. In podzols and podzolic soils, most are found in the A_1 horizon (Table 5.1). This pattern of distribution is not unexpected, since most of the organic matter in podzols and podzolics is found in the A_1 horizon. However, a similar pattern exists in soils where the organic matter is distributed more uniformly throughout the profile, so that factors other than energy supply must be limiting also. The most likely explanation of this phenomenon lies in the change which occurs in the soil atmosphere with depth. In general, as one proceeds farther from the surface, oxygen becomes depleted and the carbon dioxide concentration rises, and either or both of these

TABLE 5.1 Distribution of chemoheterotrophic microbes throughout the profile of a podzol soil*

Horizon	Depth (cm)	Numbers of microbes per gram $(\times 10^3)$			
		Aerobic bacteria	Anaerobic bacteria	Actino-mycetes	Fungi
A_1	3–8	7 800	1 950	2 080	119
A_2	20–25	1 804	379	245	50
A_2/B	35–40	472	98	49	14
B_1	65–75	10	1	5	6
B_2	135–145	1	0.4	–	3

* After Starc, A. (1942) *Arch. Mikrobiol.*, **12**, 329–52.

factors may limit the development of chemoheterotrophic micro-organisms.

Some substrates for chemoheterotrophs in soil originate from the roots of vascular plants. These substrates may be organic materials sloughed off from the roots or exuded by them. The presence of such substrates markedly affects the kinds and abundance of soil micro-organisms in the immediate neighbourhood of roots, and gives rise to what is known as the 'rhizosphere effect'. This will be discussed further in Chapter 7.

When the soil ecosystem approaches a steady state, the gross pattern of distribution of substrates does not change appreciably with the passage of time. On a microscopic scale however, there are still vast changes, and these changes occur from place to place at any one time, and from time to time in any one place. Of paramount importance is the fact that substrates for chemoheterotrophs in soil are ephemeral. Consequently the distribution of such microbes or their propagules is determined not only by the present, but also by the past, disposition of their substrates.

Types of substrates in the soil

Soil organic matter derives from several different sources, being the re-mains of dead plants and animals and their excretory products in various stages of decomposition, the final stage being known as humus (pp. 15, 103). The cells of microbes themselves also serve as substrates for succeeding generations of microbes. In fact, any organic compound that is synthesized biologically is subject to decomposition by soil microorganisms, provided the environmental conditions are appropriate.

The kinds of compounds available as microbial substrates are therefore enormous. Since each individual organism has an enzyme complex which enables it to attack only a certain number of these compounds, a knowledge of those which can be used as substrates by a particular microbe is useful in studying its ecology. Such information can be obtained from pure culture studies in the laboratory, but care is needed in transposing laboratory results to the field, for it cannot be assumed, just because an organism is capable of utilizing a specific substance in a test tube or petri dish, that it will utilize that compound as a substrate in the soil. Thus cellulose decomposing fungi will grow very well on simple sugars in pure culture, but in the highly competitive environment of the soil they may seldom have the opportunity of attacking such substrates.

While simple organic compounds do occur in soil, particularly during the decomposition of organic residues, or as exudates of plant roots, most natural substrates for microbial growth are complex, rarely being composed of a single substance. The most abundant substrates for soil microorganisms are cellulose, hemicellulose, lignin, chitin and humus.

Cellulose. Because a large part of the plant debris added to soil is cellulose, the decomposition of this carbohydrate has been closely studied. Cellulose is a long-chain polymer formed by the condensation together of adjacent glucose molecules. Decomposition of cellulose in soil is slow. Relatively few animals are able to decompose it and most of those which do depend on the cellulolytic ability of symbiotic microorganisms, such as bacteria in the rumen of cattle, and protozoa in the gut of termites. Cellulose decomposing microbes in soil include many fungi, and a few aerobic and anaerobic bacteria, actinomycetes, protozoa and myxobacteria. The heterogeneous nature of the cellulolytic microflora permits of decomposition over a wide range of environmental conditions.

Hemicellulose. Polysaccharides known as hemicelluloses are among the major plant constituents added to soil, second only in quantity to cellulose. Hemicelluloses are subject to decomposition by a wider range of microorganisms than is cellulose, and decomposition is faster. The name hemicellulose is unfortunate, because the molecule is not structurally related to cellulose. The hemicelluloses are a class of water-insoluble polysaccharides which may be extracted from plant tissues by dilute alkali; when hydrolysed with hot, dilute mineral acids they yield hexoses and pentoses, and some also uronic acids.

Lignin. Another abundant constituent of plant tissues, especially of woody plants, is lignin.* Not a great deal is known of its chemistry, except that it is a complex polymer built up of subunits of an aromatic nature, and that different kinds of lignin vary in their basic units. Lignin probably never occurs free, but usually mixed with cellulose to a greater or lesser degree. As the lignin content of plant tissues increases, the ability of soil microorganisms to decompose them decreases. The main lignin decomposers are basidiomycetes, though a few other fungi and some bacteria of the genus *Pseudomonas* have been shown to effect its breakdown.

Chitin. The most common polysaccharide whose basic unit is an amino sugar is chitin. It consists of N-acetyl glucosamine units linked together like the glucose units of cellulose. The exoskeletons of crustaceans and insects are composed of chitin. It also occurs in the hyphal walls of many fungi, and substantial quantities become incorporated in soils. Chitin utilizing microbes include bacteria and actinomycetes, and some fungi.

Humus. This is the name given to the amorphous, dark-coloured, colloidal organic material found in soils. It has a high cation exchange capacity and a high water-holding capacity. It is not a single chemical substance, but can be extracted from soil and fractionated by appropriate techniques. A small portion consists of water-soluble substances such as sugars and amino acids, but the greater part is insoluble in water. The major fraction, called humic acid, is believed to be produced by oxidative polymerization of a mixture of phenols and additional compounds derived from lignins, proteins and other metabolites of the soil biota; the properties of the resulting very large molecule derive mainly from its surface carboxyl groups. There is evidence that the chemical nature of humic acid differs from one soil type to another, so that its composition cannot be regarded as fixed.

Although humus represents the final stage of organic matter decomposition in soil, it would be a mistake to regard it simply as the resistant residue of plant and animal detritus. It is also, in fact, a product of microbial biosynthesis, and furthermore it remains subject to microbial decomposition, albeit slowly.

Microbial growth in relation to substrate

Substrates for microbial growth in soils vary not only in kind but also in amount, and this variability affects some groups of microbes more

* Lignin and cellulose together make up about 80–90 per cent of wood, there being about twice as much cellulose as lignin.

than others. The **zymogenous** microflora, normally present in the resting stage, becomes active whenever fresh organic materials are added.
The **autochthonous** or indigenous microflora, which characteristically
exists in the vegetative phase and is more or less continuously active, is
believed to utilize as substrates humic materials and the fatty residues
from cuticular waxes and cutins. Knowledge of the actual species of
microbes that break down humus is limited, but actinomycetes are
known to be involved. Both bacteria and actinomycetes are able to decompose cutins and waxes. Whether any fungi are truly autochthonous
is not certain, although some species are characteristically present in
soil as active hyphae. It can only be inferred that such fungi form part
of the autochthonous microflora, since little is known of their nutrition. There is no doubt however that soil contains a large number of
inactive fungal propagules of various kinds: 'resting hyphae', sclerotia,
and various kinds of spores, particularly chlamydospores, sporangiospores and conidia. These spores and other resting fungal structures in
soil, with the possible exception of sclerotia, appear to germinate only
when in contact with an external source of nutrients, such as roots,
germinating seeds, and decomposing plant and animal remains (see
p. 89). After germination, growth of fungi depends on a continuing
supply of energy, together with the necessary nutrients and a suitable
physical environment. As J. H. Warcup has pointed out, a source of
energy and nutrients sufficient for the growth and multiplication of a
bacterium may be barely adequate for a germinating fungal spore and
quite inadequate to sustain extensive mycelial development. Unless the
external supply is maintained, lysis of the hyphae takes place or else the
fungus forms a resting structure such as a chlamydospore.

It is not uncommon for some fungi to be closely associated with
specific substrates and to make little free growth in the soil itself.
Typical are the sugar fungi, whose capacity to germinate and grow
rapidly on simple carbohydrates permits them to burst into activity
whenever suitable substrates become available. Between the exhaustion
of one substrate and the appearance of another, most sugar fungi lie
dormant as spores. Other fungi, especially higher ascomycetes and
basidiomycetes, which have longer-lived mycelia, may make more
extensive growth through soil, travelling from substrate to substrate by
means of rhizomorphs or mycelial strands. Such behaviour is typical of
the lignin fungi which utilize, in addition to lignin, cellulose and simpler
compounds if they are available.

Effect of food supply on the soil fauna

Osmotrophs, as typified by fungi and bacteria, may or may not utilize the same substance both as a substrate for energy-yielding oxidations and as a source of nutrients. In contrast to this, the food of phago-trophs must provide both energy and nutrients. The feeding habits of large animals can be readily determined by observation, but many members of the soil fauna are too small to be observed directly, and consequently our knowledge of the food supply of soil animals is in-complete.

Food source as a basis of classification

Following the classification of chemoheterotrophs given in Chapter 3, they may be divided into biophages and saprophages, but this classifica-tion is too broad to be of much value in determining their food relationships, and each category is normally subdivided further. Saprophages include those animals which feed on dead vegetable matter (detritivores), carrion (cadavericoles) or dung (coprophages). Biophages include species which feed on living plants, especially roots, or on freshly fallen green leaves (phytophages), or on microorganisms (micro-bivores, fungivores), or on living animals as predators (carnivores) and parasites. These various classes of soil animals will be discussed briefly in turn.

Phytophages. Many different kinds of sucking insects, e.g. cicada nymphs and aphids, and numerous chewing insects, e.g. mole-crickets, beetle, fly and moth larvae, feed on plant roots. Millipedes, woodlice, slugs and snails may also feed on living plants, though normally their diet is restricted to decaying material. Termites and ants may some-times attack surface vegetation. Freshly fallen leaves are devoured by a wide variety of soil animals, many of which may occasionally attack live plants. Soil algae are ingested by certain amoebae.

Detritivores. Representatives of the majority of taxonomic groups of soil inhabiting invertebrates consume dead organic matter in varying stages of decomposition. For many of these animals, it is not certain whether their food supply is the detritus itself or the associated micro-organisms of decay. When organic matter is ingested, compounds such as hemicellulose and cellulose are usually digested through the agency of an internal symbiotic microflora, although there is evidence that a few animals synthesize their own cellulase, e.g. earthworms and molluscs, and possibly some nematodes.

Carrion feeders. The common decomposers of the carcasses of verte-brates are the larvae of flies and beetles which are not regarded as members of the soil fauna. Many soil animals do not appear to possess the enzymes necessary to digest animal protein, and hence do not feed on carrion. The bodies of many invertebrates decay rapidly in the soil, but the chitinous exoskeletons of arthropods are subject to decomposition by few animals. Fungi are the most important chitin decomposing soil organisms, though chitinase is found in the alimentary tract of some nematodes, earthworms and molluscs.

Coprophages. Apart from the dung of surface-dwelling vertebrates, which is inhabited by many, often specialized, invertebrate animals, large quantities of excrement are produced by the soil fauna itself. Faecal pellets are utilized by bacteria and fungi, together with a great variety of small arthropods, especially springtails and nematodes. Russian workers have found that enchytraeids reproduce rapidly in forest litter, provided it contains caterpillar faeces. Enchytraeid excrement is in its turn eaten by earthworms, the casts of which provide a favourable habitat for certain beetles. The reingestion of microbially enriched faeces, i.e. coprophagy, may prove to be of great significance in the functioning of the soil ecosystem.

Microbivores. Fungi and other protists constitute an important part of the diet of many soil animals which might otherwise be classified as detritivores. In fact, the food relationships of these two trophic groups (microbivores and detritivores) are often so complex and intertwined that it is impossible to separate saprophage from biophage: many soil animals can apparently be either or both, as the occasion demands. Nevertheless, there are some forms which are noted for their habit of grazing upon fungal mycelia, and fungivores may provide over half the soil faunal biomass. Included here are certain families of beetles and the larvae of some flies. Many oribatid mites are fungivorous and seem to ingest plant detritus for the decay fungi associated with it. These mites, and some springtails, may be quite selective in their choice of fungi and bacteria for food.

Carnivores. In this group also it is frequently difficult to distinguish between true carnivores (biophages) and carrion feeders (saprophages). Exclusively predatory and parasitic forms do exist however, in many taxa. Arthropods and small annelid worms are preyed upon by various centipedes, spiders and beetle larvae. Predators of the smaller members of the mesofauna include many species of mite, and numerous fly and beetle larvae. Nematodes are voracious predators of other nematodes, small enchytraeid worms, and protozoa. Many rotifers and all turbellarians are also predacious, and are relatively unselective in their choice of prey. In addition to these predatory forms, there are some which are parasitic on other animals, including many species of endozoic protozoa and nematodes, and numerous ectoparasitic mites.

Population regulation

As indicated above, restriction to one particular source of food is rare among soil animals. Predators may select from a variety of prey animals, detritivores may occasionally graze on fungal mycelia, and fungivores may change their diet and become detritus feeders should the need arise. In any soil with a well developed organic horizon, therefore, adult members of the soil fauna are unlikely to die from starvation. Nevertheless, there is some evidence that food shortages lead to increased mortality of some immature forms of soil animals, e.g. the larvae of some mites. In general however, the influence of food supply on fecundity seems to be more important in population regulation than is any effect it might have on mortality. The size of animal populations is a function of the interaction between natality and immigration on the one hand, and mortality and emigration on the other. Migration is not an important factor in the biology of most soil animals, as it is for example with leaf-eating insects. This means that the balance between natality and mortality determines population size, so that any factor which influences either the birth rate or death rate may act in a regulatory fashion to stabilize populations.

Diet may affect reproductive performance in some soil animals, although this matter has been little studied. It is known however, that a diet high in protein stimulates reproduction in earthworms, and that when protein supply is limiting, competition for food intensifies. Competition for available prey might well therefore regulate the populations of predators, though again there is little experimental evidence that such a mechanism is operative in the soil ecosystem. There are however data to show that predators themselves have a strong regulating influence on the populations of other soil animals, notably beetles, nematodes, and possibly fly larvae.

Biotic factors such as competition and predation often act in a 'density-dependent' manner, the effect on population size being a function of population density. Populations may also be regulated by environmental factors, which tend to be 'density-independent', in other words their effect is more or less constant over a wide range of population densities. Both kinds of factors are probably operative in most ecosystems, the density-independent mechanisms predominating in ecosystems of low diversity under conditions of environmental stress, the density-dependent agents in high-diversity ecosystems not subject to environmental extremes. In systems of the first kind, population fluctuations are usually large and irregular, whereas the second type of system displays relatively minor oscillations of population density around some steady state value. Furthermore, regulation appears to be achieved, in some populations, by the interaction of density-dependent and density-independent factors. For example, climatic conditions determine the length of the breeding system in many soil animals, and this independent variable probably acts in conjunction with predation to control the size of faunal populations in the soil.

The process of organic matter decomposition

Much discussion revolves around the relative contributions of the several components of the soil biota to organic matter decomposition and energy flow in the soil subsystem. The softer tissues of plants and small animals are believed to be decomposed by microbes alone, but the breakdown of more refractory tissues involves the combined activities of the soil flora and fauna. Some tissues decompose at the soil surface, releasing soluble products which diffuse into the soil. On the other hand, fresh organic matter may be incorporated directly into soil, by earthworms for example, before any decomposition takes place.

Chemical analyses of the food and faeces of microarthropods reveal little difference in the composition of ingested and egested materials: net assimilation of ingested litter by soil animals is less than 10 per cent, easily digestible sugars and proteins being the major constituents utilized. In view of this, the main contribution of the soil fauna to organic matter decomposition is thought to be an increase in the surface area available for microbial attack as a result of their comminution of the detritus. For this reason, some authorities speak of the action of animals as 'breakdown' and restrict the use of the term 'decomposition' to the activities of the microflora.

The importance of physical breakdown by the macrofauna and the larger members of the mesofauna is clearly shown when discs cut from leaves of plants are placed in nylon mesh bags and buried in the soil or litter. The results of one such experiment are shown in Fig. 5.2. Bags made from mesh with a 7 mm opening, large enough to allow entry of all microbes and most invertebrates (see Fig. 2.13), permitted more rapid decomposition of the leaf discs than those made from mesh of 0.5 mm, through which only microorganisms, mites, springtails and

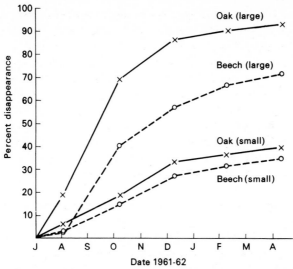

FIG. 5.2 Breakdown of plant litter by soil animals, as shown by the effect of mesh size on the decomposition of oak and beech leaves in nylon bags. The larger mesh (7 mm) admitted most invertebrates while the smaller (0.5 mm) excluded all but small nematodes and small arthropods such as mites and springtails. (From Edwards, C. A. and Heath, G. W. (1963) in *Soil Organisms*, eds J. Doeksen and J. van der Drift, North-Holland.)

other small arthropods and small nematodes could pass. Leaf discs placed in bags made from mesh of 0.003 mm size, to which only micro-organisms gained access, remained intact throughout the duration of the experiment, a period of about nine months.

These results illustrate unequivocally how the mesofauna in particular disintegrates plant litter in forest ecosystems and in the process makes it more susceptible to microbial attack. In grassland ecosystems, leaves are generally softer and more readily decomposable, and breakdown by the soil fauna has a less conspicuous role. The surface area of plant detritus in forests may be increased by up to several orders of magnitude by the action of the meso- and macrofauna. The faecal pellets which result maintain a more favourable moisture status than does unaltered plant litter, and are more readily moved down into the litter layer by percolating water or gravitational forces. Whether any significant chemical changes take place in the organic matter during its passage through the animal gut is a more contentious issue than the extent to which physical changes occur. While the composition of faecal matter is generally very similar to that of food prior to ingestion, some enzymatic degradation no doubt takes place (as a result of cellulase production, for example), and a slight rise in pH occurs, during passage through the gut. These changes, however small, when combined with better moisture relationships, make faecal material a very suitable substrate for microbial, and especially bacterial, exploitation.

Organic matter decomposition in the soil thus depends on the integrated activities of microbes and small animals. The degree of physical breakdown depends not only on the anatomy of the leaves but also on the kinds of animal involved. The various litter-feeding species have their own peculiar patterns of leaf consumption, some mining the internal parenchyma tissues, others consuming the cuticle and epidermal cells, still others reducing the leaf to a skeleton of vascular tissue, and so on. In mor soils, where the fauna consists principally of oribatid mites and collembola, plant residues with well preserved cellular structure may be found in the uppermost mineral horizon. In mull soils, where the fauna is more varied and numerous, all plant structures are completely destroyed; furthermore, many of the larger animals ingest mineral particles along with their food, thus promoting the formation of soil aggregates.

Measurement of carbon mineralization and energy flow

Qualitative studies of microbial growth in relation to substrate, e.g. successional studies (Chapter 4), or on soil animals in relation to food supply, do not throw much light on the contribution of decomposer organisms to energy flow in ecosystems, nor on the relative importance of various taxonomic groups. Unfortunately, there are considerable technical difficulties involved in working out energy budgets for the soil biota, and as a result the data on energy release and carbon mineralization by the decomposers are not nearly so extensive, nor as reliable, as those relating to energy capture and CO_2 fixation by the producers. An analysis of energy flow, or of the carbon cycle, in the soil ecosystem requires a population energy budget or carbon budget for each recognizable trophic group, to provide the basis for constructing a detailed food chain or food web. It is customary to recognize two kinds of food chains, viz. the **grazing food chain** and the **detritus food chain** (Fig. 5.3). Such a model is however inadequate to represent the complexity of the decomposer group. Little more can be deduced from it than an appreciation of the overall importance of the soil biota in the energetics of terrestrial ecosystems, relative to that of the other biotic components.

As previously indicated (p. 12), the soil as an ecosystem differs from the soil—plant system in that the autotrophic component is in-

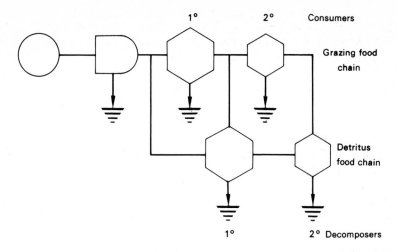

FIG. 5.3 A two-channel food chain – the standard trophic model – depicted in energy circuit language.

significant, except in those instances where the soil surface is directly exposed to insolation, in which event soil algae may become important as producers. In most soil ecosystems, however, the energy source is the bound chemical energy of organic matter produced mainly by vascular plants. A substantial amount of this photosynthate finds its way into the detritus pathway of the soil–litter system, as much as 85 per cent in a *Spartina* salt marsh in Georgia, USA (Table 5.2). In contrast, a substantial fraction (one-third) of the net production in a meadow system is grazed by herbivores. This table also indicates that in the woodland and forest ecosystems, respiration of the producer plants utilizes a larger fraction of the gross production (due to their larger biomass compared to grasslands), leaving less to be passed on to the other trophic levels. Furthermore, in the examples given, a greater proportion of the net production in woodland passes through the grazing food chain than in the marsh or pasture: phytophagous insects may thus figure more prominently in silviculture than the more conspicuous herbivorous mammals in agriculture. It would be unwise to accept this as a generality, however. The weight of evidence (e.g. p. 129) is that in forest ecosystems the detritus food chain is unquestionably the major pathway of energy flow, only a few per cent of net primary production being captured by leaf-eating insects, except when insect populations reach plague proportions and massive defoliation results. Perhaps the most important point to note about Table 5.2 is that, although gross production varies widely, net primary production is fairly constant; it is

TABLE 5.2 Fate of primary production in different ecosystems*

System	Gross primary production†	Producer respiration†	Net primary production†		
			Total	Eaten	Decomposed
Spartina salt marsh	1.17 (100)	0.10 (9)	1.07 (91)	0.07 (6)	1.00 (85)
Meadow, grazed	1.17 (100)	0.12 (10)	1.05 (90)	0.39 (33)	0.66 (56)
Beech wood, Denmark	2.35 (100)	1.00 (43)	1.35 (57)	0.95 (40)	0.40 (17)
Rain forest, Ivory Coast	5.35 (100)	4.00 (75)	1.35 (26)	0.90 (17)	0.45 (9)

* After Macfadyen, A. (1970) 'Soil metabolism in relation to ecosystem energy flow and to primary and secondary production' in *Methods of Study in Soil Ecology*, ed. J. Phillipson. UNESCO, Paris.
† Units are dry matter equivalents in kg/m²/yr.

in the partitioning of this net production among the different trophic levels that large differences occur from one ecosystem to another.

Methods of measuring soil metabolism

The realization that such a large part of the net primary production passes into the soil-litter subsystem, and is decomposed there, is fairly recent. The study of organic matter decomposition in soil has therefore assumed great significance, not only because so much of the energy captured by photosynthesis is released by it, but also (and perhaps more importantly) because it is only during this dissipation of energy that nutrients bound in the organic form are 'mineralized', and so made available for recycling through the vegetation subsystem. The cycling of carbon is discussed later in this chapter, while the mineralization of other important plant nutrients is treated in detail in Chapter 6.

Soil metabolism reflects the energy demands of the soil biota. There are several ways in which it may be determined, viz. (1) by difference, (2) by litter fall, (3) by soil respiration, and (4) by litter decomposition. These will be described in turn.

(1) Difference method

If the energy consumed by above-ground herbivores can be determined, and subtracted from net primary production, then the remainder (in a steady state system) represents energy flowing through the decomposer component. Several estimates of soil metabolism have been made in this way. While sound in theory, it results in practice in estimates which are often inaccurate and imprecise, because it compounds errors made in the determination of net primary production and herbivore consumption. Independent estimates should therefore be made of the energy input to the decomposer unit, by measuring litter fall for example.

(2) Litter fall method

In a steady state system, the annual input of litter and the amount of it which is decomposed annually should be equal. Litter fall, consisting of leaves and other plant parts, can be measured directly by catching the litter in suitably designed litter traps. Excrement of herbivorous and carnivorous animals is not usually caught in these traps, and should be determined separately; an appreciable amount of readily decomposable organic matter is added to some soil ecosystems from this source.

In forests, the annual rate of litter fall increases directly with decreasing latitude and altitude from about 100 g/m^2 in arctic/alpine forests to over 1 000 g/m^2 in equatorial lowland forests. The litter fall method is not however readily applicable to grasslands because of the difficulty of collecting litter and measuring its production accurately in grassland communities. Another defect of this method is that it fails to take into account the input of detritus from root systems, so that estimates of energy input from litter fall are underestimates because they ignore the respiration of plant roots and their associated microflora (see Chapter 7).

The decomposition constant. The amount of litter that accumulates on the surface of the mineral soil depends on the balance between the rate of litter fall and the speed with which it decays once it reaches the soil. Different kinds of forest ecosystems differ in the rates at which organic matter decomposition proceeds. The overall rate will obviously depend on such factors as the degree of lignification of the tissues being decomposed, and on the prevailing climate and weather patterns. Decomposition is generally more rapid in hot climates than in cold. This is illustrated by the fact that less litter accumulates on the soil surface in tropical forest ecosystems than in cool temperate forests, despite the fact that, as indicated above, the rate of litter production is higher in the former. The account which follows is based on the approach of J. S. Olson.

If X represents the accumulated surface litter, and L the amount of new litter added each year by the process of leaf fall, then the rate of change in X is given by the expression:

$$dX/dt = L - kX \tag{1}$$

where k is a constant which may be called the 'decomposition constant'.

For an ecosystem in steady state, X is constant, i.e. $dX/dt = 0$. Thus in the steady state condition, the following relationships hold:

$$L = kX, \ k = L/X \tag{2}$$

The decomposition constant k can therefore be estimated by measuring L and X in ecosystems assumed to be in steady state. Some values of k obtained in this fashion are: 0.025 for ponderosa pine forests in the Sierra Nevada mountains of western USA, 0.25 for southern pine forests in south-eastern USA, and 4.0 for tropical lowland rainforest in Africa (Fig. 5.4).

The decomposition constant may be used to calculate the time needed for a given fraction of the accumulated litter to decompose,

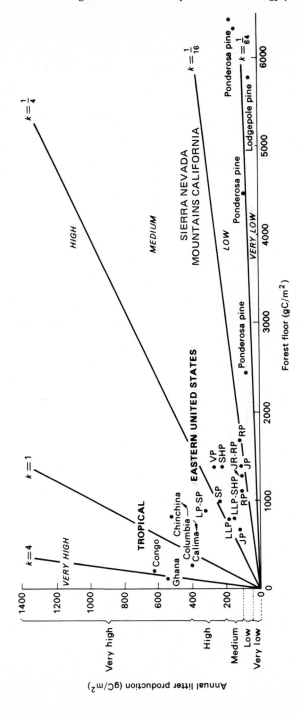

FIG. 5.4 The decomposition constant *k*, estimated for various evergreen forests from the ratio of annual litter production to the amount of litter accumulated on the forest floor. (From Olson, J. S. (1963) *Ecology*, **44**, 322–31, by permission of the Duke Press.)

assuming no further additions of litter are made. This is a special case of eq. (1) which thus becomes:

$$dX/dt = -kX \qquad (3)$$

According to this expression, the decay rate (dX/dt) is proportional to the amount of litter present. This situation is analogous to the phenomenon of radioactive decay, and we may calculate a theoretical 'half-life' for the litter analogous to the half-life of a radionuclide.

Equation (3) may be rewritten as follows:

$$\frac{1}{dX/dt} = \frac{1}{-kX}$$

$$\therefore \frac{dt}{dX} = \frac{1}{-kX}$$

Integrating, we have:

$$t = -\frac{1}{k} \int \frac{1}{X} dX$$

i.e.
$$t = -\frac{1}{k} \ln X + C \qquad (4)$$

Multiplying eq. (4) by k and rearranging, gives the following relationship:

$$\ln X = -k(t - C)$$

which may be written in exponential form as:

$$X = A e^{-kt} \qquad (5)$$

where A is a constant. If when $t = 0$, $X = X_0$, then A is replaced by X_0 and eq. (5) becomes:

$$X = X_0 e^{-kt} \qquad (6)$$

To calculate the 'half-life' of the litter, i.e. the time taken for half of the total amount present at time zero to be reduced by one half, put $X = X_0/2$ in eq. (6), which then becomes:

$$X_0/2 = X_0 e^{-kt_{1/2}}$$

Dividing by X_0, transposing, and taking logarithms, we have:

$$\ln 0.5 = -kt_{1/2}$$

$$\therefore t_{1/2} = -\ln 0.5/k = 0.693/k$$

Substituting the values of k given previously for the several ecosystems, half-times for litter breakdown are found to be over twenty years in the subalpine ponderosa pine forests, two to three years in the subtropical southern pine communities, and less than one year in tropical rainforests.

(3) Soil respiration methods

It is possible to determine the respiratory activity of the soil biota by the techniques of respirometry and/or gas analysis. Either or both O_2 uptake and CO_2 output may be measured, although most variants of the method are based on the latter. They all tend to overestimate the contribution of decomposers to total soil metabolism because it is impossible to distinguish the CO_2 evolved from roots from that respired by the soil fauna and microflora. Root respiration is largely an unknown factor, although rough estimates have been made which show the effect to be more significant in woodland and forest than in grassland.

Early methods of measuring soil respiration *in situ* frequently involved the pumping of air over the soil, and gave estimates which were far too high, because CO_2 trapped in the soil pores was included along with the respiratory output. Improved techniques involve the use of boxes or cylinders inverted over representative portions of the soil surface, these small chambers being sealed for only short periods during which measurements are recorded. Even so, sources of error remain. Root respiration is still included, for example. In addition, mechanical disturbance of the soil during installation of the chambers can stimulate metabolic activity. Finally, temperature and humidity changes within the small chambers can change the rate of CO_2 evolution from the soil—litter system.

Although soil respiration determinations must be made in the field to be of any value in ecosystem analysis, laboratory studies with the Warburg respirometer can provide realistic comparisons between various soils, even when air-dried and rewetted soil samples are used. They also provide a means of studying the effect of environmental factors on organic matter decomposition, under controlled and reproducible conditions. Other laboratory studies, involving terrestrial microcosms (terraria), may prove of value in the testing of trophic models of real soil ecosystems.

(4) Litter decomposition method

If weighed samples of litter are placed in mesh bags made of nylon or fibreglass, the decomposition rate can be determined by periodically reweighing them. By using bags of different mesh size, particular groups of soil organisms can be excluded, while those entering the bags can be readily extracted, and some idea of the relative contributions of the various taxonomic groups obtained (see Fig. 5.2).

Population energy budgets

As indicated earlier (p. 110), the traditional trophic model is inadequate for proper consideration of the energetics of the soil ecosystem. This matter has been discussed recently by R. G. Weigert and his colleagues at the University of Georgia. The problem is partly one of nomenclature, the traditional terminology (producer, consumer, decomposer)

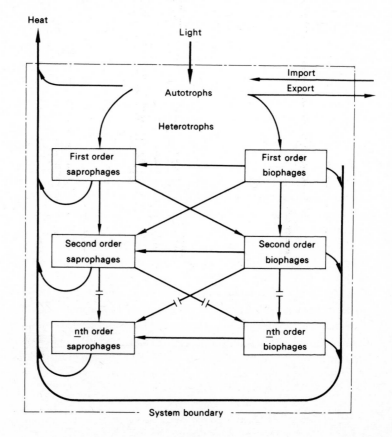

(a)

tending to obscure the primary trophic differentiation into autotrophs and heterotrophs. A further complication is the fact that the name 'decomposer' is applied generally to such a heterogeneous collection of soil organisms. An improvement over the simple trophic model, which shows a single energy pathway through the soil (the detritus food chain), is one which shows two parallel pathways, separated according to whether the energy (food) source is live or dead (Fig. **5.5**). This modified trophic model uses the classification of biophage and saprophage, introduced in Chapter 3. Saprophages might be regarded as the 'true' decomposers; biophages include both grazers and predators. The first order heterotrophs of the soil subsystem are mostly saprophages, though first order biophages may be present also, e.g. larvae and nematodes which feed on plant roots or amoebae that ingest soil algae. In addition, both higher order saprophages and biophages are a feature of the soil ecosystem.

The modified trophic model shown in Fig. 5.5 has the advantage of permitting separate consideration of saprophages subsisting at different trophic levels. It is still limited, however, by the occurrence of a single species at more than one level, and by the fact that some animals

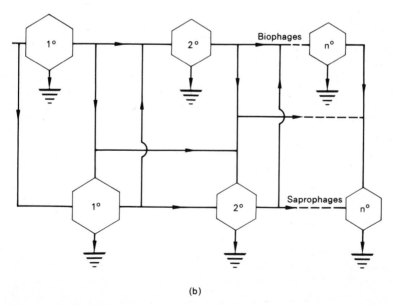

(b)

FIG. 5.5 *(a)* Modified trophic model for the soil-litter subsystem. (From Weigert, R. G. *et al.* (1970) in *Methods of Study in Soil Ecology*, ed. J. Phillipson, UNESCO, Paris.) *(b)* Energy network diagram showing details of the detritus food chain in the soil.

apparently alternate between biophagy and saprophagy. Because of these limitations, it may be better to revert to a single species population model which, although it may not so readily distinguish between biophagy and saprophagy, at least will permit the contribution of a single species to energy flow to be evaluated. In any event, whatever model is used, the determination of the **population energy budget** is basic to any analysis of ecosystem energetics.

Following Weigert *et al.*, a simplified population energy budget may be expressed by the following equation (neglecting work exchanges with the system surroundings, which are quantitatively negligible):

$$I = P + R + E \tag{7}$$

where I = ingestion or consumption, i.e. chemical energy content of ingested matter;

P = production, i.e. chemical energy content of materials synthesized;

R = respiratory heat loss, i.e. the net heat exchange between the population and its surroundings;

E = egestion, i.e. chemical energy content of egested matter.

The production component may be further subdivided into growth and yield, if necessary, and the energy equation then becomes:

$$I = G + Y + R + E \tag{8}$$

where G = growth, i.e. chemical energy content of matter represented by the increase in biomass or standing crop;

Y = yield, i.e. chemical energy content of matter lost to a subsequent level.

A simple flow diagram illustrating eq. (8) is given in Fig. 5.6. This model might serve as a basis for applying the techniques of systems analysis to a solution of the problem of energy flow in the soil eco-system. This is by no means a simple task, however: it requires each important species component to be identified and its population energy budget determined; it also presupposes a knowledge of the food web of the system. There are formidable difficulties in the way of obtaining the requisite data, especially that pertaining to the Protista. Thus techniques for clearly distinguishing living from dead microbial cells in the soil have yet to be perfected. There also remains the problem of measuring soil respiration without interference from root respiration, a task made more difficult by the fact that an important fraction of the microbiota is closely associated with living roots (see Chapter 7).

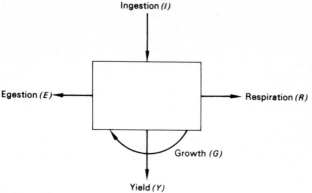

FIG. 5.6 Flow diagram for a balanced energy equation. See eq. (8). (From Weigert, R. G. *et al.* (1970) in *Methods of Study in Soil Ecology*: Proceedings of the Paris Symposium — Ecology and Conservation, 2, ed. J. Phillipson, UNESCO, Paris. Reproduced by permission of UNESCO. © UNESCO 1970.

Partitioning energy flow among the soil biota

The relative contributions of microbes and soil animals to soil metabolism is not known for certain. It is generally accepted that the microbiota (mainly fungi and bacteria) contribute far more to total soil metabolism than do the meso- or macrobiota. Something of the order of 10 per cent of the annual input of energy in litter is thought to be utilized for biosynthesis, growth and respiration by the soil fauna. The low biomass of soil animals relative to bacteria and fungi (Table 1.1) is indicative of their respective direct contributions to soil metabolism. The indirect involvement of the fauna, in stimulating microbial development (p. 108), is of course much greater.

Role of soil fauna

For adult soil animals, if it is assumed that growth and yield are negligible and that respiratory heat loss is all directed towards maintenance, eq. (8) may be simplified thus:

$$I = (r \times B) + E \qquad (9)$$

where r = respiratory heat loss of an individual;

B = biomass or standing crop.

An estimate of r, obtained in the laboratory, can be used to estimate $R(= r \times B)$, provided the biomass of the population is known, and provided the respiratory rate of the animals in question is the same under field and laboratory conditions. Such an estimate is unrealistic,

. however, because it ignores the normal age-class distribution which pertains in all naturally occurring populations. Because the respiratory rate of individuals varies with their state of maturity, a more accurate estimate could be derived by summation of the respiration of the various age (or size) classes represented in the sample. A further disadvantage of the method is that it is not applicable to the smaller members of the mesofauna, for which indirect estimates of respiration must be made, e.g. by calculating the regression of respiration on weight for a sample of the population.

Techniques are also available for making independent estimates of the other terms in eqs. (7) and (8). For example, the quantity of food ingested, I, and the amount of matter egested as faeces, E, may be determined by laboratory studies. Production, P, can be estimated by making successive measurements of biomass. This is comparatively simple and direct so far as the larger soil animals are concerned, but weighing of many of the individual smaller forms is difficult if not impossible, and for these animals, such as the smaller mites and collembola, indirect estimates of biomass must be made, e.g. from previously determined relationships between linear dimensions or surface area and weight.

An example of an energy budget for a soil animal population is provided by the data of M. D. Engelmann, for cryptostigmatid mites in a grassland soil from Michigan, USA. The values (cal/m^2/yr) for the various parameters were as follows: I, 10 248; P, 270; R, 1 965; E, 7 686. A further term which must be taken into account is mortality M, 430. Adding this term to the right-hand side of eq. (7) permits an independent estimate of I, as the sum of P, R, E and M, i.e. 10 351 cal/m^2/yr. This compares quite closely with the experimentally determined value of I, 10 248 cal/m^2/yr.

The contribution of the various trophic groups of soil animals to total faunal respiration has not been estimated reliably for many soils. The significance of individual groups will vary with their biomass, which in turn varies with locality, so that the relative importance of any particular group will change from place to place. Some larger animals, e.g. isopods, may compensate for a low metabolic rate with high biomass, while conversely, the low biomass of groups such as collembola, nematodes and enchytraeids may be offset by their high respiratory activity. Groups such as cryptostigmatid mites, which usually have a low biomass coupled with a relatively low rate of metabolism, probably make little direct contribution to organic matter decomposition in soils; the ecological significance of these animals lies in their ability to promote decomposition by bacteria and fungi. The lack of correlation

TABLE 5.3 Contribution of trophic groups of soil animals to biomass and energy flow*

Group†	Beech mor			Beech mull			Spruce mor			Spruce mull		
	Biomass (g/m²)	Energy flow (kcal/ m²/yr)	(%)	Biomass (g/m²)	Energy flow (kcal/ m²/yr)	(%)	Biomass (g/m²)	Energy flow (kcal/ m²/yr)	(%)	Biomass (g/m²)	Energy flow (kcal/ m²/yr)	(%)
Herbivores	4.7	33.6	20.4	9.3	106.5	27.3	11.3	128.3	32.9	5.9	88.4	28.4
Large decomposers	4.2	13.9	8.4	60.8	122.1	31.2	1.0	2.1	0.5	5.5	10.3	3.3
Small decomposers	3.8	76.0	46.1	2.4	93.5	23.9	1.6	113.5	29.1	1.4	113.7	36.5
Predators	2.9	41.5	25.1	1.5	68.7	17.6	1.2	145.9	37.4	1.1	99.3	31.9
Total	15.6	165.0	100.0	74.0	390.8	100.0	15.1	389.8	99.9	13.9	311.7	100.1

* Adapted from an analysis of nine soil habitats by Macfadyen, A. (1963) 'The contribution of the microfauna to total soil metabolism' in *Soil Organisms*, eds. J. Doeksen and J. van der Drift, North-Holland.

† Herbivores include nematodes, molluscs, bugs, beetles, flies, moths, etc.; large decomposers, earthworms, woodlice and millipedes; small decomposers, nematodes, enchytraeids, oribatid mites and collembola; predators, spiders, centipedes, flies, beetles, etc.

between biomass and energy flow is clearly brought out in Table 5.3. Note that the coniferous (spruce) forest soils have a higher energy flow relative to biomass than do comparable broadleaved (beech) forest soils, the difference being due mainly to small decomposers and predators. Large decomposers are much more important than small decomposers in the energetics of broadleaved than coniferous forest soils; there are relatively very few of the former in the spruce soils. Note also that the difference between mull and mor, in both biomass and energy flow, is more pronounced in the broadleaved forest than in the coniferous forest.

Role of soil microbes

As pointed out previously (p. 121), the activities of the chemoheterotrophic protists so dominate the processes of organic matter decomposition and energy flow in the soil subsystem that their contribution to total soil metabolism exceeds that of the rest of the soil biota combined. Important as these decomposers are, there are as yet no reliable direct estimates of their contribution to soil respiration, nor is it possible to say which of the two major microbial groups involved, viz. bacteria and fungi, contributes the more.

The problems involved in solving the energy balance equations for soil microorganisms have so far proved insurmountable. In the first place, it is extremely difficult to determine microbial biomass, the usual method for bacteria being to estimate population density (numbers per gram) by direct or indirect methods,* measure their average dimensions and calculate their volume, then multiply this figure by their presumed specific gravity. The accepted value for specific gravity has been 1.0, but there is evidence that this may be in error by as much as 50 per cent. Estimates of bacterial biomass indicate that it is of the order of 10 g/m² dry weight in most soils.† Bacterial populations fluctuate widely, however, and in favourable habitats bacterial biomass may exceed this value by an order of magnitude (see, for example, the live weight data of Table 1.1). It is known that direct counting procedures tend to overestimate, and indirect counting methods to underestimate, the population density of bacteria, and that both techniques are very imprecise. It should also be kept in mind that converting numbers to biomass does not increase the precision of an estimate.

---

* Brief descriptions of the techniques of soil microbiology are given in Appendix II.
† Based on the weight of 1 m² of soil to a depth of 15 cm.

Fungal biomass has usually been determined by measuring the length and average diameter of the mycelium present in a soil sample, calculating its volume, and multiplying this by a factor for specific gravity, as with bacteria. Some 10 m/g of mycelium may be present in soils, with a biomass of the order of 5 g/m^2 dry weight. When the weight of spores present is included, fungal biomass frequently exceeds that of bacteria. What proportion of the mycelia in soils is inactive or dead is however an unresolved question.

The difficulties faced by soil microbiologists in determining microbial biomass do not mean that they should give up their attempts to do so. Dependence on numbers alone gives a false impression of the relative importance of various groups. Thus the ratio of numbers of bacteria to fungi in arable soils, as determined by the dilution plate technique (see Appendix II), is frequently about 100/1, but despite this fungal biomass may be the greater.

Can eqs. (7) and (8) be solved for microorganisms? There seems to be no way of determining I experimentally, hence it must be estimated as the sum of P (or $G + Y$), R and E. The growth rate of individual populations can be measured in the laboratory, but this has yet to be successfully achieved in the soil; there is hardly any doubt however, that growth rates under natural conditions bear little relationship to those determined in pure culture. The most promising techniques for calculating microbial growth rates in the soil are based on the use of radioactive tracers or fluorescent dyes, but as yet there have been insufficient studies of this kind to allow their value to be properly assessed.

Egestion, E, is a term which has no meaning for bacteria and fungi. The exudation of waste products by these microbes is somewhat comparable, but it is necessary to recall that they also exude exoenzymes (p. 69) in addition to metabolic wastes, and so are able to 'digest' some of their substrates extracellularly, as well as disposing of their unwanted residues in this way. In any event, it seems unlikely that the rates of exudation of wastes could be satisfactorily measured in natural conditions.

The remaining term in the energy equations, R, is another which cannot yet be determined for specific groups in the field. Equation (9) cannot be applied to microbial populations, because these organisms are so minute and have such a rapid rate of reproduction that it is impossible to measure the respiration of mature individuals. A further problem arises with bacteria because many are facultative anaerobes (p. 62), and therefore the efficiency of their substrate utilization varies with change in the oxygen supply. Since aeration is a continuously variable parameter, both spatially and temporally, it is doubtful whether measurements of CO_2 output from soils would provide an unequivocal estimate of the contribution of bacteria to energy flow, even if it were possible to suppress entirely the activities of the rest of the soil biota.

It must be concluded that, at the present time, it is not practicable to prepare population energy budgets for soil fungi and bacteria, and hence it is not possible to solve the energy balance equations directly. The best that can be achieved is, knowing the total soil metabolism, to subtract from this the experimentally determined value for the metabolism of the animal component. It is in this way that the 'estimate' of 80–90 per cent as the contribution of microbial metabolism to the total has been obtained. Even this estimate is in error to the extent that total soil metabolism includes the respiration of plant roots.

One attempt has been made to prepare an energy budget for the soil

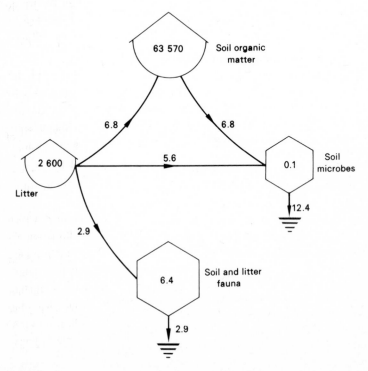

FIG. 5.7 Energy budget for the soil subsystem in a tropical rainforest. Pool sizes in kcal/m²; flow rates in kcal/m²/day. Based on data of H. T. Odum (1970) in *A Tropical Rain Forest*, eds. H. T. Odum and R. F. Pigeon, US Atomic Energy Commission.)

subsystem in tropical rainforest (Fig. 5.7). Although this model does not go beyond separating the 'decomposer' group into fauna and microflora, it does indicate the magnitude of the standing stock of energy and the rates at which this is depleted by the activities of small animals and microorganisms, and replenished by litter fall.

Total system energy budget

Solution of the energy equations for the soil biota provides a means of determining the contribution of the soil subsystem to the energetics of the whole ecosystem of which it is a part. The treatment which follows is based on that of G. M. Woodwell and D. B. Botkin.

The increase in biomass, i.e. net primary production (*NPP*), of the autotrophic component of an ecosystem, viz. the plant community, is given by:

$$NPP = GP - R_a \tag{10}$$

where GP = gross production (total amount of photosynthate produced) and R_a = photosynthate lost by respiration of the producer organisms, i.e. autotroph respiration.

The increase in biomass of the ecosystem as a whole (net community production, *NEP*) is, likewise,

$$NEP = GP - R_e \tag{11}$$

where R_e is the total respiratory loss of all components of the system.

The total community respiration is the sum of the respiration of the heterotrophs (R_h) and the autotrophs, thus:

$$R_e = R_a + R_h \tag{12}$$

Heterotroph respiration is also made up of two major components, viz. consumer respiration (R_c) and decomposer (soil) respiration (R_d), so that:

$$R_h = R_c + R_d \tag{13}$$

Substituting for GP from eq. (10) and R_e from eq. (12), we may rewrite eq. (11) as:

$$NEP = (NPP + R_a) - (R_a + R_h)$$

i.e. $$NEP = NPP - R_h \tag{14}$$

Equation (14) provides a means of estimating net community productivity. This parameter cannot be estimated from eq. (11) because there is no satisfactory method for measuring gross productivity directly (due to the impossibility of determining respiration losses by the producers during photosynthesis).

These production equations are of paramount importance in studies of ecosystem function, for their solution permits the contributions of the various components to energy flow to be assessed. As already indicated, the preparation of an energy budget is an essential first step in any serious study of the relationship between structure and function in terrestrial ecosystems. R. H. Whittaker and G. M. Woodwell and their associates have attempted to analyse an oak-pine forest ecosystem at Brookhaven, NY, in this fashion. Gas exchange techniques were used to provide several independent estimates of R_e, the average value (expressed as dry matter equivalent) being 2 129 g/m^2/yr. This figure for total respiration of the ecosystem should theoretically comprise the sum of the contributions of the several components, such as leaves and twigs, branches and stems, ground cover and the soil surface. In practice, direct measurement is possible for only some of these components. For example, the respiration of leaves and twigs cannot be measured directly because there is no way of monitoring the respiration which occurs contemporaneously with photosynthesis. Furthermore, when measuring CO_2 evolution from soil, it is impossible to avoid confounding the respiration of roots (which is part of R_a) with that of the heterotrophs (R_h). The latter can be estimated indirectly from a knowledge of litter decay rates (see p. 114) and the soil respiration data corrected accordingly to give a value for root respiration. When this is added to the respiration of stems and branches, an estimate of 1 520 g/m^2/yr for R_a is obtained.

There are no satisfactory data for net primary productivity of the plant community based on direct methods involving gas exchange, so an indirect estimate of 1 195 g/m^2/yr derived from harvest techniques must be utilized, along with that for R_a, to solve for GP in eq. (10). Thus GP = 1 195 + 1 520 = 2 715 g/m^2/yr. In turn, NEP can be calculated from GP and R_e using eq. (11): NEP = 2 715 − 2 129 = 586 g/m^2.

From this oak-pine forest, therefore, we have a solution to all the production equations given above except eq. (13). Of the gross annual production of 2 715 g/m^2, some 56 per cent is utilized for respiration by the producer organisms, leaving 1 195 g/m^2 as the net production of the plant community. Of this net primary production, a further 609 g or 51 per cent are consumed by heterotroph respiration. That an increment of 586 g/m^2 remains indicates that accretion of organic matter is still occurring in this ecosystem, in other words it has not yet attained a steady state. This is also illustrated by the fact that the ratio of gross primary production to total community respiration (GP/R_e) exceeds unity, since in ecological succession the P/R ratio approaches 1 as the ecosystem matures towards the steady state or climax.

Even though biomass is still increasing, the fraction of net primary production which is respired by heterotrophs is substantial. The relative proportions utilized by consumers and decomposers can only be guessed, since eq. (13) remains unsolved. While some members of the soil biota, viz. the biophagous animals, might be classified as consumers, their contribution to total heterotroph respiration is slight. Other consumers, including leaf-eating insects may harvest a significant fraction of net primary production, but in the forest ecosystem under consideration, 98 per cent of that not utilized for growth remains unharvested, and consequently passes directly into the decomposer system.

Biogeochemistry of carbon

Geochemistry is the science that concerns the chemical composition of the Earth and the movement of elements between different parts of the Earth's crust and the hydrosphere and atmosphere. The exchanges of elements between the living and non-living parts of the biosphere (the region of the Earth which is inhabited by organisms) are referred to as biogeochemical cycles. At the ecosystem level, they are simply called nutrient cycles. Carbon, though not one of the more abundant elements in the Earth, nevertheless plays a central role in geochemistry, because carbon compounds are essential for every known form of life. The carbon cycle, as commonly understood in biology, consists of the photosynthetic reduction of CO_2 by green plants and its subsequent respiratory release to the atmosphere by plants and microorganisms and, to a lesser degree, by animals. From a geochemical viewpoint, however, this conception of the carbon cycle is a gross oversimplification.

The most important part of the carbon cycle involves exchange between the air, the sea, and the terrestrial biosphere. Of these three reservoirs of carbon the greatest is the ocean, but it is not a uniform reservoir. It comprises an upper mixed layer, 50–100 m in depth, which contains most of the marine life, and a lower or deep sea layer. There is a 'fast' carbon cycle involving the mixed layer of the ocean, the atmosphere, and the terrestrial biosphere (green plants, animals and soil organisms), in which the turnover time* of carbon is measured in years

---

* Turnover time is the time required to replace a quantity of material equal to the amount of that substance present in the reservoir. Its reciprocal is termed the residence time.

or at the most, decades; exchange with the deep sea layer is slower, being measured in hundreds of years. Superimposed on this fast cycle is a much slower cycle, turning over about once every 100 000 years, which involves rock weathering and the dissolution and precipitation of carbonates in the ocean.

Accumulation of carbon in the lithosphere

Carbon becomes enriched in the lithosphere in a number of ways: by chemical erosion of rocks, as biogenic deposits or as humus. These will be discussed briefly in turn.

Chemical erosion

Carbonate may be formed from the silicate of primary rocks by the action of CO_2 in the presence of water, according to the reaction:

$$CO_2 + MSiO_3 \underset{\longleftarrow}{\overset{H_2O}{\longrightarrow}} MCO_3 + SiO_2$$

where M is a divalent metal. In the absence of other processes, this would tend to maintain a very low concentration of CO_2 (about 0.001 per cent) in the atmosphere. It is a common reaction in the biosphere, the CO_2 being supplied mainly by soil microorganisms; it therefore occurs most rapidly in soils high in organic matter.

Carbonate formed by this or any other process may be converted to bicarbonate by the action of water containing dissolved CO_2, as follows:

$$CO_2 + H_2O + CaCO_3 \longrightarrow Ca(HCO_3)_2$$

The bicarbonate thus formed is fully soluble and eventually finds its way to the ocean, where it is utilized for photosynthesis by phytoplankton. Approximately half of it will subsequently be deposited as exoskeletons in oceanic sediments and so returned to the lithosphere, while the remainder is respired to the atmosphere.

Biogenic deposits

Three kinds of biogenic deposits need to be considered. The most important of these, from the geochemical viewpoint, are calcareous sediments. The presence of great thicknesses of limestone ($CaCO_3$) in sedimentary deposits indicates that enormous quantities of CO_2 have left the atmosphere during geological times. Except in the case of corals,* nearly every instance of the deposition of CO_2 as $CaCO_3$ is a biological process involving microorganisms. At the present time, the chief agents of sedimentation in the deep sea are the foraminifera. Other kinds of deposit, viz. argillaceous sediments such as shales, contain reduced forms of carbon; this carbon represents CO_2 which was originally fixed photosynthetically.

Coal and petroleum are biogenic deposits which, though negligible from the geochemical viewpoint, are further examples of the involvement of the soil biota in the carbon cycle. In the formation of coal, the role of soil organisms is restricted to the modification of organic matter during the accumulation of peat, before it is exposed to the mechanical forces which ultimately determine its physical nature. The precise role of microbes in the transformation of deep oceanic sediments into petroleum is a matter of debate, though much petroleum derives from the oils synthesized and stored by diatoms. There is good evidence that bacteria are involved in the early stages of conversion of these oils into petroleum, but the later stages seem to be largely if not wholly physico-chemical.

Humus

The term humus is used to encompass the organic fraction of the soil itself, as distinguished from the organic matter of the surface litter, and as such humus is largely a product of the activities of soil organisms. It represents carbon which was first fixed by the process of photosynthesis. The actual carbon content of soils depends on the rate of organic matter production by green plants and its rate of alteration by heterotrophic organisms once it enters the soil. The balance between the two processes usually results in a net gain of organic carbon in soils, so that humus becomes a more or less permanent constituent of the lithosphere. The humus content of different soils varies greatly with climatic and other factors. In general, temperate and cold humid climates favour the accumulation of humus, whereas hot tropical conditions favour the oxidative processes which return CO_2 to the atmosphere (see pp. 5, 117).

Recalcitrant molecules

Microbiologists regard it as axiomatic that every naturally occurring

* The formation of coral is brought about by the coralline algae and coral polyps.

organic compound is mineralized by one or more groups of micro-organisms. If it were not so, then the carbon cycle would be inter-rupted, and huge accumulations of the resistant substances would occur in the biosphere. It is true that massive deposits of some organic materials, such as coal and petroleum, do exist, but the carbonaceous residues of organisms from which these biogenic deposits derive are susceptible to microbial decomposition (i.e. are biodegradable) given appropriate environmental conditions.

There are however certain organic compounds, notably synthetic chemicals, which are either non-biodegradable or which decompose extremely slowly in all environments. Martin Alexander refers to these substances as **recalcitrant**. They deserve close study because many of them have become pollutants of regional and even global significance. Among the most refractory synthetic molecules are the branched alkyl benzene sulphonate detergents and the chlorinated hydrocarbon insecti-cides. The latter are remarkably persistent in soil (Fig. 5.8), some such as DDT being of especial concern because of the way in which they become more and more concentrated as they pass from one trophic level to the next, and because they become so widely distributed in nature as food chains ramify to form complex food webs.

The carbon cycle

The fast carbon cycle, as visualized by H. Craig in 1957, is shown in Fig. 5.9. Most of the carbon in the fast cycle is found in the deep sea.

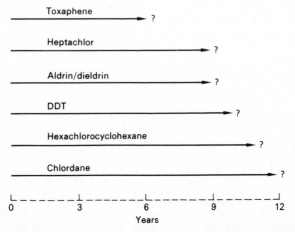

FIG. 5.8 The persistence of chlorinated hydrocarbons in soil. The question mark indicates that the compound persists longer than the time shown. (From Alex-ander, M. (1971) *Microbial Ecology*, Wiley.)

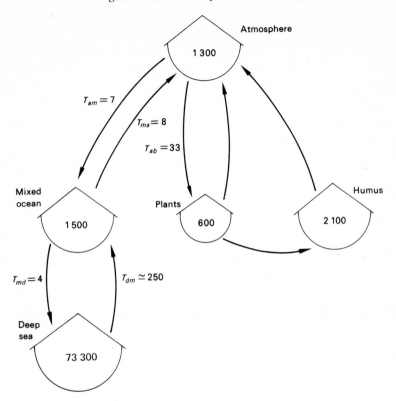

FIG. 5.9 The flow of carbon between the atmosphere, the hydrosphere and the terrestrial biosphere. Pool sizes in g/m². T is the residence time in years in exchange with the various pools. (After Craig, H. (1957) *Tellus*, **9**, 1–17.)

Even this reservoir is minute in comparison with the amount of carbon involved in the slow cycle. For example, calcareous sediments contain 28 500 times, and argillaceous sediments 10 600 times, more carbon than is present in the atmosphere. Note that there are several unknowns in the cycle. For example, the turnover time between humus and the atmosphere is not given. The radiocarbon dating technique shows that the age of humus samples from the A horizon of cool temperate podzol soils is approximately contemporary, and those from the B horizon are several hundred years old. This suggests that the turnover time of carbon in A horizon humus is of the same order as that in the mixed ocean layer, that is only a few years; in warmer regions it may even be less. The turnover time of carbon from deeper in the profile is likely to be longer, cf. the deep sea layer. In chernozem soils however, the age difference between humus from surface and sub-soil horizons appears to be less pronounced.

Selected references

Alexander, M. (1971) *Microbial Ecology.* Wiley.
Gray, T. R. G. and Williams, S. T. (1971) *Soil Microorganisms.* Oliver & Boyd.
Kevan, D. K. McE. (1962) *Soil Animals.* Witherby.
Mason, B. (1966) *Principles of Geochemistry,* 3rd edn. Wiley.
Phillipson, J. (1966) *Ecological Energetics.* Arnold.
Odum, E. P. (1971) *Fundamentals of Ecology,* 3rd edn. Saunders.
Wallwork, J. A. (1970) *Ecology of Soil Animals.* McGraw-Hill.

Alexander, M. (1965) 'Biodegradation: problems of molecular recalcitrance and microbial fallibility.' *Adv. appl. Microbiol.,* 7, 35—80.
Babiuk, L. A. and Paul, E. A. (1970) 'The use of fluorescein isothiocyanate in the determination of the bacterial biomass of grassland soil.' *Can. J. Microbiol.,* 16, 57—62.
Bray, J. R. (1964) 'Primary consumption in three forest canopies.' *Ecology,* 45, 165—7.
Burges, A. (1967) 'The decomposition of organic matter in the soil' in *Soil Biology,* eds. A. Burges and F. Raw, pp. 479—92. Academic Press.
Coleman, D. C. and McGinnis, J. T. (1970) 'Quantification of fungus — small arthropod food chains in the soil.' *Oikos,* 21, 134—7.
Craig, H. (1957) 'The natural distribution of radiocarbon and the exchange time of carbon dioxide between atmosphere and sea.' *Tellus,* 9, 1—17.
Curry, J. P. (1969) 'The decomposition of organic matter in soil. I. The role of the fauna in decaying grassland herbage.' *Soil Biol. Biochem.,* 1, 253—8.
Edwards, C. A., Reichle, D. E. and Crossley, D. A., Jun. (1970) 'The role of soil invertebrates in turnover of organic matter and nutrients' in *Analysis of Temperate Forest Ecosystems,* ed. D. E. Reichle, pp. 147—72. Springer-Verlag.
Engelmann, M. D. (1964) 'Energetics, terrestrial field studies and animal productivity.' *Adv. ecol. Res.,* 3, 73—115.
Garrett, S. D. (1951) 'Ecological groups of soil fungi: a survey of substrate relationships.' *New Phytol.,* 50, 149—66.

Jones, D. and Griffiths, E. (1964) 'The use of thin soil sections for the study of soil microorganisms.' *Plant Soil*, 20, 232–40.

Kevan, D. K. McE. (1968) 'Soil fauna and humus formation.' *Trans 9th Congr. Int. Soil Sci. Soc.*, 2, 1–10.

Lindeman, R. L. (1942) 'The trophic-dynamic aspect of ecology.' *Ecology*, 23, 399–418.

McBrayer, J. F. and Reichle, D. E. (1971) 'Trophic structure and feeding rates of forest soil invertebrate populations.' *Oikos*, 22, 381–8.

Macfadyen, A. (1963) 'The contribution of the microfauna to total soil metabolism' in *Soil Organisms*, eds. J. Doeksen and J. van der Drift, pp. 3–17. North Holland Publishing Co.

Macfadyen, A. (1970) 'Soil metabolism in relation to ecosystem energy flow and to primary and secondary production' in *Methods of Study in Soil Ecology*, ed. J. Phillipson, pp. 167–72. UNESCO.

Mason, W. H. and Odum, E. P. (1969) 'The effect of coprophagy on retention and bioelimination of radionuclides by detritus-feeding animals' in *Symposium on Radioecology*, eds. D. J. Nelson and F. C. Evans pp. 721–4. University of Michigan.

Odum, E. P., Connell, E. and Davenport, L. B. (1962) 'Population energy flow of three primary consumer components of old field systems.' *Ecology*, 43, 83–96.

Odum, E. P. and Smalley, A. E. (1959) 'Comparison of population energy flow of a herbivorous and a deposit-feeding invertebrate in a salt marsh ecosystem.' *Proc. natn. Acad. Sci., USA*, 45, 617–22.

Odum, H. T. (1970) 'Summary; an emerging view of the ecological system at El Verde' in *A Tropical Rain Forest*, eds. H. T. Odum and R. F. Pigeon, pp. I-191–I-281. US Atomic Energy Commission.

Olson, J. S. (1963) 'Energy storage and the balance of producers and decomposers in ecological systems.' *Ecology*, 44, 322–31.

Oglesby, R. T., Christman, R. F. and Driver, C. H. (1967) 'The biotransformation of lignin to humus – facts and postulates.' *Adv. appl. Microbiol.*, 9, 171–84.

Ovington, J. D. (1965) 'Organic production, turnover and mineral cycling in woodlands.' *Biol. Rev.*, 40, 295–336.

Norkrans, Birgitta (1967) 'Cellulose and cellulolysis.' *Adv. appl. Microbiol.*, 9, 91–130.

Perrin, R. M. S., Willis, E. H. and Hodge, C. A. H. (1964) 'Dating of humus podzols by residual radiocarbon activity.' *Nature, Lond.*, 202, 165–6.

Reiners, W. A. (1968) 'Carbon dioxide evolution from the floor of three Minnesota forests.' *Ecology*, 49, 471–83.

Reiners, W. A. and Reiners N. M. (1970) 'Energy and nutrient dynamics of forest floors in three Minnesota forests.' *J. Ecol.,* **58**, 497—519.

Shanks, R. E. and Olson, J. S. (1961) 'First-year breakdown of leaf litter in Southern Appalachian forests.' *Science,* **134**, 194—5.

Swincer, G. D., Oades, J. M. and Greenland, D. J. (1969) 'The extraction, characterization, and significance of soil polysaccharides.' *Adv. Agron.,* **21**, 195—235.

Tamm, C. O. and Holmen H. (1967) 'Some remarks on soil organic matter turn-over in Swedish podzol profiles.' *Meddr. Norske Skogforsves.,* **85(23)**, 69—88.

Teal, J. M. (1962) 'Energy flow in the salt marsh ecosystem of Georgia.' *Ecology,* **43**, 614—24.

Weigert, R. G., Coleman, D. C. and Odum, E. P. (1970) 'Energetics of the litter—soil subsystem' in *Methods of Study in Soil Ecology,* ed. J. Phillipson, pp. 93—8. UNESCO.

Whittaker, R. H. and Woodwell, G. M. (1969) 'Structure, production and diversity of the oak-pine forest at Brookhaven, New York. *J. Ecol.,* **57**, 155—74.

Witkamp, M. (1966) 'Rates of carbon dioxide evolution from the forest floor.' *Ecology,* **47**, 492—4.

Woodwell, G. M. and Botkin, D. B. (1970) 'Metabolism of terrestrial ecosystems by gas exchange techniques: the Brookhaven approach' in *Analysis of Temperate Forest Ecosystems,* ed. D. E. Reichle, pp. 73—85. Springer-Verlag.

Woodwell, G. M. and Marples, T. G. (1968) 'The influence of chronic gamma irradiation on production and decay of litter and humus in an oak-pine forest.' *Ecology,* **49**, 456—65.

6 Microbiological processes and nutrient cycling

By virtue of their effect on nutrient circulation in the biosphere, microbes have great significance in the biogeochemistry of the elements. Availability of nutrients markedly influences plant vigour and consequently, productivity. Microbial processes affecting nutrient availability thus have a vital role in ecosystem function. Microbes may however affect plants adversely as well as beneficially. For example, they can on occasion compete with plants for nutrients, but only if they have an adequate supply of energy. In other instances, plant nutrients are made available by microorganisms in the course of meeting their energy demands. Therefore, in order to determine how microorganisms affect the availability of plant nutrients, we must consider separately the various kinds of energy-yielding processes which were discussed in Chapter 3.

To recapitulate, the energy sources for life are two: the radiant energy of the sun, and the chemical bond energy contained in organic and inorganic compounds. Radiant (solar) energy is the basis of photosynthesis. Bacterial photosynthesis is a strictly anaerobic process, and this requirement for anaerobic conditions, coupled with the fact that they can utilize light of longer wavelengths than green plants, restricts the activities of photosynthetic bacteria to aquatic environments such as lakes and estuaries. They are therefore unlikely to play any part in promoting nutrient availability in soils and so will not be considered further. There are two other groups of photosynthetic microorganisms, the algae and the blue-green algae. Some blue-green algae can fix atmospheric nitrogen, and in some ecosystems (e.g. in rice culture) they may play a significant part in maintaining soil fertility. While photosynthesis by soil algae may be important in certain ecological situations, in general it is not the photosynthetic microorganisms, but those which obtain their energy from chemical processes which are of greatest significance in plant nutrition, and we will be concerned only with these. Three kinds of oxidation—reduction reactions provide energy for microorganisms (Table 3.1) and these are termed, according to the nature of the final hydrogen-acceptor, respiration, anaerobic respiration or fermentation. The fact that some microbes can respire aerobically so long as oxygen is present, but when the oxygen supply becomes limiting switch to anaerobic respiration or fermentation as a source of energy, does not detract from the value of examining the processes themselves, since it is these which are important in nutrient cycling rather than the microorganisms *per se.*

Aerobic processes and nutrient cycling

In the aerobic process of respiration, the hydrogen-donor or substrate may be either organic or inorganic. Of the inorganic hydrogen-donors which may be used, only reduced nitrogen compounds and reduced sulphur compounds are of any significance in the context of plant nutrition. We will return to these later, after first examining the role of respiration carried out with organic substrates.

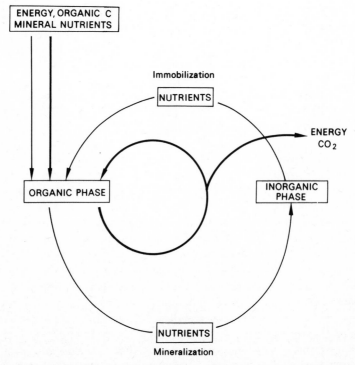

FIG. 6.1 The mineralization—immobilization cycle in the soil. Energy flow shown by broad lines, nutrient pathways by narrow lines.

Respiration with organic substrates

A great variety of organic compounds can serve as hydrogen-donors for microbial respiration. The effect of such energy-yielding oxidations on the supply of plant nutrients is entirely indirect, that is nutrients become available only as by-products of the microbial respiration of organic substrates. When inorganic ions are produced by the oxidation of organic compounds, the process is termed **mineralization**; when inorganic molecules are assimilated into microbial protoplasm, we speak of **immobilization**. It is a basic concept of soil microbiology that mineralization and immobilization of nutrients proceeds concurrently, so that there is a continual biological turnover, or **mineralization—immobilization cycle**, in the soil. The energy needed to keep this cycle running is that released during the oxidation of organic compounds, added to the soil as plant and animal residues or stored in the soil organic matter. The cycle operates continuously but more or less intensely, depending

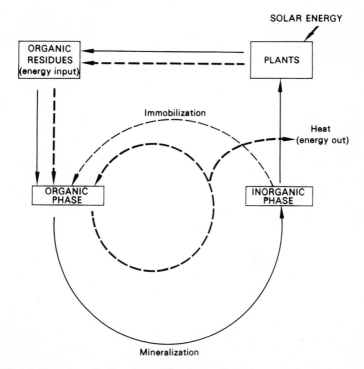

FIG. 6.2 The mineralization—immobilization cycle under conditions of energy deficit, resulting in net mineralization. Energy flow shown by broad lines, nutrient pathways by narrow lines. Broken lines indicate interrupted or intermittent flow.

on the supply of readily decomposable substrates (Fig. 6.1). Not all the energy released during oxidation is captured by the decomposing microbes, a considerable quantity being dissipated as heat. A large amount of carbon also escapes from the system as carbon dioxide, but the mineralized nutrients are not usually lost and are available again and again for microbial use. Unless the energy supply is renewed therefore, by the addition of fresh substrates in the form of plant debris, a stage will be reached when inorganic ions accumulate, and we can speak of **net mineralization** (Fig. 6.2). In these circumstances, nutrients will be readily available for plant uptake. Conversely, if readily decomposable substrates are added to the system, there tends to be a surplus of energy, the demands of the microflora for inorganic ions become greater than the mineralization outflow, and any source of inorganic ions in the soil will be drawn upon by microorganisms, resulting in **net immobilization** (Fig. 6.3). Under these conditions, the supply

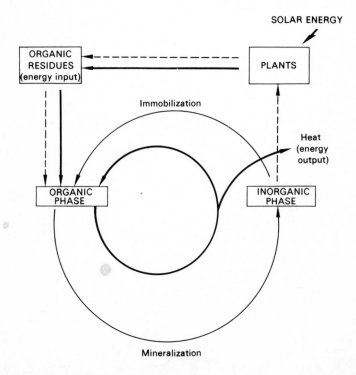

FIG. 6.3 The mineralization–immobilization cycle under conditions of energy surplus, resulting in net immobilization. Energy flow shown by broad lines, nutrient pathways by narrow lines. Broken lines indicate interrupted or intermittent flow.

of nutrients available for plants becomes depleted. The three diagrams can be combined (Fig. 6.4) using the energy network diagrams of H. T. Odum described in Chapter 1 (p. 10).

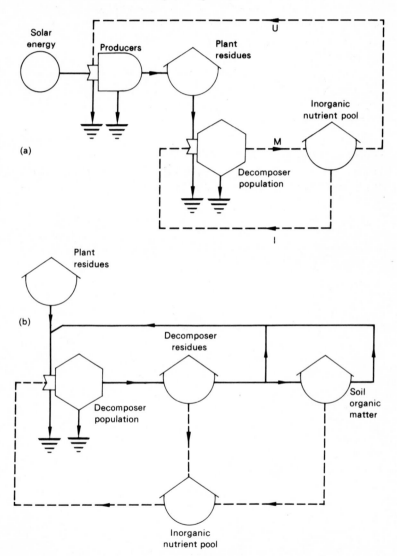

FIG. 6.4 Energy network diagram of the mineralization—immobilization cycle. *(a)* Generalized picture of the cycle in the soil—plant system. *(b)* Detail of the cycle in the soil. Major energy flows shown as solid lines, pathways of low energy compounds (inorganic nutrients) as broken lines. M, mineralization; I, immobilization; U, plant uptake.

Implicit in the concept of a mineralization–immobilization cycle is the assumption that plants cannot compete successfully with microbes for inorganic nutrients, and only when there is net mineralization can plants satisfy their nutrient requirements. This is most likely correct for nitrogen, the plant nutrient required in greatest amount by microorganisms, and may on occasions be true for sulphur and phosphorus also. The demands of microbes for other nutrients are relatively modest, and plants are unlikely to suffer from deficiencies of them as a result of microbial competition. Not surprisingly therefore, research tends to be centred on the nitrogen turnover cycle. Even here, the addition of fresh substrates to soil will affect plant growth adversely only if these substrates are high in energy in relation to nitrogen. The primary limiting factor for growth of heterotrophic microbes is energy supply, and since this in turn is dependent upon carbon content, highly carbonaceous amendments will cause greater immobilization of mineral soil nitrogen than highly proteinaceous materials.

Many kinds of chemoheterotrophs are involved in mineralization–immobilization cycles. Fungi are especially prominent, particularly in forest ecosystems where low soil pH often restricts the activities of bacteria. Ascomycetes and imperfect fungi, notably *Penicillium*, *Fusarium*, *Aspergillus* and *Trichoderma*, and phycomycetes such as *Mucor* and *Rhizopus*, are among the fungi most frequently isolated on soil dilution plates (see Appendix II); population densities are usually in the range of 10^4-10^6 propagules (spores or hyphal fragments) per gram of soil. Other isolation techniques have shown that, in addition to these well known genera, various basidiomycetes are widespread and active in soils. As primary colonizers of fresh plant detritus, the former group might be expected to have the larger role in organic matter turnover.

This is borne out by a study of mycelial production and depletion during ten weeks' incubation of a sandy podzolic soil from subtropical Eastern Australia, when it was found that hyaline non-septate hyphae (Phycomycetes) and pigmented septate hyphae (Ascomycetes and Fungi Imperfecti) together accounted for more than 90 per cent of total mycelium colonizing nylon gauze buried in the soil, while clamp-bearing hyphae (Basidiomycetes) represented less than 2 per cent of the total. The addition of glucose greatly stimulated the growth of the two major groups of fungi, resulting in net immobilization of added amino-nitrogen (Table 6.1). A closer analysis of mycelial production and depletion at intervals during the incubation period revealed that the activity of the phycomycetes was subject to greater fluctuations than that of the septate fungi.

TABLE 6.1 Effect of glucose on disposition of labelled amino-nitrogen and on production of fungal mycelium in a podzolic soil*

Treatment	Nitrogen fraction (ppm^{15}N)			Length of hyphae (μm/mm^2)	
	Inorganic	Organic		Phycomycetes	Ascomycetes + Fungi imperfecti
	NH$_4^+$	Hydro-lysable	Non-hydro-lysable		
Minus glucose	34.5	25.5	8.9	312	239
Plus glucose	7.8	41.4	15.5	618	898

* Values tabulated are means for serial samplings during ten weeks incubation. The differences between treatment means are all highly significant statistically. Nitrogen was added as glycine (CH$_2$.^{15}NH$_2$.COOH). The data is from J. M. Jones (1968) PhD thesis, University of New England.

Among bacteria, the gram-positive rods *Arthrobacter* and *Coryne-bacterium*, and the aerobic sporeformer *Bacillus*, make up a large proportion of the microflora. The gram-negative rods known as fluorescent pseudomonads (*Pseudomonas* spp.) are also active in organic matter decomposition; they have great biochemical versatility, being able to use a far wider range of organic compounds as carbon and energy sources than any other group of microorganisms. Bacterial populations in fertile soils fall between 10^6 and 10^9 cells per gram.

Mineralization and immobilization of nitrogen

Ammonia is a waste product of microbial metabolism, and any NH$_4$-N that accumulates in soil represents the quantity of substrate nitrogen in excess of microbial requirement. Since organic matter added to soil will normally supply both carbon and nitrogen, whether NH$_4$-N will accumulate depends in part on the relative proportions of carbon and nitrogen in the additive. This explains a well known phenomenon in agriculture, viz. that incorporating the residues of one crop just before another is sown may result in a temporary nitrogen deficiency in the second crop. The duration of the period of net immobilization depends on the nature of the organic matter added, that is on its carbon and nitrogen status, and its incorporation in the soil must be properly timed in relation to the date of sowing if the new crop is not to suffer from nitrogen deficiency. This realization has led to much research on the effect of the ratio of readily available energy to readily available nitrogen in crop residues or organic manures, a rough approximation of which is given by the carbon:nitrogen (C/N) ratio of the additives. Agronomic experience has shown that when organic matter containing about 1.8 per cent N is added to soil there is neither net gain nor net loss of mineral nitrogen, whereas organic amendments containing less than 1.2 per cent deplete inorganic nitrogen reserves rapidly. In natural materials with a carbon content of about 40 per cent, these N levels correspond to C/N ratios of 20/1 and 30/1 respectively: organic matter with a C/N ratio wider than 30/1 favours net immobilization, while material with a ratio narrower than 20/1 causes net mineralization.

The concept of a critical C/N ratio of about 20/1 was developed for arable soils in the temperate regions of the northern hemisphere. In such soils, only materials having a C/N ratio of less than 20/1 are likely to provide available nitrogen for plants when incorporated in the soils at the beginning of the growing season. The concept cannot be applied uncritically to another situation, however. The C/N ratio of leaf litter entering forest soils is much wider than 20/1, yet several tons of this material are decomposed each year in productive forests, apparently without detriment to their growth rate. For example, some 5 000 to 8 000 kg/ha of litter is incorporated each year in the blackbutt (*Eucalyptus pilularis*) forest soils of Eastern Australia, yet this litter when fresh has a C/N ratio exceeding 100/1, declining only to about 40/1 before the comminuted fragments enter the soil. Apparently it is not only the C/N ratio of organic amendments that is important, but also their chemical nature. The nitrogen requirements for breakdown of lignified material is less than for more succulent tissue, seemingly because the less readily decomposable substrate promotes less microbial activity and hence there is less microbial protoplasm to be synthesized. Also there is evidence that wood-decaying fungi are able to conserve nitrogen by autolysis of the mycelium and re-use of the nitrogen it contains, and are thus able to promote rapid decomposition of lignified tissues despite their low C/N ratios.

Forms of organic nitrogen in soils

Only a very small portion of the organic nitrogen in soils appears to be protein, but this fraction, which probably represents the protein of living microbial cells, is very important as a source of mineral nitrogen for plant growth. Some of the ammonium released during the decomposition of proteins and amino sugars combines with quinones and polyphenols to form products of greater stability against microbial attack, and this reaction occurs also with a certain proportion of the ammonium added as fertilizer; it is often called ammonium fixation.

Amino acids released during the process of decomposition can combine with quinones too, producing relatively resistant humic acid polymers. Although the chemical nature of about half the total nitrogen in soil remains obscure, 20—40 per cent of it is known to occur as bound amino acids and 5—10 per cent as combined amino sugars. That these compounds do not occur free in soils is evidenced by the fact that they provide excellent substrates for a wide variety of microorganisms in the laboratory. It seems that only a very small portion of the total soil organic matter participates in the mineralization—immobilization cycle at any one time. The great bulk of organic matter that enters the soil, once partially decomposed, is more or less stabilized against further microbial attack. It is in this form that it is called humus, and as such it constitutes a passive organic phase existing contemporaneously with, but outside, the turnover cycle.

Urea hydrolysis

An important reaction which liberates mineral N is the hydrolysis of urea:

$$CO(NH_2)_2 + 2H_2O \rightarrow (NH_4)_2CO_3$$

The conversion of urea to ammonium carbonate brings about a rapid increase in soil reaction, and if the pH rises above 8, substantial amounts of ammonia may be evolved. This is because the equilibrium between ammonium ions in the soil solution and free ammonia shifts towards the production of more ammonia at high pH:

$$NH_4^+ + OH^- \rightleftarrows H_2O + NH_3$$

The resulting combination of high pH and free ammonia makes the environment unsuitable for most other bacteria. When synthetic urea is used as a fertilizer, plants can be damaged as a result of urease activity in two separate but related ways: firstly, if the pH rises above 9.5, ammonia toxicity can result from the presence of as little as 1—2 ppm NH_4-N; secondly, because *Nitrobacter* spp., which oxidize NO_2^- to NO_3^-, are more sensitive to high pH than are *Nitrosomonas* spp., which oxidize NH_4^+ to NO_2^-, nitrite toxicity can occur as a result of the accumulation of NO_2^- ions.

Urea is a typical product of animal excretion and large amounts are constantly being added to soils and natural waters; smaller quantities derive from the decomposition of nucleic acids. Urea hydrolysis is brought about by a limited number of heterotrophic soil bacteria but since the reaction liberates little energy, they cannot use it as a source of energy. Instead they satisfy their carbon and energy demands by oxidizing amino acids (most of them cannot oxidize carbohydrates). If urea is mixed with peptone and inoculated with soil, the organisms which predominate are spore formers, mainly *Bacillus pasteurii* and *Sporosarcina ureae*. These bacteria grow best in alkaline media, up to pH 11, and can hydrolyse urea in concentrations up to 10 per cent. Non-spore forming urea hydrolysing bacteria also exist, but these can only operate at urea concentrations below 3 per cent; examples are *Micrococcus ureae, M. aureus,* and certain yeasts including *Rhodotorula* and *Cryptococcus.* Hydrolysis is due to the enzyme urease, and its production is not restricted to the urea bacteria. On the contrary, many other bacteria and fungi possess the enzyme and can therefore use urea as a source of nitrogen. While none of these can tolerate high concentrations of urea, they are nevertheless likely to be responsible for much of the urea decomposition which occurs in acid soils, since the bacteria which hydrolyse urea are very sensitive to acidity.

Heterotrophic nitrification

Oxidation of ammonium compounds, once thought to be the sole province of the chemoautotrophic nitrifying bacteria (p. 150), is now known to be accomplished by a variety of chemoheterotrophs. In fact, heterotrophic nitrification, as it is called, is not an uncommon microbiological phenomenon, at least *in vitro,* though its biogeochemical significance may be slight. The organisms concerned apparently derive no energy from the oxidations.

Two groups of heterotrophic nitrifiers exist, one oxidizing ammonium and the other, various organic nitrogen compounds. Among the ammonium oxidizers are the actinomycete genera *Streptomyces* and *Micromonospora,* the bacteria *Bacillus* and *Pseudomonas,* and the fungus *Aspergillus flavus.* In pure cultures, isolates of these organisms rarely produce more than 1 or 2 ppm NO_2-N, though amounts up to and exceeding 5 ppm have been recorded. Usually the process proceeds no further and nitrite disappears through assimilation, but *A. flavus* oxidizes peptone as far as nitrate. The second group of heterotrophic nitrifiers produce nitrate from a variety of organic nitro-compounds such as the nitrophenols, and from oximes of several organic acids including pyruvic, oxaloacetic and α-ketoglutaric. Among the organisms concerned are species of *Corynebacterium* and the actinomycete *Nocardia.* The significance of heterotrophic nitrification is difficult to assess, but the rate of production of nitrate is known to be less, by at least an order of magnitude, than in autotrophic nitrification. The consensus of opinion is that heterotrophs are unimportant in the formation of nitrate in soils generally, but they may be of significance in unusual habitats, where their relative inefficiency might be compensated for by their large numbers. In acid forest soils in particular, where only small populations of autotrophic nitrifiers exist, the contribution of heterotrophic nitrification to the mineralization process may be far from negligible.

Mineralization and immobilization of sulphur

Transformations of sulphur in soils resemble in many ways the microbial conversions of nitrogen. Soil organic matter contains a variety of complex sulphur compounds including bound forms of the sulphur-containing amino acids cystine, cysteine and methionine. Sulphur is taken up by plants mainly as sulphate (SO_4^{2-}) and is reduced to sulphydryl ($-SH$) within plant tissues. Mineralization of plant debris is therefore an essential part of the soil sulphur cycle. As in the mineralization of organic nitrogen, the extent of mineral sulphur formation is governed to some degree by the sulphur content and the C/S ratio of the organic matter.

Mineralization and immobilization of phosphorus

As with nitrogen and sulphur, there is a large reservoir of organic phosphorus in soils which is unavailable to plants. While much of the phosphate taken up by plants is provided by the weathering of primary minerals, the microbial oxidation of organic substrates is an important supplementary source of inorganic phosphate. The mineralization process is especially important in virgin soils, both the total amount of phosphorus mobilized and the percentage of total organic phosphorus mineralized being greater in virgin soils than in their cultivated counterparts. The mineralization–immobilization cycle of phosphorus is analogous to the turnover cycles of nitrogen and sulphur but it is doubtful whether plants ever suffer from phosphorus deficiency as a result of microbial competition.

Incomplete oxidations and biological weathering

The major end product of the decomposition of organic matter under aerobic conditions is carbon dioxide, and in this event the oxidation of organic compounds is regarded as complete. Certain microbes, however, carry out incomplete oxidations, so that carbon compounds other than

CO_2 may accumulate. The best known example is the oxidation of ethyl alcohol to acetic acid by the acetic acid bacteria, a reaction which is utilized in the commercial production of vinegar. Other bacteria produce organic acids, for example many bacteria of the genus *Pseudomonas* oxidize glucose to gluconic acid and subsequently to 2-ketogluconic acid (Fig. 6.5), which is a powerful chelating agent. Chelation may be of importance in the solubilization of mineral silicates such as felspar and mica, and cations such as Ca^{2+}, once released from the crystal lattice of the mineral, may be held by the chelating agent in a form available to plants. In addition, phosphate might be released from apatite by chelation of Ca^{2+}, or from iron and aluminium phosphates by chelation of Fe^{3+} and Al^{3+}.

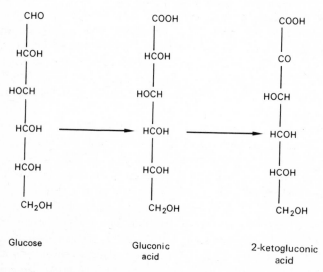

FIG. 6.5 Oxidation of glucose to gluconic acid and subsequently to 2-keto-gluconic acid, as carried out by certain soil microorganisms.

Primary minerals in nature are subject to the combined influence of physical and chemical weathering. Organisms contribute to both kinds of weathering, but especially to the latter. Physical forces result in the comminution of rocks thereby increasing the surface area of exposed silicate minerals to the action of chemical agents. Acid production by plant roots and microorganisms has long been associated with the release of metallic ions from primary minerals, ever since Julius von Sachs demonstrated, over a century ago, the ability of plant roots to etch the surface of marble. That carbonic acid and organic acids of microbial or plant origin act as agents of solubilization and as sources of hydrogen for ion exchange (p. 176) is widely accepted, but there is considerable doubt as to their significance in the weathering process, especially since carbonic acid is weak and highly labile, and many of the organic acids credited as weathering agents occur only at low concentrations. Apart from acidity *per se*, however, the chemical degradation of rocks and minerals can be mediated by chelation. Most of the metallic cations found in silicate minerals readily chelate with appropriate organic molecules to form stable ring structures, and soil organic matter contains numerous chelating agents. Some of these are, like ketogluconic acid, products of the microbial respiration of simple substrates, while others are formed during the microbial conversion of plant residues to humus.

Speculation on the role of microorganisms in the weathering process arises as a result of the presence of bacteria and fungi in the weathered crusts of rocks. The microorganisms isolated from this habitat have been tested in pure cultures for their ability to dissolve silicates such as felspars and micas, and many common fungi and bacteria possess this attribute. Among the most active bacteria are the fluorescent pseudomonads which are capable of producing 2-ketogluconic acid. The most active fungi are species of *Botrytis, Mucor, Penicillium* and *Aspergillus*. The ketogluconic acid producing pseudomonads also release phosphate from insoluble phosphates, including apatite, by chelation of calcium. It is one thing however to demonstrate a mechanism for the breakdown of finely ground phosphate and silicate minerals in the laboratory, but quite another to determine the significance of such processes in nature. In the field, three factors are operative which are normally not taken into account in the laboratory: other microorganisms are present, competing for available substrates; minerals are not pulverized; and an energy source or carbon substrate is scarce or lacking. The latter constitutes the major obstacle to accepting the significance of biological weathering since (with the exception of algae in lichens) all the microorganisms so far implicated are heterotrophs. In view of their dependence on an organic carbon source, the most likely habitat in nature where they could act as primary agents for rock weathering is the rhizosphere. Various sugars including glucose are exuded by plant roots and these could conceivably be converted by the rhizosphere microflora into carbohydrate acids and used as chelating agents to solubilize primary minerals. This will be discussed further in Chapter 7.

Respiration with inorganic substrates

The bacteria which use inorganic hydrogen-donors as substrates for aerobic respiration are able to utilize CO_2 as a source of carbon for cell synthesis. One group of these chemoautotrophic bacteria is of particular significance to plant nutrition and mineral cycling, viz. the nitrifying bacteria. Another group of some importance is the sulphur-oxidizing bacteria.

Nitrification

The mineralization of organic nitrogen can be differentiated into the processes of ammonification and nitrification (Fig. 6.6). **Ammonification** concerns the production of ammonium by heterotrophic soil microorganisms, and has been dealt with previously (p. 143). **Nitrification** refers to the oxidation of ammonium to nitrite and nitrate by autotrophic bacteria. T. Schloesling and A. Müntz were the first to prove that nitrification was a biological process, by demonstrating in 1877 that it could be stopped by sterilizing agents such as chloroform. The nitrifying bacteria fall into two physiological groups. The first, typified by *Nitrosomonas*, oxidizes ammonium to nitrite:

$$2NH_4^+ + 3O_2 \longrightarrow 2NO_2^- + 4H^+ + 2H_2O$$

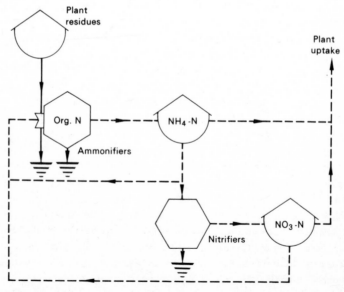

FIG. 6.6 The mineralization of organic nitrogen by soil microorganisms, showing the sequential stages of ammonification (production of NH_4^+) and nitrification (production of NO_3^-). The hexagonal symbol, normally used to designate a heterotrophic population, has been rotated through 30° to represent the nitrifiers, which are chemoautotrophs, and so distinguish them from the chemohetero-trophic ammonifiers.

The second, represented by *Nitrobacter,* oxidizes nitrite to nitrate:

$$2NO_2^- + O_2 \longrightarrow 2NO_3^-$$

The nitrifiers have long been considered to be obligate chemoautotrophs, but *Nitrobacter* was recently shown capable of utilizing acetate as a sole source of carbon and energy so that, strictly speaking, the term 'facultative autotroph' is more appropriate. Switching to a heterotrophic mode of nutrition does not increase the growth rate of *Nitrobacter,* but presumably it has some survival value in environments where nitrite is limiting.

The energy yields for both stages of the nitrification process are low, and the nitrifiers grow very slowly: even under optimum conditions, their mean generation time is about ten hours. The growth rate of heterotrophic nitrifiers (p. 146) is much faster, nevertheless the autotrophs are thought to be responsible for the bulk of the biological oxidation of ammonium in most soils.

The activity of the nitrifying bacteria is markedly influenced by certain environmental conditions, chief among which is soil pH. In acid environments their activity is greatly reduced, even in the presence of an adequate amount of substrate. In pure culture, their optimum pH is between 7.5 and 8.0. In soils, nitrate production falls off rapidly below pH 6.0 and generally is negligible below pH 5.0. Nitrification can however occur at a soil pH of 4.0 and nitrifying bacteria have been detected in even more acid soils. Another important environmental variable is the soil oxygen supply; both *Nitrosomonas* and *Nitrobacter* are obligate aerobes, hence adequate soil aeration is essential to their function. Population densities are very low, and in acid soils may be only of the order of 100 cells per gram. They rarely exceed 10^5 per gram even in neutral and alkaline soils, unless ammonium fertilizers have been added.

Under most conditions in nature, the oxidation of ammonium proceeds as far as nitrate, so that nitrite does not normally accumulate in soils; this is fortunate because nitrite is toxic to plants and microbes. Where it does occur it is usually the result of the combined effects of alkalinity and high ammonium levels, as described previously (p. 145). In arable soils, nitrate is considered to be the principal form in which nitrogen is assimilated by plants, hence from the agronomist's viewpoint the nitrifying bacteria play a key role in the soil nitrogen cycle and in the maintenance of soil fertility. In grassland and forest soils, the nitrifiers may not be so important (Fig. 6.7). Arable soils of the temperate regions, unless they are very acid, contain a fairly constant but very low level of ammonium, and a variable but higher amount of nitrate. The NO_3-N concentration commonly ranges from 2–20 ppm (mg/kg),

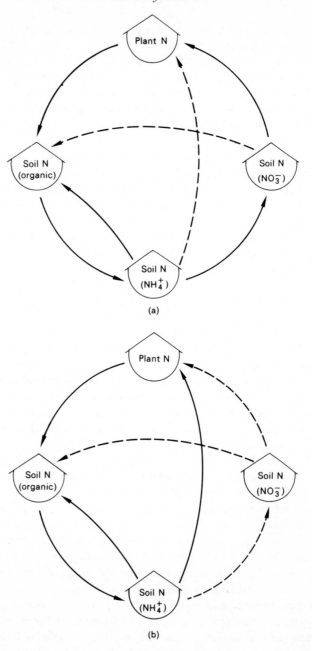

FIG. 6.7 The soil nitrogen cycle. *(a)* The 'nitrate model', as typified by arable soils. *(b)* The 'ammonium model', as found in many permanent grassland and forest soils. Major pathways shown as solid lines, minor pathways as broken lines.

and in favourable circumstances rises to over 50 ppm. It varies throughout the year according to agronomic practice, tending to accumulate in fallow soils and to disappear under cropping. As E. W. Russell has pointed out, however, soil in fallow will accumulate nitrate only if four conditions are satisfied. First, sufficient readily decomposable organic matter must be present to provide ammonium as an energy source for the nitrifiers. Second, the soil must be kept free of weeds otherwise these may utilize the nitrate as rapidly as it is produced. Third, the soil must be kept moist but not necessarily continuously. Fourth, there must not be too much rain or else nitrate will be lost by leaching.

It is generally assumed that nitrification plays little or no part in the nitrogen economy of permanent grassland and forest soils, and that grasses and trees absorb nitrogen almost entirely as ammonium. While direct experimental proof of this assumption is lacking, there is much circumstantial evidence to support it. According to F. E. Chase and colleagues, there are large areas of the Earth's land surface 'in which, because of soil or climatic conditions, coupled with dense perennial plant cover, nitrate does not occur and plants must subsist on an ammonium diet'.

Grassland soils of the cool temperate zone in the northern hemisphere maintain a low but fairly constant level of NH_4-N, about 3−9 ppm throughout the year, but they contain very low or negligible amounts of nitrate nitrogen (1−2 ppm) which distinguishes them from soils under crops or fallow. A depression of nitrification might be expected in old, permanent grassland soils since these are frequently acid, and hence contain few nitrifying bacteria. In addition, there is some evidence which points to a direct inhibition of nitrifiers by grass root exudates. In many instances however, the absence of nitrification under pasture cannot be explained, and many grassland soils nitrify well if incubated in the laboratory; furthermore, it is common experience that nitrification will proceed rapidly in the field if old pastures are ploughed out. Not all grassland soils behave in this fashion, however. In Southern Australia, with a warm, intermittently dry summer and a cold, wet winter, J. R. Simpson found that soils from an old *Phalaris*-subterranean clover pasture accumulate nitrate during summer and autumn (cf. fallow soils), the levels sometimes reaching 40 ppm NO_3-N during the summer and falling to about 2 ppm in winter and early spring; NH_4-N tends to remain at about 4−5 ppm throughout the year.

The levels and forms of mineral nitrogen in forest soils depend on their pH and the type of humus. Nitrification is generally much more active in mull than in mor soils. Many forest soils are moderately to strongly acid, and in consequence the activity of nitrifying bacteria in these soils is likely to be inhibited. The level of NH_4-N in lateritic podzolic soils from dry sclerophyll eucalypt forest in South East Queensland is relatively constant at 7—9 ppm, while NO_3-N rarely occurs in detectable amounts. The native microflora in these soils shows a marked preference for ammonium and seemingly has limited ability to utilize nitrate. Table 6.2 shows how nitrate remains largely unincorporated during incubation even though the bacterial population rises with the addition of lime, whereas ammonium is rapidly immobilized by the microflora and subsequently mineralized.

Whether these observations apply in general to forest soils is not known. If forest soil microbes are indeed limited in their capacity to utilize nitrate then what nitrate is produced under natural conditions must be either taken up by the trees or else lost to the system by denitrification (p. 158) or leaching. Alternately, the low levels of nitrate commonly found in undisturbed forest ecosystems might be explained by postulating that nitrification plays a minor role in such ecosystems. This is difficult to accept in view of the known presence of nitrifying bacteria in many forest soils and the necessity of providing nitrate as an electron-acceptor in the denitrification process (without which the nitrogen cycle is incomplete). In any event, there are certainly some forest soils which have considerable potential for nitrification when the tree cover is disturbed or when they are limed, even though they may contain little or no nitrate in the virgin condition. Others do contain significant amounts of nitrate naturally, especially in the tropics where the phenomenon may be related to an alternating cycle of wetting and drying imposed by prevailing climatic regimes. For reasons that are not entirely clear, there is rapid oxidation of organic matter in a soil that has been remoistened after drying, the flush of decomposition lasting several days. This could well explain the high fluctuating nitrate levels (5—25 ppm N) but a low and fairly constant ammonium level (4 ppm N) found by D. J. Greenland in soil from tropical high forest in Ghana.

S. L. Jansson has proposed that two soil nitrogen cycles must be considered, viz. an external cycle, involving uptake and assimilation of nitrogen by plants, and an internal cycle in which various forms of nitrogen are cycled between the organic and inorganic phases by microbiological processes. The external cycle is governed and determined by the internal cycle, in which the key form of nitrogen is ammonium (Fig. 6.8). This is subject to continuous consumption and renewal by the microflora, whereas nitrate constitutes a more or less transitory pool of surplus inorganic nitrogen not needed in the internal cycle. Jansson further postulated that nitrifiers are weak competitors for

TABLE 6.2 Effect of lime on microbial populations and on mineralization and immobilization of $^{15}NH_4$-N or $^{15}NO_3$-N during incubation of a sandy podzolic soil*

Treatment	Soil pH	Fungi per gram (×10⁵)	Bacteria per gram			Organic N		Inorganic N	
			Ammonifiers (×10⁶)	Nitrifiers	Denitrifiers (×10⁶)	Non-hydro-lysable (%)†	Hydro-lysable (%)†	NH₄⁺ (%)†	NO₃⁻ (%)†
K^{15}NO₃ minus lime	4.7	2.91	2.94	*ca.* 60	0.07	2.4	2.6	0.4	94.5
K^{15}NO₃ plus lime	7.4	1.91	11.18	*ca.* 80	0.53	1.9	2.5	0.4	95.1
Significance level‡	***	***	***	ns	***	ns	ns	ns	ns
(^{15}NH₄)₂SO₄ minus lime	4.6	3.43	3.88	*ca.* 40	0.24	6.0	22.4	64.6	6.9
(^{15}NH₄)₂SO₄ plus lime	7.3	2.55	18.81	*ca.* 1400	1.36	14.6	27.7	42.4	15.2
Significance level‡	***	***	***	***	***	**	***	***	***

* After Jones, J. M. (1968) PhD thesis, University of New England.
† Percentage of total labelled nitrogen.
‡ One, two or three asterisks indicate that means differ at the 5%, 1% or 0.1% levels of probability, respectively; ns indicates that the differences are not significant.

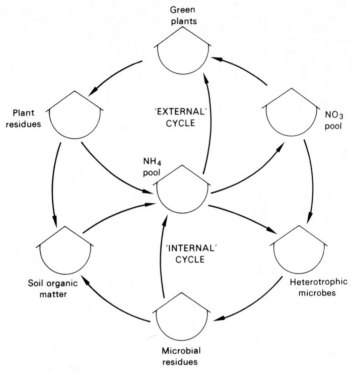

FIG. 6.8 The flow of nitrogen through the soil–plant system, based on S. L. Jansson's concept of ammonium as the key form of soil nitrogen.

NH_4-N compared with heterotrophic microorganisms, and green plants weak competitors for NH_4-N in comparison with nitrifiers. Some of these concepts are relatively new and as yet unconfirmed, but an emphasis on the overriding importance of ammonium is clearly compatible with the hypothesis that nitrification is not essential for the nutrition of vascular plants in many grassland and forest ecosystems. The agronomic significance of nitrate is not to be doubted, but it is likely that its major functional role in natural ecosystems is not to provide nitrogen for the producers, but rather to serve as an electron acceptor in denitrification. The biogeochemistry of nitrogen is discussed in Chapter 9.

Sulphur oxidation

The colourless sulphur bacteria use inorganic sulphur compounds, or elemental sulphur, as substrates for aerobic respiration. During this process, hydrogen sulphide is oxidized to sulphur, and sulphur and thiosulphate are oxidized to sulphate:

$$2H_2S + O_2 \longrightarrow 2S + 2H_2O$$
$$2S + 2H_2O + 3O_2 \longrightarrow 2SO_4^{2-} + 4H^+$$
$$S_2O_3^{2-} + H_2O + 2O_2 \longrightarrow 2SO_4^{2-} + 2H^+$$

There are two groups of autotrophic sulphur-oxidizers. One, the filamentous sulphur bacteria, are closely related to the blue-green algae. They occur in specialized habitats such as hot springs and on the surface of estuarine mud, and need not concern us here. The other group are gram-negative rods with polar flagella (if motile), and are assigned to the genus *Thiobacillus*. The thiobacilli are found in soils, but not in large numbers unless sulphur compounds are added deliberately. Under normal conditions, most soils contain less than 200 thiobacilli per gram, though higher populations, of the order of 1 000 cells per gram, occur when appropriate substrates are present. At the low population densities normally holding, they can hardly play a major role in sulphate formation. It seems more likely that sulphate production in most soils is achieved by other means, for example as a by-product of the decomposition of sulphur-containing proteins, which is brought about by a variety of heterotrophic bacteria and fungi that are more abundant and widespread than the thiobacilli. For example, of more than 200 strains of sulphur-oxidizing microbes isolated from Australian soils, 61 per cent were heterotrophic bacteria (31 per cent *Arthrobacter* spp., 11 per cent *Bacillus* spp.) and 22 per cent were facultative *Thiobacillus* spp., while only 13 per cent were autotrophic thiobacilli. Nevertheless, in soils where microbial transformations of sulphur are confined to the activities of heterotrophs, the rate of sulphur oxidation may be inadequate for satisfactory plant nutrition.

Not all of the sulphate in soils is the product of biological oxidations *in situ*. A substantial proportion of soil sulphate derives from rain; its origin will be discussed later when anaerobic processes are considered (p. 161). It should also be kept in mind that in well aerated soils sulphides, sulphur and thiosulphate can be slowly oxidized by purely chemical processes. Such processes are however insignificant in comparison with biological oxidations of reduced sulphur, provided soil temperature and moisture regimes are favourable for microbial activity.

Anaerobic processes and nutrient cycling

Two kinds of anaerobic energy-yielding processes are known among chemoheterotrophic microbes, viz. anaerobic respiration where the hydrogen-acceptor is inorganic, and fermentation in which an organic molecule serves as the hydrogen-acceptor. Some anaerobic processes affect the supply of plant nutrients directly, others indirectly. In well aerated soils, direct competition between anaerobes and plant roots for available nutrients seems unlikely. Since the energy-yielding reactions of anaerobes are independent of oxygen however, they are able to maintain ion uptake when conditions are no longer suitable for active ion accumulation by roots. Therefore in badly aerated and infertile soils, it is conceivable that anaerobes could compete with plants for nutrients.

Anaerobic respiration

Of the three possible hydrogen-acceptors known to participate in this process, only two — nitrate and sulphate — have any significance for plant nutrition. Nitrate reduction, or **denitrification**, is a process of very great geochemical significance, being the principal means by which nitrogen escapes from the biosphere to the atmosphere. This aspect of the process will be taken up in Chapter 9. In the present context, viz. that of plant nutrition, nitrate reduction represents a loss of available nitrogen. Sulphate reduction plays an analogous role in the sulphur cycle: not only does it reduce the availability of sulphur to plants, but it also represents the major pathway for transferring sulphur from the biosphere to the atmosphere. The analogy between the two cycles is not so close as might appear however, as we shall see.

Nitrate reduction: denitrification

The organisms capable of utilizing NO_3^- as an electron-acceptor in energy-yielding oxidations are all bacteria. They have a wide distribution over the surface of the Earth, both in terrestrial and aquatic habitats, and in the air. Soil is a particularly efficient denitrifying system. Ammonium ions derived from the mineralization of organic matter first appear near the soil surface, and by virtue of their positive charge are adsorbed on the negatively charged soil colloids and so prevented from moving down through the soil profile. At or near the surface, oxygen levels are high and conditions favourable for nitrification. The nitrate ions so formed, being negatively charged, are no longer held by the colloids but are leached to lower levels where the oxygen concentration is lower. Provided suitable organic substrates are present, the nitrate can serve as a hydrogen-acceptor for denitrifiers, the end products being nitrous oxide or molecular nitrogen, which diffuse out of the soil and are lost to the atmosphere (Fig. 6.9). Whenever anaerobic conditions prevail in soil, for example following waterlogging, denitrification becomes the dominant process of the nitrogen cycle. It not only occurs in waterlogged soils however, but is a normal reaction in all soils, since pockets of anaerobiosis exist temporarily even under conditions of good aeration.

Only a few genera of bacteria can denitrify, but those which can are widespread. *Pseudomonas* and *Achromobacter,* and to a lesser extent the spore-forming *Denitrobacillus,* are among the principal genera of soil bacteria involved. Many of these same bacteria are active in proteolysis, ammonification and other organic matter decomposition processes, and begin to reduce nitrate only when conditions for aerobic respiration no longer exist. Although most denitrifiers are heterotrophs, at least two autotrophic denitrifying bacteria are recognized, viz. *Thiobacillus denitrificans* which oxidizes sulphur, and *Micrococcus denitrificans* which oxidizes hydrogen. Fungi, being for the most part obligate aerobes, are not involved in denitrification.

Denitrification is generally considered to take place in at least two stages, nitrate first being reduced to nitrite, then nitrite to molecular nitrogen:

$$NO_3^- + H_2 \longrightarrow NO_2^- + H_2O$$
$$2NO_2^- + 4H_2 \longrightarrow N_2 + 4H_2O$$

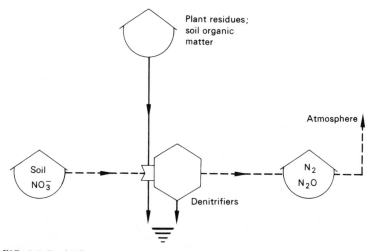

FIG. 6.9 Denitrification in soil, an example of anaerobic respiration in which nitrate ions are used as electron acceptors for the oxidation of reduced carbon compounds.

When the concentration of nitrate is high, denitrifying bacteria may produce nitrous oxide (N_2O), which escapes to the atmosphere as such, or is further reduced to N_2 when the nitrate concentration falls. Other factors which affect the evolution of N_2O are soil reaction and the identity of the denitrifying bacteria. The effect of soil reaction is complex, the optimum pH varying with nitrate concentration and the organisms involved. Active denitrification, by removing nitrate, tends to cause a rise in the pH of the system, hence the buffering capacity of the soil exerts a strong influence on the nature and extent of denitrification.

There has been much controversy concerning the effects of oxygen on denitrification. Some workers have claimed that certain bacteria can denitrify aerobically, however it seems likely that where such results have been obtained, they are due in part to experimental error. For example, in actively growing cultures it is possible that lower oxygen tensions may exist in places, even though efforts are made to ensure adequate aeration. This can in fact be demonstrated by the use of a sensitive instrument such as a polarograph. In passing, it should be mentioned that chemical decomposition of nitrate can apparently take place in certain circumstances, especially during the nitrification of ammonium fertilizers in acid, sandy soils.

Sulphate reduction

Sulphate (SO_4^{2-}) may act as the electron-acceptor in anaerobic respiration, and in the process is reduced to sulphide (S^{2-}):

$$SO_4^{2-} + 4H_2 \longrightarrow S^{2-} + 4H_2O$$

Sulphite (SO_3^{2-}) and thiosulphate ($S_2O_3^{2-}$) are alternate electron-acceptors. The microbial reduction of sulphate is a step in the soil sulphur cycle analogous to denitrification in the nitrogen cycle. Unlike denitrification however, which is carried out by a number of facultative anaerobes, sulphate reduction is restricted to relatively few species of bacteria, the most widespread of which is *Desulphovibrio desulphuricans*. This organism influences soil fertility directly by reducing the amount of SO_4^{2-}, which is the principal form in which sulphur is absorbed by plants. Its activity in soils, like that of denitrifiers, is greatly enhanced by waterlogging, which provides the necessary reducing conditions. In flooded soils, such as occur in rice paddies, the sulphide concentration may exceed 50 ppm within a few days of inundation.

Sulphate reduction is most characteristic of estuarine muds where it

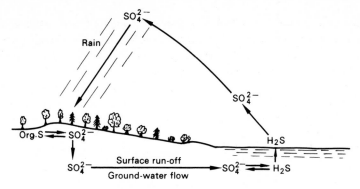

FIG. 6.10 A simplified outline of the sulphur cycle. Sulphate reduction, a form of anaerobic respiration, produces H_2S in the littoral zone which diffuses into the atmosphere where it is oxidized spontaneously to sulphate, dissolved in water and returned to the land in rain. Sulphate absorbed by plants is incorporated in organic compounds which are subsequently mineralized (usually aerobically) to produce sulphate again which returns to the sea via ground water and surface streams.

is one of the dominating microbiological processes. In an indirect way, this has a more profound influence on plant nutrition than have the activities of sulphate reducers in the soil itself. The ocean is the great reservoir of sulphate and is the major source of sulphur for terrestrial plants and animals, which require it as a component of proteins and certain vitamins. Sulphate moves from the ocean to the land as a component of rainwater, and the greater part of the sulphate found in rainwater apparently derives from the spontaneous oxidation of H_2S which emanates from the shallow waters of the littoral zone. On the surface of marine sediments, sulphate-reducing bacteria convert dissolved sulphate to H_2S, in which form it escapes to the atmosphere where it is oxidized spontaneously to sulphate, taken up in water and finally deposited on the land in rain. The sulphur cycle is illustrated diagrammatically in Fig. 6.10.

Fermentation

In fermentation, organic molecules act as both hydrogen-donors and hydrogen-acceptors. Being a strictly anaerobic process, fermentation makes a minor contribution to organic matter decomposition in well aerated soils. In such soils aerobes, especially fungi, are the major decomposers of plant residues. There are fermentative bacteria capable of decomposing cellulose, but they are more abundant than fungi only in anaerobic habitats, such as waterlogged peats. Nevertheless since most soils, especially those of heavy texture, contain micro-habitats where anaerobic conditions exist from time to time, fermentation no doubt plays some part in mineralization—immobilization cycles. Sugars are the most readily and widely used substrates for fermentation, but a variety of other substances, including various organic acids, amino acids, purines and pyrimidines can be fermented by some bacteria. The different kinds of fermentation are classified according to their major end products.

The simplest possible fermentation consists of the splitting of a simple six-carbon sugar into two molecules of the three-carbon lactic acid. It is not only typical of the so-called lactic acid bacteria, but is also characteristic of animal tissues as well as certain protozoa and fungi. In the lactic acid fermentation, pyruvic acid, produced by glycolysis of a monosaccharide, acts as the final hydrogen-acceptor. Two kinds of lactic acid bacteria are known: (a) homofermentative forms, in which lactic acid is virtually the sole product of glucose fermentation; and (b) heterofermentative forms, which produce carbon dioxide, ethyl alcohol and sometimes acetic acid, in addition to lactic acid. The heterofermentative forms are characteristically plant inhabitants. They are thought to exist normally on plant surfaces, growing at the expense of exudations. They also flourish in decaying plant tissues, where they soon dominate the bacterial flora because their acid production inhibits the growth of most other bacteria. They are not considered a part of the normal soil microflora.

The butyric acid fermentation is typical of *Clostridium*, a genus of anaerobic spore formers. It is also found in *Bacillus macerans* and some anaerobic protozoa. The process involves the conversion of sugars and related compounds to butyric and acetic acids, carbon dioxide and hydrogen, plus a variety of alcohols. Many butyric acid bacteria are nitrogen-fixers, e.g. *Cl. pasteurianum.* The chief substrates for these fermentations are soluble sugars, starch and pectin. Pectin decomposing clostridia are the principal agents in the retting, i.e. softening, of flax and other fibres. Another group of clostridia ferment amino acids, with the production of fatty acids, ammonia and carbon dioxide.

Many of the bacteria which carry out fermentations are, like the denitrifiers, facultative anaerobes. The end products of fermentation include many organic acids which may assist in the solubilization of primary minerals. The carbon dioxide produced may also contribute to rock weathering, through the formation of carbonic acid. It is doubtful however whether these effects are any more pronounced than the effects of organic acids and carbon dioxide produced by microorganisms which respire aerobically.

Selected references

Alexander, M. (1961) *Introduction to Soil Microbiology.* Wiley.

Gray, T. R. G. and Williams, S. T. (1971) *Soil Microorganisms.* Oliver & Boyd.

Rose, A. H. (1968) *Chemical Microbiology,* 2nd edn. Butterworth.

Russell, E. W. (1961) *Soil Conditions and Plant Growth,* 9th edn. Longman.

Alexander, M. (1964) 'Biochemical ecology of soil microorganisms.' *A. Rev. Microbiol.* **18**, 217−52.

Alexander, M. (1965) 'Nitrification' in *Soil Nitrogen,* eds. W. V. Bartholomew and F. E. Clark, pp. 307−43. American Soc. Agronomy.

Birch, H. F. (1958) 'The effect of soil drying on humus decomposition and nitrogen availability.' *Plant Soil,* **10**, 9−31.

Birch, H. F. (1960) 'Nitrification in soils after different periods of dryness.' *Plant Soil,* **12**, 81−96.

Bollen, W. B. and Wright, E. (1961) 'Microbes and nitrates in soils from virgin and young-growth forests.' *Can. J. Microbiol.,* **7**, 785−92.

Boyle, J. R., Voigt, G. K. and Sawhney, B. L. (1967) 'Biotite flakes: alteration by chemical and biological treatment.' *Science* **155**, 193−5.

Bremner, J. M. (1967) 'Nitrogenous compounds' in *Soil Biochemistry,* eds. A. D. McLaren and G. H. Peterson, pp. 19−66. Marcel Dekker.

Chase, F. E., Corke, C. T. and Robinson, J. B. (1967) 'Nitrifying bacteria in soil' in *The Ecology of Soil Bacteria,* eds. T. R. Gray and D. Parkinson, pp. 593−611. Liverpool University Press.

Clark, F. E. and Paul, E. A. (1970) 'The microflora of grassland.' *Adv. Agron.,* **22**, 375−435.

Cowling, E. G. and Merrill, W. (1966) 'Nitrogen in wood and its role in wood deterioration.' *Can. J. Bot.,* **44**, 1539−54.

Duff, R. B., Webley, D. M. and Scott, R. O. (1963) 'The solubilization of minerals and related materials by 2-ketogluconic acid producing bacteria.' *Soil Sci.* **95**, 105−14.

Florence, R. G. (1965) 'Decline of old-growth redwood forests in relation to some soil microbiological processes.' *Ecology,* **46**, 52−64.

Greenland, D. J. (1958) 'Nitrate fluctuations in tropical soils.' *J. Agric. Sci.,* **50**, 82−92.

Harmsen, G. W. and van Schreven, D. A. (1955) 'Mineralization of organic nitrogen in soil.' *Adv. Agron.*, 7, 299–398.

Jansson, S. L. (1958) 'Tracer studies on nitrogen transformations in soil with special attention to mineralization–immobilization relationships.' *K. Lantbr. Högsk. Annlr*, 24, 101–361.

Moore, D. R. E. and Waid, J. S. (1971) 'The influence of washings of living roots on nitrification.' *Soil Biol. Biochem.*, 3, 69–83.

Odu, C. T. I. and Adeoye, J. C. (1970) 'Heterotrophic nitrification in soils – a preliminary investigation.' *Soil Biol. Biochem.*, 2, 41–5;

Quastel, J. H. (1965) 'Soil metabolism.' *A. Rev. Pl. Physiol.*, 16, 217–40.

Schmidt, E. L. (1954) 'Nitrate formation by a soil fungus.' *Science*, 119, 187–9.

Simpson, J. R. (1954) 'Mineral nitrogen fluctuations in soils under improved pasture in southern New South Wales.' *Aust. J. agric. Res.*, 13, 1059–72.

Skerman, V. B. D. and Macrae, J. C. (1957) 'The influence of oxygen on the reduction of nitrate by adapted cells of *Pseudomonas denitrificans.*' *Can. J. Microbiol.*, 3, 215–30.

Skinner, F. A. (1967) 'The anaerobic bacteria of soil' in *The Ecology of Soil Bacteria*, eds. T. R. G. Gray and D. Parkinson, pp. 573–92. Liverpool University Press.

Smith, W. H., Bormann, F. H. and Likens, G. E. (1968) 'Response of chemoautotrophic nitrifiers to forest cutting.' *Soil Sci.*, 106, 471–3.

Swaby, R. J. (1962) 'Effect of microorganisms on nutrient availability' in *Trans. Int. Soc. Soil Sci., Comm. IV and V*, ed. G. J. Neale, pp. 159–72. International Soil Conference, Palmerston North, New Zealand.

Vitolins, I. and Swaby, R. J. (1967) 'Activity of sulphur-oxidizing microorganisms in some Australian soils.' *Aust. J. Soil Res.*, 7, 171–93.

Wadleigh, C. H. (1955) 'Mineral nutrition of plants as related to microbial activities in soils.' *Adv. Agron.*, 7, 75–87.

Wallace, W. and Nicholas, D. J. D. (1969) 'The biochemistry of nitrifying organisms.' *Biol. Rev.*, 44, 359–91.

Webley, D. M., Henderson, M. E. K. and Taylor, I. F. (1963) 'The microbiology of rocks and weathered stones.' *J. Soil Sci.*, 14, 102–12.

Whitehead, D. C. (1964) 'Soil and plant-nutrition aspects of the sulphur cycle.' *Soils and Fert.*, **27**, 1—8.

Wijler, J. and Delwiche, C. C. (1954) 'Investigations on the denitrifying process in soil.' *Plant Soil*, **5**, 155—69.

7 The rhizosphere

The topics dealt with in Chapters 5 and 6, concerning the microbial contributions to energy transformations and nutrient turnover in soils, involve rather loose associations between plants and microorganisms. These plant—microbe relationships exist because the heterotrophic soil microflora depends primarily upon plant detritus for its energy supply, and because the growth of plants is determined in large measure by the activity of both heterotrophic and autotrophic soil microbes. The present chapter is concerned with a much closer plant—microbe inter-action, that which occurs in the immediate vicinity of plant roots. The soil in this region is a highly favourable habitat for microorganisms, and has a characteristic microflora which is quite distinct from the general soil population. This unique environment which is under the influence of plant roots is called the **rhizosphere**. Within this zone, interactions between plants and microorganisms can greatly affect crop production and soil fertility and hence, at the ecosystem level, energy flow and nutrient cycling.

The concept of the rhizosphere was introduced in 1904 by L. Hiltner. Its extent is variable, there being no sharp boundary between it and the neighbouring soil. The roots of plants are frequently sur-rounded by a mucilaginous layer varying in composition from a rela-tively simple oligosaccharide to a complex pectic acid polymer permeated by loose cellulose microfibrils. Electron micrographs give a graphic picture of this boundary zone between roots and soil, indicating that the space between the cell walls and mineral soil particles may be filled with mucilaginous material (Fig. 7.1). This region of 'mucigel' approximates to the definition of the term **rhizoplane** which is the name sometimes given to root surface itself and the closely adhering soil. Actually, the influence of plant roots extends beyond the muci-laginous zone into the surrounding soil especially if the soil is not a fertile one. The extent of the rhizosphere is generally of the order of millimetres or less, though an effect has been discerned at a distance of more than 1 cm in sandy soils.

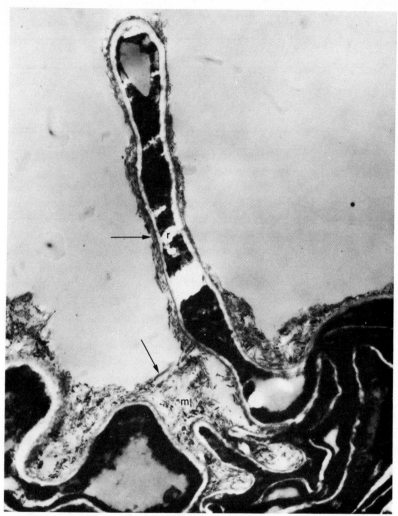

FIG. 7.1 The boundary layer between plant roots and soil. Electron micrograph of root hair (r) of pea, showing the zone of mucigel (m) outside the epidermis. The arrows indicate soil particles embedded in the mucigel. From Greaves, M. P., and Darbyshire, J. F., (1972), *Soil Biol. Biochem.*, 4, 443−9.

Composition of the rhizosphere population

A measure of the root influence, as determined by dilution platecounts, is given by the *R/S* ratio, which is the ratio of microbial numbers per unit weight of rhizosphere soil, *R*, to the numbers in a unit weight of adjacent non-rhizosphere soil, *S*. The rhizosphere effect is considerably greater for bacteria than for other protists (Table 7.1).

TABLE 7.1 The rhizosphere effect: typical *R/S* ratios for various microbes

Type of organism	R/S ratio
Bacteria	10—50
Fungi	5—10
Protozoa	1—3
Algae	1—2

With bacteria, qualitative as well as quantitative effects are common. Gram-negative bacteria are favoured over gram-positive, and non-spore formers over spore formers. Short gram-negative rods respond most, and invariably make up a greater percentage of the rhizosphere microflora than of the normal soil population. The short, gram-negative rods that are greatly stimulated in the rhizosphere fall mainly into three genera, namely *Pseudomonas, Achromobacter* and, to a lesser extent, *Agrobacterium.* Anaerobic bacteria are also greatly stimulated in the rhizosphere, and this is attributed to reduced oxygen supply resulting from root and microbial respiration.

The high bacterial density in the rhizosphere undoubtedly results in a high degree of microbial competition and the selection pressures arising from this tend to favour rapidly growing and biochemically versatile organisms over slower growing and less versatile strains. This would suggest that the rhizosphere microflora has a greater ability to effect rapid biochemical changes than the general soil population.

The nutrient requirements of the bacterial component of the rhizosphere biota have been studied by means of an empirical scheme for classifying soil bacteria, devised in 1943 by A. G. Lochhead and F. E. Chase. This classification recognizes seven nutritional groups of bacteria, distinguished according to their ability to grow on media of varying degrees of complexity. Some bacterial isolates can grow on a simple medium containing only glucose and mineral salts whereas others require preformed amino acids or B-vitamins, or unidentified growth factors contained in yeast extract or soil extract. Lochhead and Chase's nutritional classification reveals a consistent, preferential enhancement of organisms that either require no special growth factors or else require amino acids only (Table 7.2). At the same time, the proportion of bacteria with complex nutritional requirements declines, even though their actual numbers increase. The selection for bacteria whose growth is enhanced by amino acids is presumably the result of the high level of amino acids in the rhizosphere. These amino acids are derived from plant exudates, decomposition of dead roots and microorganisms, and from exudates of microbial cells. In general, the rhizo-

TABLE 7.2 Incidence of nutritional groups of bacteria in the rhizosphere of oats*

Requirements for maximum growth	Percentage of whole pop.		Total count per gram	
	Control soil	Rhizosphere	Control soil ($\times 10^6$)	Rhizosphere ($\times 10^6$)
No special growth factors †	13	33	32	690
Amino acids	2	11	5	230
B vitamins	9	11	22	230
Amino acids + B vitamins	2	1	5	21
Yeast extract	27	19	67	400
Soil extract	23	18	57	380
Yeast extract + soil extract	24	7	60	150

* After Wallace, R. H. and Lochhead, A. G. (1949) *Soil Sci.*, **67**, 63–9.
† Capable of growing in a simple medium containing sugar and inorganic salts only.

sphere bacteria are less fastidious than those which live beyond the region of root influence.

In contrast to their effect on bacteria, roots do not have such a marked influence on the total number of fungi. However, specific genera are stimulated, in other words the rhizosphere effect for fungi is more qualitative than quantitative. The imperfect fungi *Fusarium* and *Cylindrocarpon* are among the more prominent rhizosphere inhabitants but many other genera are represented, especially the phycomycetes *Mucor* and *Rhizopus*. An extreme example of this tendency is the virtual dominance of a single fungal species on the surface of mycorrhizal roots of the ectotrophic kind. This special case of the rhizosphere effect will be considered in Chapter 8. The spores of many common soil fungi, which normally lie dormant, will often germinate in the rhizosphere.

Alteration of the microbial environment by plant roots

Stimulation of microorganisms in the rhizosphere is assumed to be caused by substances coming from roots, partly as a result of exudation and partly due to autolysis of moribund and dead root cells. Different plant species and also different parts of the root system of the same plant, may have distinctive rhizosphere microfloras. The causes of these differences, which may be both qualitative and quantitative, are not known for certain, though some of the effects can be attributed to differences in rooting habit, tissue composition, and in the products of root exudation. The age of the plant also affects the composition of the rhizosphere flora. A rhizosphere effect is detectable in seedlings only a few days old, and this must primarily be due to the stimulatory properties of root exudates. As the plant matures, dead and sloughed-off root tissues add appreciably to the rhizosphere effect. With the approach of senescence, the rhizosphere population gradually declines, and eventually becomes indistinguishable from the normal soil microflora. Unlike the heterotrophic soil microflora in general, the rhizosphere population is not appreciably altered, either qualitatively or quantitatively, by the addition of crop residues, animal manures, or mineral fertilizers. This is only to be expected, since the existence of an assured energy source makes the rhizosphere a habitat more or less independent of fluctuations in substrate availability, which is the major limiting factor for the heterotrophic soil microflora generally.

The nature of root exudates

This topic has been studied in great detail by A. D. Rovira, and the account which follows is based largely on his reviews. Root exudates include carbohydrates, amino acids and other organic acids, vitamins, nucleic acid derivatives, and various miscellaneous compounds. The amounts exuded, while adequate for the support of large populations of microorganisms, are often too low to be detected without the use of sensitive analytical methods such as chromatography. In studying root exudates, careful attention to aseptic technique is essential, since it has been shown that non-sterile roots exude greater quantities of amino acids than roots grown in axenic culture. A corollary to this observation is that the rhizosphere microflora itself contributes to the root exudate effect observed in soils, and the relative contribution of the two components — roots and microbes — may be difficult to assess in nature. Growth factors in particular may be contributed primarily by microorganisms, in other words bacteria with less specialized growth factor requirements may synthesize and release metabolites needed by more specialized nutritional types.

Among the carbohydrates exuded, at least ten sugars, including an oligosaccharide, have been identified in the exudates of a wide range of plant species. The hexoses glucose and fructose are generally the most abundant, and others which have been detected include the pentoses xylose, ribose, arabinose, and the disaccharides sucrose and maltose. The wide range of sugars recorded in root exudates suggests that exudation of sugars is a general phenomenon which probably has little or no effect in determining the actual composition of the rhizosphere microflora associated with any particular species of plant.

In contrast to their exudation of carbohydrates, plants appear to differ greatly with respect to the amounts and kinds of amino acids they exude. The most abundant amino acids exuded by ten and twenty-one day-old pea plants are homoserine, threonine and glutamine and by oats, lysine, serine and glycine; a total of twenty-two amino compounds has been found in pea root exudates compared to only fourteen in oat root exudates. In addition the total amount of exudate from peas is many times that produced by oats. Such qualitative and quantitative differences between the exudates of different plant species grown under identical conditions are likely to have far reaching effects on the composition and density of the rhizosphere population.

Various other organic acids, including several members of the tricarboxylic acid cycle, occur in root exudates of several plant species. These organic acids could not only provide readily available substrates for many microorganisms, but in addition they might have important secondary effects in the rhizosphere soil such as alteration of pH and chelation of metal ions (see p. 148).

The most common vitamins found in root exudates are biotin and thiamine. The levels recorded are generally low and probably insufficient to meet the needs of all the vitamin requiring microbes in the rhizosphere. Many of these microbes, perhaps the majority, depend on the exudates of less fastidious microorganisms rather than on root exudates. The nucleic acid derivatives, adenine, guanine, uridine and cytodine, are also released from the roots of plants. Exoenzymes such as phosphatase and invertase have been found associated with roots, too. And finally, a great variety of miscellaneous compounds is found in root exudates including phenol derivatives and other substances toxic to microorganisms. Thus not all the effects of plant root exudates are necessarily beneficial for the rhizosphere microflora.

Factors affecting exudation

Apart from the effect of plant age, discussed above, the conditions under which plants are grown also affect exudation. It is increased under high light and temperature regimes. If soil is allowed to dry out to the stage where plants wilt, then re-wetted, there is a rapid release of amino acids from the roots as the plants regain turgor. Microorganisms themselves can affect the pattern of exudation by changing the permeability of root cells, by altering root metabolism, and by modifying some of the materials released from roots. Furthermore, the root sur-face is not uniformly populated and this may change the exudate pattern from place to place along the root.

Other factors affecting the proliferation of microbes in the rhizosphere

Although organic materials originating from roots — exudates, slough-ings, etc. — appear to be the primary determinants of the rhizosphere effect, there are additional factors which may be important in making the soil adjacent to plant roots a favourable habitat for microorganisms. For example, the assimilation of nutrients by plants may lower the concentration available for microbial use, favouring those groups which can compete more successfully or which have very low nutrient require-ments. Again, root respiration may alter the pH and the availability of some nutrients in rhizosphere soil, and by utilizing oxygen favour the growth of microaerophiles and anaerobes. Furthermore, soil physical properties can be altered by plant growth, as when root penetration improves soil structure, leading to increased aeration and a consequent stimulation of the oxidative processes of aerobic microbes.

The rhizosphere in relation to nutrient cycling

The activities of the rhizosphere microflora affect the circulation of nutrients through their influence on plant nutrition. The effect of microbial processes on nutrient availability in the rhizosphere thus pro-vides a basis for considering the regulatory role of this root—microbe interaction. Before discussing it, however, it is pertinent to review briefly the state of knowledge concerning the uptake of nutrients from the soil. A more detailed treatment may be found in the work of Epstein (see under 'Selected references').

Soil as a source of mineral nutrients

Salts exist in soil in a number of different states: (i) as water-soluble salts dissolved in the soil solution; (ii) as sparingly soluble or insoluble substances containing exchangeable ions; and (iii) as insoluble sub-stances from which ions are not readily obtained by exchange reactions.

The composition of the soil solution varies with soil type, and for all ions except phosphate its concentration increases as soil moisture content decreases. The level of phosphate is relatively independent of soil moisture content, presumably because the soil solution is nearly saturated with rather insoluble phosphates: even in phosphate-rich soils, the soil solution rarely contains more than 1 ppm phosphorus.

An equilibrium is maintained between the exchangeable ions and the soil solution, and in this way exchangeable ions become available for plant growth, i.e. by replacing ions in the solution phase as these are utilized by plants. Although both anions and cations can exist in exchangeable form adsorbed on soil colloids, exchangeable anions are present in limited supply only. The exchangeable cations are of greater importance in plant nutrition, and these comprise principally Ca^{2+}, Mg^{2+}, K^+ and Na^+. In acid soils, H^+ ions make up a substantial proportion of the exchangeable cations, and this leads to infertility, since the nutrient cations are displaced into the soil solution where they are subject to leaching.

The greater part of the mineral salts content of soil is present as relatively insoluble substances from which ions do not readily exchange. For example, montmorillonite contains much potassium in non-exchangeable form and apatite consists of insoluble calcium phosphates. Such substances are slowly transformed by the process of weathering, which leads gradually to increased solubility and exchangeability of ions. The rate of weathering varies greatly for different minerals and is affected by pH, soil moisture content and temperature. Contact between plant roots and soil increases the rate of weathering, both by mechanical effects which tend to break up larger soil particles, and by the chemical effects of carbonic acid and organic acids produced by the roots.

Mechanisms of ion uptake

Certain aspects of nutrient uptake by cells were discussed in Chapter 3 in relation to the nutrition of microorganisms. The entry of ions into plant roots is accomplished by both passive and active mechanisms, and the relative significance of these varies with soil conditions and plant species. That part of the root in which passive uptake processes such as diffusion and ion exchange operate consists of the cell wall and intercellular spaces. This 'apparent free space', as it is termed, lies outside the outer cytoplasmic membrane or plasmalemma. It is made up of the so-called 'outer space', which is freely accessible to diffusion, and the 'Donnan free space' which represents that fraction of the tissue available for ion exchange reactions. The apparent free space of roots extends from the epidermis to the innermost layer of cortical cells, the

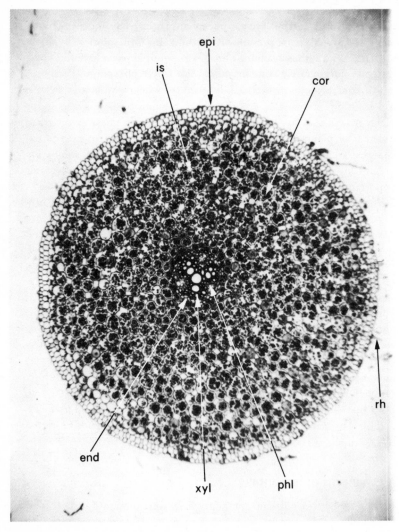

FIG. 7.2 Cross section of the primary root of buttercup, *Ranunculus acris*: rh, root hair; epi, epidermis; cor, cortex; is, intercellular space; end, endodermis; xyl, xylem; phl, phloem. (Photo by G. Wray.)

endodermis, but does not include the tissues of the stele (Fig. 7.2).

By means of diffusion and exchange reactions, nutrient ions from the external medium migrate into the apparent free space of roots. This process may be hastened by the mass flow of ions in water moving towards roots under the influence of the transpirational pull of leaves. Once the ions reach the plasmalemma, however, the semipermeable and selective properties of this membrane impede their further progress by passive means. Only by active processes can ions be transported across cell membranes and accumulated in vacuoles at concentrations many times that found in the soil solution.

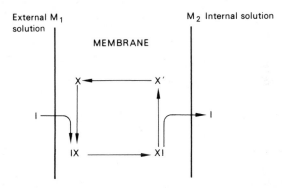

FIG. 7.3 Diagrammatic representation of the 'carrier' concept in the active uptake of ions from the soil solution (From Sutcliffe, J. F. (1962) *Mineral Salts Absorption in Plants*, Pergamon Press.)

The energy expended in active accumulation of ions is provided by the metabolic reactions of the cell. The transport process itself is believed to involve the reversible binding of ions to a constituent of the cytoplasmic membrane known as a **carrier**, although the operation of such a system has not been demonstrated unequivocally. The carrier concept (Fig. 7.3) visualizes an ion (I) reacting with its carrier (X) at or near the outer (M_1) surface of the membrane, either by adsorption, exchange adsorption, or chemical combination. Neither the carrier nor the ion carrier complex (IX) can move into the medium, but the complex is mobile in the membrane, and moves to the other side (M_2), where it undergoes a spatial rearrangement which brings the ion into a position contiguous with the inner boundary of the membrane. The complex then breaks down, releasing the ion to the internal solution ('inner space'), and forming a carrier precursor (X') which is incapable of leaving the membrane or of reaccepting an ion. The precursor is transported back across the membrane to M_1 and reconverted to the carrier, which can then combine with another ion.

Absorption of ions from soil

So far as is known, anions are absorbed almost entirely from the soil solution. A reservoir of certain anions, e.g. phosphate, is present as insoluble substances, but this is not true of nitrate which must be continually replenished by microbial activity. The extent to which plants can facilitate release of strongly held anions, such as phosphate, is debatable, but their capacity to release cations from the solid state has been recognized since the nineteenth century (p. 148). Two hypotheses are advanced to explain the uptake of cations from soil.

(a) *CO_2 hypothesis* Respiratory CO_2 from roots reacts with water to produce carbonic acid, which diffuses to the surface of the soil particle, where H-ions exchange for adsorbed cations. These in turn enter the soil solution where they diffuse to the root surface and are absorbed either by exchange for H-ions or in association with anions (Fig. 7.4(*a*)). It seems likely that this mechanism plays an important part in the release of exchangeable ions from the solid phase into the soil solution.

(b) *Contact exchange hypothesis* Cation exchange may occur between soil and root without the intervention of the soil solution. H. Devaux first drew attention to the cation exchange properties of plant roots in 1916, but it was H. Jenny and R. Overstreet who in 1938 elaborated the idea of 'contact exchange'. Adsorbed ions are not held rigidly at the site of adsorption but vibrate around this point, so that from time to time they occupy a finite volume, the 'oscillation volume'. When the oscillation volumes of two adsorbed ions overlap, contact exchange can occur (Fig. 7.4(*b*)).

It has been argued that the surface area of soil particles in contact with roots is too small for contact exchange to be of significance in plant nutrition, but at the microscopic and submicroscopic level this is not so, and there is no doubt that contact exchange can take place. It is likely to be important, however, only in circumstances where ionic concentrations are very low, such as in skeletal soils containing a high proportion of relatively unweathered minerals, or in other special situations.

Availability of nutrients to plants

Dissociated ions in the soil solution, and the majority of exchangeable ions adsorbed on colloidal surfaces, are generally thought to be readily available to plant roots. Non-exchangeable ions in primary minerals and organic matter are usually believed to be not readily available although it is known that certain clay minerals such as illite may supply sufficient non-exchangeable potassium to support natural vegetation indefinitely or even some crops. Furthermore the release of ions from

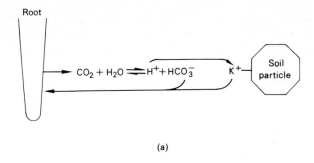

(a)

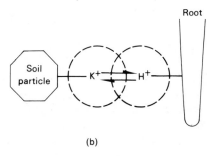

(b)

FIG. 7.4 The role of plant roots in the uptake of cations from the soil. *(a)* the CO_2 mechanism. *(b)* the contact exchange hypothesis. (For explanation, see text.)

primary minerals has an important pedogenic function in that it is the point of initiation of many nutrient cycles, hence any factor which accelerates this process is significant in ecosystem function. It is in this context that the effect of the rhizosphere microflora on the nutrition of plants needs to be discussed. This is conveniently done under several headings.

Release of non-exchangeable ions

Mineralization of organic matter. It has been suggested (p. 168) that the rhizosphere microflora should have a greater ability than the general soil population to effect rapid biochemical changes, and there is some evidence to support this contention. It has been found, for example, that the enzymatic activity of barley roots is increased by the presence of a root surface microflora, and as a result of this the plant's ability to utilize urea and some organic phosphates is increased. Ammonifying bacteria characteristically respond to the proximity of living roots, and

R/S ratios in excess of 50/1 are not uncommon for this group. This should lead to greater mineralization of organic nitrogen in the rhizosphere, a prediction which can be confirmed by incubating samples of rhizosphere and non-rhizosphere soil in the laboratory, and comparing the amount of NH_4-N released after a standard period of time. Such results do not however conform with field evidence, which indicates that less mineralized nitrogen is present in soil under crops than in fallow, even when allowance is made for the amount of nitrogen taken up by the plants. This apparent anomaly was explained by the studies of W. V. Bartholomew and F. E. Clark, using the heavy isotope of nitrogen (^{15}N) as a tracer, which showed that although the net amount of nitrogen mineralized in cropped soil is only about half that in uncropped soils, the total quantity mineralized is greater under the crop. The difference is due to the fact that most of the nitrogen mineralized under a plant cover is rapidly assimilated again by the microflora.

This example illustrates the general principle discussed in Chapter 6, viz. the availability of plant nutrients is the resultant of the opposing processes of mineralization and immobilization. Theoretically, the overall effect in the rhizosphere could be detrimental as often as it is beneficial, and examples of this are known. On balance, however, the effect is more likely to be beneficial, for the nutrients mainly involved in these microbial transformations are the anions nitrate, sulphate and phosphate. Since these are normally absorbed by plants from the soil solution, it could be argued that the cyclic turnover through organic and inorganic forms, which is mediated by microorganisms, minimises loss through leaching and provides a continual supply of anions at the root surface.

TABLE 7.3 Bacterial populations on mycorrhizal and non-mycorrhizal roots of yellow birch seedlings*

Kinds of bacteria	*Numbers per gram of dry roots*	
	Mycorrhizal roots	*Non-mycorrhizal roots*
Methylene blue reducers	5.8×10^8	5.0×10^7
Glucose fermenters		
acid producing	4.6×10^7	5.0×10^5
gas producing	5.8×10^7	1.0×10^4
Ammonifiers	1.2×10^8	1.3×10^7
Fluorescent pigment producers	2.7×10^5	1.0×10^4

* Adapted from Katznelson, H., Rouatt, J. V. and Peterson, E. A. (1962) *Can. J. Bot.*, **40**, 377–82.

A rhizosphere effect which may be of particular significance in the nutrition of some forest trees is illustrated by a comparison of the surface microflora of mycorrhizal and non-mycorrhizal roots of yellow birch, a species which forms ectomycorrhizas (see Chapter 8). Table 7.3 shows that there are greater numbers of diverse metabolic groups of bacteria on mycorrhizal roots and this implies a greater availability of nutrients in their vicinity. The increase in methylene blue reducing and glucose fermenting bacteria indicate that certain kinds of oxidizable and fermentable substrates would be broken down more rapidly in the presence of mycorrhizas than in their absence. Especially in the rich humus layers, where mycorrhizas abound, the potential ammonifying capacity of their rhizosphere microflora could be of particular importance in the nitrogen nutrition of the trees.

Solubilization of minerals. It has long been known that plant roots can increase the rate of rock weathering by the production of CO_2 and organic acids (see Chapter 6). The combined respiratory activities of roots and microorganisms result in greater CO_2 production from rhizosphere than non-rhizosphere soil; it has been variously estimated that microbial respiration accounts for one-third to two-thirds of this carbon dioxide. Enhanced production of CO_2 in the rhizosphere, where it would dissolve in the soil water to form carbonic acid, should lead to increased solubility of primary minerals, and a consequent increase in the availability of nutrient ions.

Some of the organic acids produced in the course of plant and microbial metabolism, for example citric, oxalic and tartaric acids, are known to be chelating agents and, as indicated previously (p. 148), chelation may affect nutrient availability. However, while organic acid production and exudation in the rhizosphere is undoubtedly higher than in the general body of the soil, there seems to be no data on the relative contributions of roots and microorganisms. One cannot therefore postulate a plant—microbe interaction of significance in plant nutrition solely on the premise that relatively high concentrations of organic acids occur in the rhizosphere. On the other hand, the demonstration of a preferential stimulation in the rhizosphere of microbes that produce known chelating agents would be strong evidence in support of such an hypothesis. Stimulation of 2-ketogluconic acid producing bacteria (p. 148) has indeed been found in the root region of crop plants, by D. M. Webley and R. B. Duff, population densities reaching 10^6 per gram fresh weight of roots and R/S ratios being of the order of 300/1; furthermore, the relative proportion of 2-ketogluconic acid producers increases 50-fold from 0.025 per cent of the total bacterial population in non-rhizosphere soil to about 1.25 per cent in the vicinity of roots.

Supporting evidence for the role of rhizosphere microorganisms as agents of biological weathering derives from the finding that roots of coniferous seedlings and their associated microflora can mobilize potassium from the crystal lattices of micas and felspars. This is in accord with reports of a seasonal variation in microbial population density in the rhizosphere of some tree species, a variation paralleled by changes in the concentration of available potassium in the rhizosphere soil.

The presence of a rhizosphere microflora appears to enhance the ability of plants to absorb phosphorus from insoluble fertilizers such as tricalcium phosphate. Whether this can be ascribed to a preferential stimulation of phosphate-dissolving bacteria in the rhizosphere is uncertain, however, for the evidence on this point is contradictory.

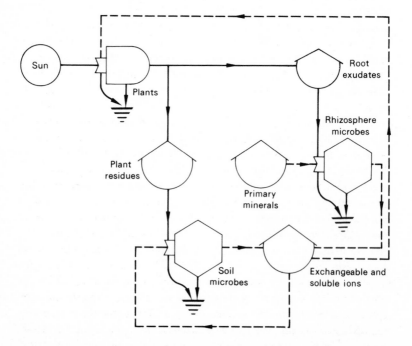

FIG. 7.5 Energy network diagram showing the postulated role of the rhizosphere microflora in the initiation of nutrient cycles. The loss of photosynthate as root exudate enhances microbial growth and leads eventually to a preferential stimulation of chelate-producing microbes in the rhizosphere. This in turn facilitates the solubilization of primary minerals which act, through a positive feedback mechanism, to increase the productivity of the system. In immature ecosystems, this could well be a major cause of successional change.

Solubilization of primary minerals by the rhizosphere microflora may not release inorganic ions sufficiently rapidly to meet the total nutrient requirements of plants, but whether or not such a rhizosphere effect contributes substantially to plant nutrition, it could still be significant in nutrient cycling. Quantitative data in support of this hypothesis has yet to be acquired, however. An energy network diagram, depicting the possible role of the rhizosphere microflora in this regard, is presented in Fig. 7.5.

Release of exchangeable ions

Cation exchange capacity of roots. The maximum number of readily exchangeable cations, including H^+, held by a given weight of plant roots, i.e. cation exchange capacity (CEC), varies widely among species. In general dicotyledons have higher root CEC than monocotyledons. Species with thick, mucilaginous roots have higher CEC than those with fine, fibrous roots; on a surface area basis, the CEC of thick roots may be 10–100 times that of thin ones. There is no general agreement concerning the significance of cation exchange in nutrient uptake by plants, although the weight of evidence favours the view that exchange adsorption (Fig. 7.4(b)), is unrelated to the actual process of metabolic accumulation. Nevertheless, as indicated previously (p. 176), when ions are present in soil at extremely low concentrations, the cation exchange properties of roots might well affect their ability to absorb such ions.

The role of microorganisms in contact exchange phenomena is largely hypothetical. The great catalytic powers of bacteria result from their large surface/volume ratio which permits rapid interchange of materials between bacterial cells and their environment, but whether ion exchange mechanisms play a part in these transfers is unknown. If they do, then it is conceivable that the presence of a rhizosphere microflora would increase the CEC of roots. Many bacteria excrete a colloidal slime layer or capsule, consisting of organic polymers of limited solubility. The presence of dense populations of bacteria in the rhizosphere might therefore lead to an increase in root CEC, but since plant roots themselves exude mucilaginous substances (p. 166), it would be difficult to determine the relative contributions of plant and microbial exudates.

CO$_2$ evolution by roots. The increased production of CO_2 in the rhizosphere which results from a high level of microbial activity in that region, has already been mentioned (p. 179). Its significance for the release of exchangeable ions is as a source of additional hydrogen-ions to exchange with metallic cations adsorbed on soil colloids (Fig. 7.3(a)).

Uptake of dissociated ions from the soil solution

It has been shown by several workers that the presence of micro-organisms on plant roots greatly modifies the absorption and utilization of phosphate by these roots. Not only is the rate of uptake affected, but the pattern of translocation and the direction of metabolism are altered also. The effects are most pronounced when the external supply of phosphate is low, and are not always directed towards increased uptake and incorporation by the plant. It is evident that the rhizosphere microflora influences nutrient absorption even from the solution phase.

Other effects

Many reports of increased nitrogen fixation have been made following attempts to establish large populations of *Azotobacter* (p. 233) in the rhizosphere, and inoculation of seed with *Azotobacter* is regularly practised in Russian agriculture. Even in the absence of inoculation, some investigators have found *Azotobacter* to be preferentially stimulated in the rhizosphere, while others have found no evidence of a rhizosphere effect. Climatic or soil differences may account for these conflicting results, at least in part.

Recent evidence supports the view that rhizospheric nitrogen fixation may be significant in the nitrogen economy of some grassland and forest ecosystems. This is discussed further in Chapter 9. In cultivated soils, however, many of the crop responses resulting from inoculation with free-living nitrogen fixers are undoubtedly due to factors other than increased supply of nitrogen to the plant. It is possible that auxin biosynthesis in the rhizosphere might stimulate the growth of plants, for many rhizosphere microorganisms are known to synthesize growth promoting substances.

Selected references

Alexander, M. (1961) *Introduction to Soil Microbiology.* Wiley.
Epstein, E. (1972) *Mineral Nutrition of Plants: Principles and Perspectives.* Wiley.
Gray, T. R. G. and Williams, S. T. (1971) *Soil Microorganisms.* Oliver & Boyd.

Barber, D. A. (1968) 'Microorganisms and the inorganic nutrition of higher plants.' *A. Rev. Pl. Physiol.*, **19**, 71—88.

Bartholomew, W. V. and Clark, F. E. (1950) 'Nitrogen transformations in soil in relation to the rhizosphere microflora.' *Int. Congr. Soil Sci. Trans.*, **4 (2)**, 112—13.

Bowen, G. D. (1959) 'The uptake of orthophosphate and its incorporation into organic phosphates along roots of *Pinus radiata*.' *Aust. J. biol. Sci.*, **22**, 1125—35.

Bowen, G. D. (1969) 'Nutrient status effects on loss of amides and amino acids from pine roots.' *Plant Soil*, **30**, 140—2.

Bowen, G. D. and Rovira, A. D. (1969) 'The influence of microorganisms on growth and metabolism of plant roots' in *Root Growth*, ed. W. J. Whittington, pp. 170—99. Butterworths.

Estermann, E. F. and McLaren, A. D. (1961) 'Contributions of rhizosphere organisms to the total capacity of plants to utilize organic nutrients.' *Plant Soil*, **15**, 243—60.

Foster, R. C. and Marks, G. C. (1967) 'Observations on the mycorrhizas of forest trees. II. The rhizosphere of *Pinus radiata* D. Don.' *Aust. J. biol. Sci.*, **20**, 915—26.

Gerretsen, F. C. (1948) 'The influence of microorganisms on the phosphate intake by the plant.' *Plant Soil*, **1**, 51—81.

Jenny, H. and Grossenbacher, K. (1963) 'Root—soil boundary zones as seen in the electron microscope.' *Soil Sci. Soc. Am. Proc.*, **27**,273—7.

Jenny, H. and Overstreet, R. (1938) 'Contact effects between plant roots and soil colloids.' *Proc. natn. Acad. Sci. USA*, **24**, 384—92.

Katznelson, H. (1965) 'Nature and importance of the rhizosphere' in *Ecology of Soil-borne Plant Pathogens*, eds. K. F. Baker and W. C. Snyder, pp. 187—207. University of California Press.

Katznelson, H., Rouatt, J. V. and Payne, T. M. B. (1954) 'Liberation of amino acids by plant roots in relation to desiccation.' *Nature, Lond.*, **174**, 1110—11.

Katznelson, H., Rouatt, J. V. and Peterson, E. A. (1962) 'The rhizosphere effect of mycorrhizal and non-mycorrhizal roots of yellow birch seedlings.' *Can. J. Bot.*, **40**, 377—82.

Kulaj, G. A. (1962) 'The dissolving of alumino-silicates in the rhizosphere of forest plantations.' *Izv. Akad. Nauk. Ser. Biol.*, **6**, 915—20.

Neal, J. L., Bollen, W. B. and Zak, B. (1964), 'Rhizosphere microflora associated with mycorrhizae of Douglas-fir.' *Can. J. Microbiol.*, **10**, 259—65.

Nicholas, D. J. D. (1965) 'Influence of the rhizosphere on the mineral nutrition of the plant' in *Ecology of Soil-borne Plant Pathogens*, eds.

K. F. Baker and W. C. Snyder, pp. 210-16. University of California Press.

Papavizas, G. C. and Davey, C. D. (1961) 'Extent and nature of the rhizosphere of *Lupinus*.' *Plant Soil*, 14, 215—36.

Rovira, A. D. (1956) 'Plant root excretions in relation to the rhizosphere effect. I. The nature of root exudate from oats and peas.' *Plant Soil*, 7, 178—94.

Rovira, A. D. (1965*a*) 'Plant root exudates and their influence upon soil microorganisms' in *Ecology of Soil-borne Plant Pathogens*, eds. K. F. Baker and W. C. Snyder, pp. 170—84. University of California Press.

Rovira, A. D. (1965*b*) 'Interactions between plant roots and soil microorganisms.' *A. Rev. Microbiol.*, 19, 241—66.

Rovira, A. D. (1969) 'Diffusion of carbon compounds away from wheat roots.' *Aust. J. biol. Sci.*, 22, 1287—90.

Rovira, A. D. and McDougall, B. M. (1967) 'Microbial and biochemical aspects of the rhizosphere' in *Soil Biochemistry*, eds. A. D. McLaren and G. H. Peterson, pp. 417—63. Marcel Dekker.

Skyring, G. W. and Quadling, C. (1969) 'Soil bacteria: comparisons of rhizosphere and nonrhizosphere populations.' *Can. J. Microbiol.*, 15, 473—88.

Smith, W. H. (1969) 'Release of organic materials from the roots of tree seedlings.' *For. Sci.*, 15, 138—43.

Sperber, J. I. (1958) 'The incidence of apatite-solubilizing organisms in the rhizosphere and soil.' *Aust. J. agric. Res.*, 9, 778—81.

Spyridakis, D. E., Chesters, D. E. and Wilde, S. A. (1967) 'Kaolinization of biotite as a result of coniferous and deciduous seedling growth.' *Soil Sci. Soc. Amer. Proc.*, 31, 203—10.

Voigt, G. K. (1963) 'Biological mobilization of potassium from primary minerals' in *Forest—Soil Relationships in North America*, ed. C. T. Youngberg, pp. 33—46. Oregon State University Press.

Wallace, R. H. and Lochhead, A. G. (1949) 'Qualitative studies of soil microorganisms. VIII. Influence of various crop plants on the nutritional groups of soil bacteria.' *Soil Sci.*, 67, 63—9.

Webley, D. M. and Duff, R. B. (1965) 'The incidence, in soils and other habitats, of microorganisms producing 2-ketogluconic acid.' *Plant Soil*, 22, 307—13.

8 Mycorrhiza

Root-infecting fungi are considered to be parasitic if they cause disease in the host plant, or mycorrhizal if they cause no damage to the host except under unusual circumstances. Separation of root-infecting fungi into such groups is convenient for the purpose of discus: ion, but the boundaries are not sharp. Mycorrhizal fungi themselves form a heterogeneous group. Some are closely related in their general behaviour to pathogenic root-infecting fungi: indeed, several well-known root disease fungi form mycorrhizas with orchids. At the opposite end of the spectrum some mycorrhizal associations appear to be little more than specialized cases of the rhizosphere effect.

The name **mycorrhiza** is derived from the Greek and means, literally, 'fungus root'. It was first applied in 1885 by A. B. Frank to the composite organs of the Cupuliferae. Similar structures were soon described from many other angiosperms, and also from many conifers. They are characterized by a complete sheath of fungal tissue which encloses the ultimate rootlets of the root system, together with an intercellular infection of the epidermis and cortex (though penetration of the cortical cells sometimes takes place to a limited extent). Such mycorrhizas are called ectotrophic, or ectomycorrhizas. They form a well defined group, distinct in morphogenesis and histogenesis from most other kinds of association between fungi and roots. The term mycorrhiza has however gradually been extended to embrace certain kinds of fungus—root associations in which the hyphae regularly penetrate the cortical cells of the host. These mycorrhizas are called endotrophic, or endomycorrhizas, and in these forms the external mantle of mycelium is usually lacking. Some endomycorrhizas do have a well developed sheath however, for example the so-called arbutoid mycorrhizas, and these constitute a link between the ectotrophic and endotrophic kinds of infection.

Ectotrophic mycorrhiza
This is a common mycorrhiza of forest trees in the families Pinaceae,

Betulaceae, Fagaceae, Dipterocarpaceae and Myrtaceae. Infection is a normal and regular event in nature, the mycorrhizal fungi being mainly higher Basidiomycetes.

Structure and development of ectotrophic mycorrhizas

Mycorrhizas occur on so-called short roots, that is small laterals of determinate length, but generally not on the main axes, or long roots, which are capable of elongating indefinitely. By comparison with un-infected rootlets, mycorrhizas are visibly swollen. In most families — both angiosperm and gymnosperm — mycorrhizas branch racemosely, however the genus *Pinus* is exceptional in having dichotomously branched mycorrhizas (Fig. 8.1). Pines are peculiar in another respect also, the differentiation into long and short roots being sharper than in most other trees.

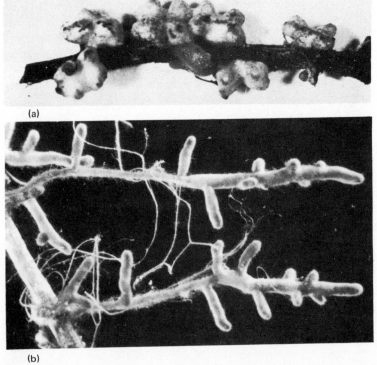

(a)

(b)

FIG. 8.1 Gross morphology of ectomycorrhizal root systems. *(a) Pinus*, showing the dichotomous branching of infected short roots typical of this genus. *(b) Eucalyptus,* showing the racemosely branched mycorrhizas found in most genera other than *Pinus* (magnification x2). Note the absence of root hairs on the mycorrhizal roots, and the presence of numerous fungal rhizomorphs. (*(b)* From Chilvers, G. A. and Pryor, L. D. (1965) *Aust. J. Bot.*, **13**, 245–59.)

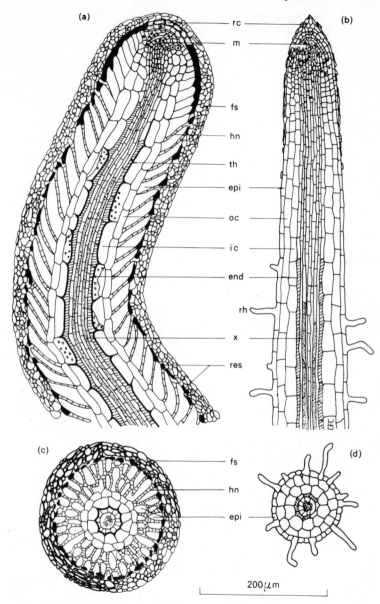

FIG. 8.2 Anatomy of ectomycorrhizas of *Eucalyptus* compared to uninfected roots. *(a)*, *(b)* median longitudinal sections of mycorrhiza and non-mycorrhizal root, respectively. *(c)*, *(d)* transverse sections of mycorrhiza and uninfected root, respectively. rc, root cap; m, meristematic region; fs, fungal sheath or mantle; hn, Hartig net; th, thickened walls of inner cortex; epi, epidermis; oc, outer cortex; ic, inner cortex; end, endodermis; rh, root hair; x, lignified protoxylem; res, collapsed residues of cap cells. (From Chilvers, G. A. and Pryor, L. D. (1965) *Aust. J. Bot.*, **13**, 245–59.)

A typical ectomycorrhiza has many short branches, so that groups of lateral rootlets are formed which may be completely enclosed by mycelium. In section (Fig. 8.2), the rootlet is seen to be bounded by a layer of fungal pseudoparenchyma which may comprise one-quarter of the total volume of the mycorrhiza and two-fifths of its total dry weight. This is the **sheath** or **mantle**, the surface of which is fairly smooth, although some hyphal connections to the surrounding soil may be visible. The inner portion of the sheath is connected to hyphae which ramify between the cells of the epidermis and outer cortex, forming a mycelial network called the **Hartig net**. The fungus never penetrates the endodermis in normal mycorrhizas. Hyphae occasionally penetrate into the cells of the cortex, but the degree of penetration is not extensive when compared to that found in endomycorrhizas.

Infection of long roots does occur, but such infection is usually limited to the presence of the Hartig net: the sheath is normally (though not always) lacking. Infection of long roots is of great significance however, since it provides the means whereby the short roots become infected as they emerge from the pericycle. It is believed that the root system is first infected, via a young short root, from a source of inoculum in the soil such as a germinating basidiospore, and thereafter the fungus spreads intercellularly throughout the cortex of the main root axes.

Factors affecting mycorrhiza formation

Ectotrophic mycorrhizas are formed typically by trees of temperate forests growing on brown earth or podzolized soils. Mycorrhizas are far more abundant in soil with mor humus, and in general are better developed in acid than in neutral or alkaline soils. An inverse relationship generally exists between nutrient availability and the degree of mycorrhizal infection in *Pinus*: the greater the availability of nutrients, the fewer the mycorrhizas. The effect of increased availability of nitrate is clearly shown in Table 8.1. This table also shows the effect of soil reaction on mycorrhiza development. It has often been assumed that the poor development of mycorrhizas on trees growing in neutral or alkaline soils is due solely to the fact that the mycorrhizal fungi are acidophilic. However, the data tabulated show that mycorrhizas develop more profusely at pH 7.5 where the soil nitrate level is low, than at pH 5.8 where a much greater amount of nitrate is present. Subsequent investigations, by C. Theodorou and G. D. Bowen, indicate that high nitrate levels inhibit the infection process, irrespective of soil pH, and that the nitrate effect is enhanced at high pH (8.0) because fungal growth in the rhizosphere is inhibited by the alkaline conditions.

TABLE 8.1 Effect of soil nitrate level and soil reaction on mycorrhiza development in *Pinus**

Treatment	Soil nitrate (ppm N)	Soil pH	Mycorrhiza (%) †
Nil	12.7	6.3	25.83
Lime	21.3	7.5	16.86
NH_4NO_3	71.4	5.8	7.21
Lime + NH_4NO_3	115.3	6.9	8.19
LSD for $p < 0.05$	12.3	0.2	5.26
LSD for $p < 0.01$	16.7	0.3	7.25

* After Richards, B. N. and Wilson, G. L. (1963) *For. Sci.*, 9, 405–12.
† Transformed data (arcsine transformation).

There have been two schools of thought concerning the effect of nutrient supply on mycorrhiza development. A. B. Hatch examined this relationship in 1937 and concluded that the predisposing factor in mycorrhiza formation was plant nutrient status, especially that of N, P and K: where the internal concentrations of these nutrients were high and properly balanced, few mycorrhizas would form. On the other hand, E. J. Björkman claimed in 1942 that the production of mycorrhizas was conditioned primarily by the presence of free soluble sugars in the root tissues; this occurs whenever carbohydrate synthesis exceeds carbohydrate utilization. Neither of these hypotheses provides an adequate explanation of mycorrhiza formation, and other factors including the production of growth regulating substances are doubtless involved. The process is complex and our knowledge of it is far from complete. For a detailed treatment, the reader is referred to J. L. Harley's monograph, *The Biology of Mycorrhiza*.

The physiology and ecology of ectomycorrhizal fungi

Knowledge of the identity and cultural behaviour of the fungi of ectotrophic mycorrhiza is due mainly to the researches of the Swedish mycologist Elias Melin and his associates, begun in the early 1920s. The results of these studies have permitted certain generalizations to be made concerning the physiology of mycorrhizal fungi. Most of the fungi of ectomycorrhizas are Basidiomycetes, the family Agaricaceae being represented by several genera including *Amanita* and *Tricholoma*. These two genera, together with the genus *Boletus* of the family Boletaceae, contain the majority of mycorrhiza forming fungi. The family Russulaceae, containing the genera *Russula* and *Lactarius*, is also well represented but has not been so widely studied. In addition to these hymenomycetes, some gasteromycetes will form ectomycorrhizas, e.g. *Scleroderma* and *Rhizopogon*. The imperfect fungus *Cenococcum graniforme* also forms ectotrophic mycorrhizas.

Most of the pure culture studies of mycorrhizal fungi have concerned species which form sporocarps regularly and hence can be readily identified. There are now grounds for believing that there are many fungi capable of forming ectomycorrhizas which fruit rarely or not at all, and which therefore have never been cultured. It is possible that these fungi may be more important in mycorrhizal associations in nature than the few dozen species that have been intensively studied in the past.

In contrast to the legume—rhizobium symbiosis (Chapter 9), the mycorrhizal association is not one of close specificity. *Cenococcum graniforme* is the least specific, being found on a wide range of species among both gymnosperms and angiosperms. *Boletus elegans* is the most specific, associating only with *Larix* so far as is known. Between these extremes are many fungal species of intermediate host range. Most host species seem capable of forming mycorrhizas with a number of different fungi, and a single host tree may associate with several species of fungi at the same time. The question of specificity assumes some importance in relation to the introduction of exotic trees in reforestation projects, and it sometimes becomes necessary to introduce the appropriate mycorrhiza forming fungi, in order to ensure the success of the reforestation venture.

Ectotrophic mycorrhizal fungi are not obligate symbionts in the sense that they cannot be grown in the absence of the host. On the contrary, a number have been isolated and studied in pure culture. Nevertheless, under natural conditions, many of them are probably incapable of leading an independent saprophytic existence in the soil. This viewpoint draws support from the knowledge that most ectomycorrhizal fungi (unlike many litter decomposing basidiomycetes) are unable to decompose cellulose or lignin, and require simple sugars as sources of carbon; furthermore, they have poor competitive saprophytic ability, being readily overgrown in culture by fast growing sugar fungi (p. 76). It thus seems unlikely that ectomycorrhizal fungi can obtain the sugars essential for growth from any source other than the living roots of their hosts. Exceptions to this generalization exist, however. For example, *Boletus subtomentosus*, unlike most other mycorrhizal fungi, can complete its life cycle and produce sporocarps when isolated from its host by trenching, and *Cenococcum graniforme* is widespread in soils even where there is no known host. Both these species have been found capable of utilizing polysaccharides in pure culture, so too can some mycorrhiza forming species of *Tricholoma* and *Lactarius*.

In addition to a simple energy substrate, some mycorrhizal fungal have a requirement for accessory growth factors. E. Melin and his associates have shown that pure cultures of most mycorrhizal fungi are partially or completely dependent on thiamine (vitamin B_1) or one of its constituent moieties, pyrimidine or thiazole. Certain species are deficient for other vitamins as well. Unidentified growth promoting substances have also been found in root exudates, not only of the coniferous host, but in the exudates of several herbaceous angiosperms as well. Amino acids may also exert a stimulating effect, but the nitrogen requirements of mycorrhizal fungi do not differentiate them from other basidiomycetes. In common with many other fungi and bacteria, they make better growth on ammonium and simple organic nitrogen compounds than on nitrate; some indeed appear to lack the enzyme nitrate reductase.

In general, it can be said that the physiological properties of ectotrophic mycorrhizal fungi are shared by many other root-surface or rhizosphere inhabiting fungi, and do not provide a clue as to why they should enter into such a peculiar morphological association with the roots of certain trees.

Endotrophic mycorrhiza

A rational discussion of endomycorrhizas is much more difficult than one of ectomycorrhizas, because they do not form such a natural unit and are much more diverse in their morphology. They may however be divided into two large groups according to whether the mycelium of the endophyte is non-septate (Phycomycete) or septate (Ascomycete, Imperfect or Basidiomycete). The two types of hyphae are not specifically associated with any particular taxonomic groups of plants, the septate forms showing the nearer affinity to the taxonomic status of the host, one sub-group being typified by members of the order Ericales and another being characteristic of the family Orchidaceae. Only the phycomycete forms will be considered here.

Phycomycete (vesicular-arbuscular) mycorrhiza

This is by far the most abundant kind of mycorrhiza. Infected roots do not usually show the marked morphological peculiarities common to ectomycorrhizas. Many look superficially like uninfected roots, quite undistorted and with root hairs. Some however lack root hairs and have

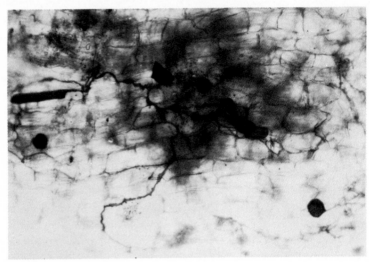

(a)

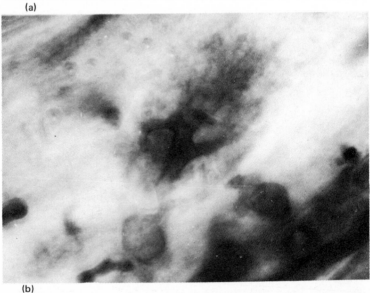

(b)

FIG. 8.3 Vesicular-arbuscular mycorrhiza. *(a)* Mycorrhizal rootlet of *Araucaria cunninghamii*, showing darkly stained fungal hyphae with terminal swellings or vesicles. *(b)* Arbuscule in *Trifolium subterraneum* root, produced by inoculation with spores of *Endogone araucareae*. The arbuscule is the structure in the centre; its subtending hypha (swollen to form a small vesicle) may be seen below it to the left. (Photos by D. I. Bevege.)

a recognizable morphology. They are called **vesicular-arbuscular (V-A)** mycorrhizas, after two kinds of organs – vesicles and arbuscules – which occur in infected tissues (Fig. 8.3).

The aseptate hyphae ramify within and between the cells of un-specialized tissues, such as the root cortex. They do not enter the stele or tissues containing chlorophyll. Within infected cells, coils of hyphae may be formed, or the cells may contain complex branched hyphal systems known as **arbuscules**. Arbuscules are the result of profuse dichotomous branching of hyphae which finally are no longer distinguishable as such but appear as a granulated mass of protoplasm intimately mixed with the protoplasm of the host cell. They are thought to be involved in nutrient transfer between the symbionts. Intercalary or apical swellings are often found on the main hyphae, and are called **vesicles**. They are sometimes very large and thick walled, and distort the cells or intercellular spaces in which they develop. Vesicles contain large amounts of oil and probably serve as storage organs. There is never any sheath formed around the root surface, although occasionally a loose weft of hyphae may be present, extending up to about 1 cm into the surrounding soil. Microscopically, the external mycelium is frequently dimorphic with slender, thin walled, septate branches arising from characteristic angular projections in coarser, irregularly thickened, non-septate hyphae. The extramatrical mycelium may also carry spherical or ellipsoid spores usually about 100−300 μm in diameter, though sometimes attaining a diameter of 800 μm; these spores may be contained within rudimentary sporocarps. External vesicles are sometimes present, too. A diagrammatic picture of a V-A mycorrhiza is given in Fig. 8.4.

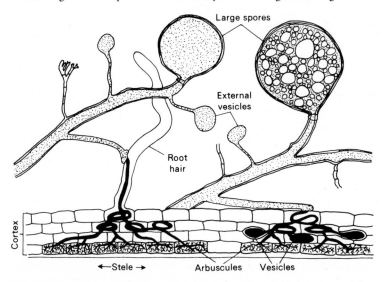

FIG. 8.4 Diagrammatic representation of vesicular-arbuscular mycorrhiza. (From Nicolson, T. H. (1967) *Sci Progr., Oxf.*, **55**, 561−81.)

Vesicular-arbuscular mycorrhizas are found in practically every taxonomic group of plants, and the list of species not infected is probably shorter than the list of those which are. They are common in many staple crop plants, having been recorded from date palms, coffee, tea, cocoa, rubber and citrus. Those gymnosperms which do not have ectomycorrhizas are usually found to have V-A mycorrhizas, for example the coniferous families of the southern hemisphere, Araucariaceae and Podocarpaceae; many members of the Cupressaceae also form V-A mycorrhizas. In addition, they occur in several angiosperm families of great economic importance, such as Leguminosae (including those nodulated by the N_2-fixing bacterium, *Rhizobium*), Rosaceae and Gramineae.

Identity of the endophyte

At the turn of the century, P. A. Dangeard gave the name *Rhizophagus* to a fungus causing V-A mycorrhizas on poplar (*Populus*). In the 1920s, B. Peyronel found hyphal connections between mycorrhizal roots of various alpine plants and fruiting bodies of the fungus *Endogone* in nearby soil, and in 1953 B. Mosse confirmed Peyronel's observation by finding fructifications of *Endogone* attached to extramatrical mycelium on the roots of strawberry. J. W. Gerdemann in 1955 described a wet-sieving technique for isolating *Endogone* spores from soil, and showed that V-A mycorrhizas were produced on a wide range of plants following inoculation with these spores. Since that time, it has become apparent that *Endogone* spores (Fig. 8.5) are widespread in soils.

The genus *Endogone* represents a highly specialized group of mycorrhizal fungi, so far as is known active only when attached to living plant tissues. With rare exceptions, it has not so far been cultured on artificial media. There have been reports of successful isolation of *Rhizophagus*, some forms of which resemble *Endogone* very closely, and which some authors consider to be an imperfect genus belonging to the same family. *Endogone* is a zygomycete of the order Mucorales, and two main groups have been recognized by T. H. Nicolson and J. W. Gerdemann, viz. those which form zygospores (*E. heterogama, E. gigantea, E. calospora*) and those which form chlamydospores (*E. mosseae, E. macrocarpa*). Recently a new species of *Endogone* (*E. araucareae*) has been described,* which produces both zygospores and chlamydospores and which forms mycorrhizas with hoop pine (*Araucaria cunninghamii*), an indigenous Australian conifer.

---

* D. I. Bevege (1971) PhD thesis, University of New England.

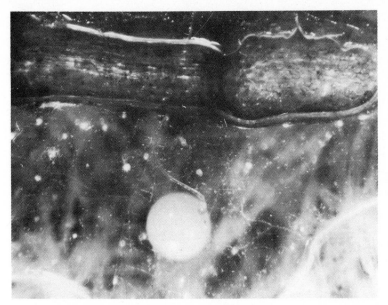

FIG. 8.5 Zygospore of *Endogone araucareae* developed on a hypha emanating from an endomycorrhizal root of *Araucaria cunninghamii.* The spore is approximately 350 μm in diameter. (From Bevege, D. I. (1971) PhD thesis, University of New England.)

Initiation and development of infection

Infection is initiated from hyphal appressoria which are formed on the roots, ingress in perennial plants being confined to the younger roots which show no evidence of secondary growth; penetration may take place via root hairs or directly through the epidermis. In most plants infection is not systemic and each new rootlet is infected afresh from the soil. In *Araucaria* however, which has the heterorhizal condition of long and short roots, infection can spread from long roots to emerging short roots.

The hyphae are frequently found coiled in the cells of the outer cortex, while arbuscules generally develop in the inner cortex (Fig. 8.4). Arbuscules tend to be localized in the younger tissues, but the fungus never invades meristematic regions. In the older cortical tissues, arbuscules undergo digestion and, more or less concurrently, vesicles are formed. When spores occur within the roots, they too are found in the older parts. Some indication of the intensity of infection in mycorrhizal plants is given by Table 8.2.

The factors affecting endophyte development have not been so widely studied as in ectomycorrhizas. Partly this is due to the difficulty

TABLE 8.2 Intensity of mycorrhizal infection in *Araucaria cunninghamii* roots*

Source of root	Root type	Percentage infected†	Vesicles per cm	Spores per cm
Fertilizer trial age 4 yrs ⎱	Short	98.0	9.6	0
⎰	Long	48.8	8.7	0
Underplanting age 7 yrs ⎱	Short	73.6	10.8	0
⎰	Long	39.9	10.0	0
Pot trial age 2 yrs ⎱	Short	88.9	15.8	3.5
⎰	Long	32.6	55.5	2.3

* Data of Bevege, D. I. (1971) PhD thesis, University of New England.
† Percentage infection in long roots is based on the total number of 'short root equivalents', found by dividing the total length of long roots in the sample by the length of the average short root (approx. 1 mm).

of designing a satisfactory method of assessing the degree or intensity of infection. In addition, the methodological problems of establishing infection in axenic culture (see below) complicate any critical experimental approach to this question. In general, endophyte development appears to vary with the successional stage at which the host plant occurs, and seasonal variation in spore numbers has been recorded in association with horticultural and cereal crops. Spore numbers are purportedly higher in cultivated soils than in their non-cultivated counterparts, and spore populations are very low in some natural communities. The spore frequency in soil beneath hoop pine trees in rainforest in Eastern Australia, however, varies from about 100 to 2 100 per kilogram, which is about the same frequency as that reported for agricultural soils in Britain.

Judging from the work of Barbara Mosse, highly specialized conditions are required for the establishment of infection. She was able to obtain axenic cultures of *Endogone* and a green plant, using as inoculum surface-sterilized spores which had previously been stimulated to germinate aseptically by the presence of a soil diffusate. Germ tubes of the fungus would not penetrate plant roots unless pectolytic enzyme solutions, or sterile filtrates of bacterial cultures, were added along with the fungus. Infection could however be achieved without such supplements in three-organism cultures, e.g by *Endogone* in the presence of a pectinase producing bacterium such as *Pseudomonas*. Infection may not always be dependent upon such complex microbial interactions, since D. I. Bevege has shown that *E. araucareae* alone can form mycorrhizas on hoop pine seemingly without an exogenous enzyme source.

Nutrient interchange in mycorrhizas

If mycorrhizal associations have any regulatory role in nature, it is likely to be through their effect on one of the major functional processes in ecosystems, viz. energy flow or nutrient circulation. For example, if the presence of mycorrhizas increases the rate of transfer of chemical elements from lithosphere to biosphere, one might be justified in assuming that this particular plant—microbe interaction was in fact significant in ecosystem regulation.

Effect of ectomycorrhizas on nutrient uptake

Since most ectotrophic mycorrhizal fungi are unable to utilize complex polysaccharides, they are unlikely to promote rapid breakdown of litter and humus and so affect the nutrition of their hosts in this way. There are however exceptions to this generality, for example several species of *Tricholoma* have the capacity to utilize cellulose as a carbon and energy source. It is not inconceivable that, among the many unidentified fungi that have been isolated directly from mycorrhizas during the past decade, there are others with litter decomposing capabilities. If this is so, then it is not unreasonable to suppose further that trees harbouring such symbionts might be to some degree independent of normal mineralization processes. This hypothesis remains to be substantiated however, whereas there is much accumulated knowledge which indicates that mycorrhizal fungi can influence the nutritional status of their hosts in other ways.

There is considerable experimental evidence to support the view that mycorrhizas function very efficiently as nutrient absorbing organs. This is illustrated by Table 8.3, which shows clearly the superiority of

TABLE 8.3 Effect of *ectomycorrhiza* **on yield and nutrient uptake of** *Pinus elliottii* *

Fungus	Dry weight of seedlings (g)†	Nutrient content of seedlings (mg)†		
		N	P	K
Nil (uninoculated)	0.26	2.44	0.22	2.27
Rhizopogon roseolus	1.39	13.03	1.37	12.54
Suillus granulatus	1.58	15.26	1.64	14.80
E8.22‡	2.81	38.92	3.86	35.60

* After Lamb, R. J. and Richards, B. N. (1971) *Aust. For.*, **35**, 1—7.
† Differences between treatments highly significant in all cases.
‡ Unidentified fungus isolated from roots of mature *P. elliottii*.

mycorrhizal over non-mycorrhizal plants, when both are grown in a peat–sand substrate at low levels of available nutrients. This table also indicates that certain unidentified fungi may be more effective symbionts, in the seedling stage at least, than some of the better known mycorrhizal fungi. One of the first to demonstrate the beneficial effects of ectomycorrhizas was A. B. Hatch, who in 1937 pointed out that infection of roots by mycorrhizal fungi increased the effective root surface for the absorption of nutrients. This was brought about in three ways: the life of infected roots was prolonged, their degree of branching was enhanced, and their diameters were increased. A second effect of mycorrhizal infection, of great significance in nutrient absorption, is that a layer of fungal pseudoparenchyma is interposed between the root surface and the soil. When considering nutrient interchange between host and fungus, it must therefore be kept in mind, as J. L. Harley has stressed, that a typical ectomycorrhiza consists of four interconnected tissue systems: (i) an external mycelium in the soil, (ii) the fungal sheath or mantle, (iii) the hyphae ramifying between the epidermal and cortical cells of the host and forming the Hartig net, and (iv) the host cortex and stele.

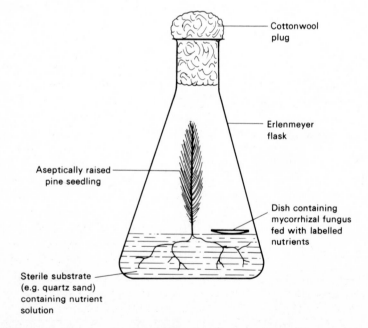

FIG. 8.6 Technique used by E. Melin and H. Nilsson to demonstrate transport of nutrients to pine seedlings through extramatrical hyphae of ectomycorrhizas. For explanation, see text.

E. Melin and H. Nilsson, in a series of papers published during the 1950s, described an elegant technique to demonstrate that hyphae emanating from the mycelial sheath can transport nutrients to the roots of the host. They grew pine seedlings in aseptic sand cultures and then introduced pure cultures of mycorrhizal fungi in shallow dishes placed on the surface of the sand (Fig. 8.6). In the course of time the hyphae grew over the edge of the dish, through the sand, and eventually formed mycorrhizas on the rootlets. By inserting isotopically labelled nutrient solutions in the dishes, they demonstrated the movement of PO_4^{3-}, Ca^{2+}, NH_4^+ and amino-N through the hyphae to the roots and into the tops of the seedlings. Just what contribution translocation of nutrients through fungal hyphae from zones of uptake remote from the root surface makes in nature has never been properly assessed. There are undoubtedly some situations, for example in coarse textured mineral soils, where hyphae ramify several centimetres away from mycorrhizas. On the other hand G. D. Bowen reported that he could find little movement of hyphae from *Pinus radiata* mycorrhizas in litter (up to 0.1 mm only). The surface of the sheath itself however is active in ion absorption: radioautographs of excised mycorrhizal roots of pine exposed to ^{32}P show a greater accumulation of phosphate than non-mycorrhizal roots.

J. L. Harley and his students at Oxford have elucidated many of the mechanisms of nutrient absorption, by using excised mycorrhizas of beech *(Fagus sylvatica)* in short-term experiments. Rates of absorption of infected roots are about five times as great for PO_4^{3-}, and about twice as great for K^+, as in uninfected roots. As in the study of nutrient uptake by excised roots of non-mycorrhizal plants, it has been found that absorption is an aerobic process, and the process of ion accumulation is linked to respiration, occurring only at the expense of metabolic energy. Mycorrhizal roots are also similar to uninfected roots in that their absorption rate is influenced by temperature, and will not proceed in the presence of metabolic inhibitors. Furthermore, both mycorrhizal and non-mycorrhizal roots show the property of selective absorption, such as preferential uptake of K^+ from a mixture of metallic cations.

In summary therefore, Harley's studies have shown the process of nutrient uptake by mycorrhizas to be similar to that shown by other absorbing organs, though seemingly more efficient. The presence of the fungal sheath, however, complicates this simple view of mycorrhizas as highly efficient ion absorbing organs. A large proportion of the ions absorbed are retained initially in the sheath or mantle, as much as 90 per cent in the case of PO_4^{3-}. Release of accumulated PO_4^{3-} to the whole system is a gradual process, dependent on temperature and oxygen

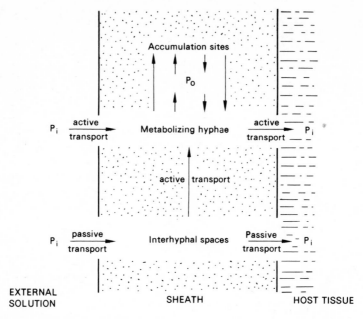

FIG. 8.7 Diagrammatic view of the passage of phosphate through the sheath of an ectomycorrhiza. (Adapted from Harley, J. L. (1969) *The Biology of Mycorrhiza, 2nd edn. Leonard Hill.*)

supply. Apparently the transfer of PO_4^{3-} from sheath to core is, like uptake from an external solution, dependent upon the expenditure of metabolic energy in respiration. It is most rapid when PO_4^{3-} is absent from the external medium. Harley's postulated scheme for the passage of phosphate through the sheath is shown in Fig. 8.7. Phosphate is absorbed actively by the sheath and accumulated in the living hyphae. Once the accumulation sites are fully occupied, phosphate may diffuse directly to the host tissue provided the concentration gradient between the external solution and the plant cells is sufficiently steep. At the phosphate concentrations which normally pertain in the soil solution however, this is unlikely to occur, so that ecologically the diffusional pathway is insignificant. Instead, it is highly probable that, under natural conditions, the host draws its phosphate from the fungal sheath by mechanisms involving active transport. This pattern of nutrient absorption in mycorrhizas is not qualitatively different from that which exists in uninfected roots, only quantitatively so. The latter are quite capable of accumulating and storing nutrients in the cortex before passing them on to the shoot. As J. L. Harley and D. H. Lewis have succinctly stated, 'mycorrhizas differ essentially from the root by

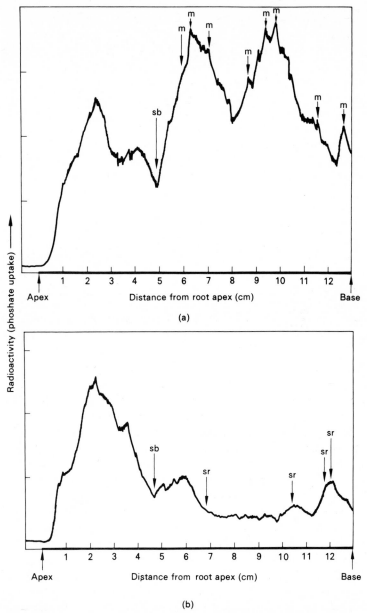

FIG. 8.8 Root scans of mycorrhizal *(a)* and uninfected roots *(b)* of *Pinus radiata,* showing how ectomycorrhizas permit the root system to retain a high capacity for absorbing ^{32}P from a $5 \times 10^{-6}M$ solution of KH_2PO_4 for a relatively long period of time: m, position of mycorrhiza; sr, position of uninfected short root; sb, commencement of suberization. (From Bowen, G. D. and Theodorou, C. (1967) *Proc. 14th IUFRO Congr., Munich,* **24,** 116–38.)

possessing an extra fungal cortex into which very rapid accumulation is possible'.

Other workers, using intact seedlings of *P. radiata,* have confirmed the findings of the Oxford group on the uptake of PO_4^{3-} by excised beech mycorrhizas. These whole-plant experiments clearly show the greater ability of mycorrhizal plants to take up PO_4^{3-} from the substrate, and reinforce the view that the sheath acts as a primary reservoir of accumulation from which PO_4^{3-} passes steadily into the host. A somewhat different pattern of absorption has been found for sulphate however, both with intact pine seedlings and excised beech mycorrhizas, indicating that this anion is not metabolised by the fungus, but has a free pathway through the sheath into the host tissue.

G. D. Bowen and C. Theodorou in 1967 emphasized one aspect of mycorrhiza formation which, although pointed out by Hatch thirty years before, is often overlooked. This is the longevity of mycorrhizas in comparison with uninfected roots. They showed, by means of a root scanning technique, that some uninfected portions of the root system of *P. radiata,* viz. the zones of cell elongation, were just as efficient at absorbing ^{32}P as were mycorrhizas (Fig. 8.8.). Mycorrhizas however persist in one position in the soil for considerable periods of time whereas the highly efficient uninfected portion of the root 'moves' through the soil as the root elongates. The limiting factor in phosphate uptake from soil is not usually the plant's ability to absorb phosphate, but rather the rate at which phosphate ions are brought to the root surface. Whether this occurs mainly by diffusion or mass flow, the distance ions will move increases with time. Therefore an organ which is active in nutrient uptake for long periods has the potential to absorb ions from a much greater volume of soil than an ephemeral structure.

Transfer of carbon from host to fungus in ectomycorrhizas

The first direct evidence that photosynthate moved from plant to fungus was provided by E. Melin and H. Nilsson in 1957. They raised Scots pine *(P. sylvestris)* seedlings in axenic culture with *Rhizopogon roseolus* or *Boletus variegatus,* allowed them to photosynthesize $^{14}CO_2$, and found that the products of photosynthesis were rapidly transported to the root tips and to the mycelium of the mycorrhizal fungus. More recent evidence of the movement of sugars from host to fungus in ectotrophic mycorrhizas comes from the studies of D. H. Lewis and J. L. Harley, reported in 1965. The main soluble carbohydrates found in beech mycorrhizas are the sugars glucose, fructose, sucrose and trehalose, and the sugar alcohol mannitol, the latter two compounds being widespread as storage carbohydrates in the fungi generally. They could not be detected in uninfected beech roots, which indicates that their existence in mycorrhizas is due to the presence of fungal tissue. Mycorrhizas placed in a solution of ^{14}C-labelled glucose accumulated mainly trehalose and glycogen, in a solution of labelled fructose they accumulated mannitol, and when fed with labelled sucrose, they accumulated all three storage carbohydrates (Table 8.4).

TABLE 8.4 **Percentage distribution of** ^{14}**C, absorbed as sucrose from an external solution, in excised beech roots***

Type of root	Insoluble carbohydrates†	Soluble carbohydrates				
		Trehalose	Sucrose	Glucose	Mannitol	Fructose
Mycorrhizal	54.0	17.2	2.6	0.9	24.4	0.9
Uninfected	22.5	0	47.5	19.0	0	11.0

* Data of D. H. Lewis, and J. L. Harley. From Harley, J. L. (1965) 'Mycorrhiza' in *Ecology of Soil-borne Plant Pathogens,* eds. K. F. Baker and W. C. Snyder. University of California Press.
† Mainly glycogen.

Irrespective of which of the three sugars were fed to mycorrhizas, ^{14}C activity occurred almost entirely in fungal storage carbohydrates, about two-thirds of them in the sheath and the remainder of the Hartig net. Uninfected roots, on the other hand, accumulated only glucose, fructose and sucrose; these sugars could also be found in the core tissue of mycorrhizas. To test the hypothesis that simple sugars move from host to fungal tissue and are there converted to fungal storage carbohydrates, Lewis and Harley prepared agar blocks containing ^{14}C-labelled sucrose, and attached mycorrhizal roots to them after first removing a ring of sheath from the base of the mycorrhiza, so that the only fungal tissue in direct contact with the agar was the Hartig net. After an appropriate period, the distribution of ^{14}C-labelled carbohydrates among the components of the mycorrhizas was determined. A typical result is shown diagrammatically in Fig. 8.9. In the basal part of the core the ^{14}C label was found mainly in sucrose, with slight activity in trehalose due to the presence of the Hartig net. In the middle zone, where the sheath was present as well, sucrose and mannitol were about equally labelled, with smaller amounts present as trehalose and the two hexoses. The apical section was dissected into sheath and core before analysis. In the core, most of the activity was in sucrose, as in the basal part, again with some activity in trehalose and hexoses. In contrast, the

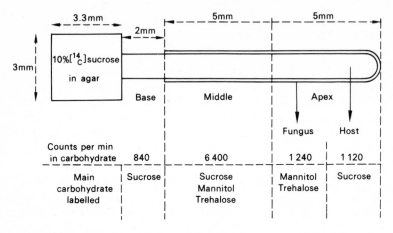

FIG. 8.9 Transfer of carbohydrate from host to fungus in ectomycorrhizas of *Fagus sylvatica*, as shown by the experiments of D. H. Lewis and J. L. Harley. The upper part of the diagram indicates the method; the centre, the amount of labelled carbon in the carbohydrates of various regions after twenty hours; the bottom, the most highly labelled carbohydrates present after twenty hours. For further explanation, see text. (From Harley, J. L. (1965) in *Ecology of Soil-borne Plant Pathogens*, eds. K. F. Baker and W. C. Snyder, University of California Press.)

apical sheath showed most activity in the fungal carbohydrates mannitol and trehalose, while sucrose activity was greatly reduced.

The fact that the ^{14}C label remained predominantly as sucrose in both basal and apical cores indicates that sucrose can move through the host tissue of beech mycorrhizas. From there it moves to the fungal tissues of Hartig net and sheath where it is converted to mannitol and trehalose. Furthermore, there is no reciprocal flow of carbohydrates from fungus to host since, compared to mycorrhizal roots, uninfected beech roots show little or no ability to absorb and utilize trehalose and mannitol.

Lewis and Harley's theory is that the fungus of ectotrophic mycorrhizas absorbs sugars from the host and converts them into reserve carbohydrates peculiar to itself, and in this way maintains a concentration gradient favouring additional movement of sugars from host to fungus. Furthermore, since re-utilization of these fungal storage carbohydrates by the host is insignificant, the fungus gains an additional advantage in that it does not have to share its energy reserves with the host. This state of affairs, i.e. where the recipient converts the transferred carbohydrate into a form unavailable to the donor, exists also in the lichen symbiosis (p. 94), and indeed appears to be a common feature of mutualistic symbiosis between autotrophs and heterotrophs.

Effect of vesicular-arbuscular mycorrhizas on growth and nutrient status of plants

Because of the problems associated with culturing *Endogone* (p. 194), it has been difficult to design experiments which would provide a critical test of the effect of V-A mycorrhizas on plant growth. Nevertheless, evidence has accumulated that they enhance the growth of the host under certain circumstances. Barbara Mosse in 1957 tested the effect of inoculating apple seedlings, grown in autoclaved soil, with *Endogone* sporocarps; inoculated seedlings were larger than uninoculated and had generally higher nutrient contents. In 1959 G. T. S. Baylis raised seedlings of *Griselinia littoralis* (Cornaceae) in non-sterile soil and transplanted them to autoclaved soil deficient in phosphorus; a proportion of the transplants became mycorrhizal, grew better and took up more phosphorus than uninfected plants. Some care is needed when interpreting the results of experiments carried out in autoclaved soils, since it has been shown that heating may produce toxins which can be destroyed by a number of different microorganisms. Especially in experiments such as those just described, where the method used to infect seedlings would have introduced other soil microbes as well as the mycorrhizal fungus, it can be argued that the beneficial results obtained are due primarily to the destruction of toxins produced during sterilization. J. W. Gerdemann in 1964 used soil which had been steam-sterilized ('partially sterilized') rather than autoclaved, and also added leachings from sporocarps to his control plants in an attempt to introduce at least some of the microorganisms which were present as contaminants of his inoculum. These experiments showed that inoculation with *Endogone* sporocarps increased the yield and phosphorus uptake of maize seedlings growing in phosphate deficient soils.

Benefit to the host seems more likely to result from mycorrhizal infection when conditions for growth are least favourable. For example, in 1966, M. J. Daft and T. H. Nicholson produced endotrophic mycorrhizas on tobacco, tomato and maize seedlings in sand culture by inoculating them with spores of *Endogone,* and found that growth was stimulated most under conditions of low phosphate availability; yield differences were greatest when phosphorus was supplied as bone meal and least when it was in the form of dicalcium phosphate. Even where inoculation failed to stimulate growth, it still resulted in increased phosphorus uptake. The enhanced growth and better phosphorus status of hoop pine seedlings resulting from infection by *Endogone* is illustrated in Table 8.5; non-mycorrhizal seedlings showed symptoms of gross phosphorus deficiency. Further evidence of improved phosphorus

TABLE 8.5 Effect of vesicular-arbuscular mycorrhiza on yield and nutrient status of two-year old *Araucaria cunninghamii* seedlings growing in a steam-sterilized krasnozem soil*

| Parameter | Mycorrhizal status | | Significance of difference† |
	uninfected	infected	
Dry weight (g)	7.8	72.6	***
P concentration, roots (%)	0.050	0.122	***
N concentration, roots (%)	0.90	0.89	ns

* Data of D. I. Bevege (1971) PhD thesis, University of New England.
† Three asterisks indicate that the differences were significant at the 0.1% level of probability; ns means not significant.

nutrition brought about by V-A mycorrhizas comes from T. M. Morrison and D. A, English, who in 1967 reported that excised mycorrhizal roots of kauri pine (*Agathis australis*) absorbed much more ^{32}P from a solution of H_3PO_4 than uninfected roots, and presented evidence to show that phosphorus uptake was metabolically dependent.

The spore isolation methods introduced by Gerdemann have permitted the establishment of V-A mycorrhizas under reasonably controlled conditions. Barbara Mosse's technique for obtaining two organism cultures of fungus and plant (p. 196) provided a further advance. G. D. Bowen and B. Mosse have used two-organism cultures and radioactive tracer techniques to study short term uptake of phosphorus by endotrophic mycorrhizas of clover and onion. They found that mycorrhizal roots took up approximately twice the phosphate that uninfected roots did from 5×10^{-6}M $KH_2{}^{32}PO_4$ solution. Autoradiographs of whole roots revealed that the mycorrhizal portions were the most radioactive, while autoradiography at the cellular level showed that a considerable amount of the activity was in the fungal tissues. The higher rate of uptake by infected parts of the root system is therefore probably due largely to uptake by the fungus and not to the stimulation of normal uptake mechanisms of the host cells following upon infection.

The evidence for increased phosphorus uptake by plants carrying V-A mycorrhizas, especially under conditions of low phosphate availability, is indisputable. It has also been shown that plants with V-A mycorrhizas can fix small amounts of atmospheric nitrogen, but there is no substantive evidence that the mycorrhizal association is in any way involved in this. In the light of current knowledge, it would be better to ascribe such fixation to the activities of bacteria in the rhizosphere (see Chapter 9). The ecological significance of these endotrophic mycorrhizas would therefore seem to stem primarily from improved phosphorus nutrition of the host plant, and perhaps a more rapid absorption of other nutrients consequent on the resulting stimulus to its respiratory metabolism.

Movement of nutrients from host to endophyte in vesicular-arbuscular mycorrhizas

Compared to ectotrophic mycorrhizas, very little is known about the transfer of materials from plant to fungus in V-A mycorrhizas. At first sight, since the association seems to be obligate for the fungus, it is reasonable to assume that its energy source is soluble carbohydrate in the host root. Unpublished autoradiographs of D. I. Bevege and G. D. Bowen indicate that when *Araucaria* seedlings raised in soil are allowed to photosynthesize $^{14}CO_2$, more ^{14}C finds its way into infected than uninfected roots, but whether the label is primarily in the fungal hyphae or in the host tissue is not known. T. H. Nicolson recently queried whether a sufficient supply of substrate could be obtained from the host to support the great development of extramatrical mycelium which sometimes occurs around phycomycete mycorrhizas. He has suggested that the fungus obtains specific growth factors from the root but derives most of its nutrients and energy from the rhizosphere or surrounding soil. The exact nature of the benefits conferred on *Endogone* by the mycorrhizal association therefore remains an open question.

Mycorrhizas in nutrient cycling and energy flow

Energy network diagrams for non-mycorrhizal and ectomycorrhizal ecosystems are presented in Fig. 8.10. The details of the mineralization—immobilization cycle have been omitted for the sake of clarity. Plants and soil microorganisms are shown as drawing on the same inorganic nutrient pool, and the two nutrient cycles are assumed to be competitive. However, in the mycorrhizal system the mycorrhizal fungus is interposed between the nutrient pool and the plant. In both systems, productivity is determined by the operation of a work gate through which energy flow from the sun is controlled by the supply of nutrients from the inorganic pool in the soil. The competitive flow towards the heterotrophic soil microbes (i.e. the immobilization rate) is governed at another work gate by the energy flow from plant residues. This is a function of the size of the plant residue reservoir which in turn depends on the rate of energy capture by the producers.

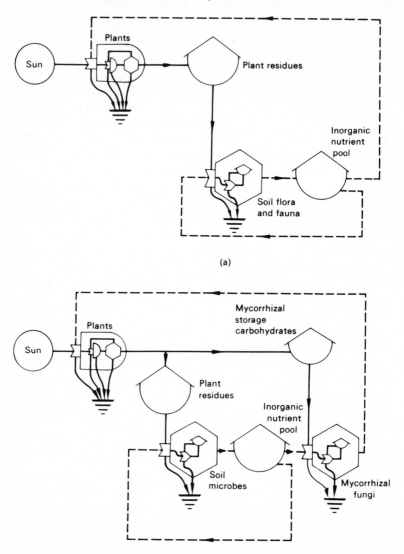

FIG. 8.10 Energy network diagrams of hypothetical ecosystems. (*a*) Non-mycorrhizal system. (*b*) Ectomycorrhizal system.

The presence of an additional module in the mycorrhizal system (Fig. 8.10(*b*)) has important implications for the processes of energy flow and nutrient cycling. The movement of plant sugars into the fungal symbiont activates the work gate which regulates nutrient flow into the mycorrhiza and thence to the host. Being independent of plant residues as an energy source, the mycorrhizal fungus competes successfully with free-living soil microorganisms for mineral nutrients. In low fertility soils, which are the typical habitat of ectomycorrhizal plants, the role of mycorrhizas is seen as speeding the passage of essential elements through the nutrient cycle, and minimizing losses from the system through leaching. Productivity is increased by ectomycorrhizas through their ability to increase the concentration of limiting nutrients at the work gate which controls the flow of solar energy into the plants.

The mechanism which initiates this increase in ecosystem productivity is the diversion of photosynthate into fungal storage carbohydrates. The amount so diverted seems to be only a small fraction of the total produced, even though the mycorrhizal fungus contributes substantially to root respiration. In the oak-pine forest studied by G. M. Woodwell and his co-workers at Brookhaven (see Chapter 5), root respiration was estimated not to exceed 424 g/m^2/yr dry matter, or 28 per cent of total autotroph respiration. According to a recent calculation of J. L. Harley, ectomycorrhizas are responsible for at least one-quarter of the root respiration of beech. If this value applies also to the ectomycorrhizal oaks and pines, then only about one-sixteenth of the total producer respiration (R_a) is accounted for by the mycorrhizal fungi. Since in this forest, R_a represents 56 per cent of gross production, it follows that for every 100 g carbon fixed by photosynthesis, 16 g are consumed by root respiration, and of this amount 4 g is respired by the mycorrhizas. The proportion of total community respiration (R_e) contributed by autotrophs will however vary throughout succession, being greater earlier and smaller later. The relative contribution of mycorrhizal fungi to producer (autotroph) respiration will likewise change as succession proceeds. Although there is no experimental evidence to support such a contention, it seems reasonable to suppose that this will be greater in the early stages, when net primary production and the annual demand for nutrients is highest. The Brookhaven forest is in a late stage of succession $(GP/R_e = 1.3)$, and in less mature forests the amount of gross production diverted into fungal storage carbohydrates might be expected to exceed the 4 per cent calculated for this ecosystem. Nevertheless, it is still likely to represent only a small proportion (probably less than 10 per cent) of the total photosynthate produced.

The ecological significance of vesicular-arbuscular mycorrhizas is not so apparent as that of the ectotrophic kind. In agronomic practice, where crops are grown on high fertility soils, they may be of no great importance, although it is well to remember that nutrient uptake by mycorrhizal roots might represent the norm even in agriculture. It is in natural communities however that this plant—microbe interaction is likely to be of greatest significance. Particularly on infertile soils, phycomycete mycorrhizas could well havȩ a regulatory function in ecosystems similar to that postulated for ectotrophic mycorrhizas.

Other regulatory functions of mycorrhizas

In addition to their direct effects on nutrient cycling and energy flow, there is evidence that ectomycorrhizas have a protective function against certain root disease organisms. Many mycorrhizal fungi produce antibiotics in pure culture which inhibit the growth of other microbes, including some pathogenic root infecting fungi. One of these is *Leucopaxillus cerealis* var. *piceina* which forms ectomycorrhizas with shortleaf pine *(P. echinata)*, a tree which is susceptible to littleleaf disease caused by the root-rot fungus *Phytophthora cinnamomi*. D. H. Marx and C. B. Davey have shown that fully developed mycorrhizas formed by this and other fungi on shortleaf and loblolly pines resist attack by the pathogen under controlled conditions in the laboratory, and have isolated and identified the antibiotic agent. They further showed that various morphological forms of naturally occurring mycorrhizas of shortleaf pine were resistant to infection; mycorrhizas with incomplete fungal mantles did permit some infection to occur but the pathogen did not invade the Hartig net region. Thus it seems probable that ectomycorrhizas have an additional regulatory function in forest ecosystems, as agents of biological control against root pathogens.

Selected references

Harley, J. L. (1969) *The Biology of Mycorrhiza*, 2nd edn. Leonard Hill.

Baylis, G. T. S. (1959) 'Effect of vesicular-arbuscular mycorrhiza on the root growth of *Griselinia littoralis* (Cornaceae).' *New Phytol.*, **58**, 274—80.

Baylis, G. T. S. (1967) 'Experiments on the ecological significance of phycomycetous mycorrhizas.' *New Phytol.*, **66**, 231—43.

Björkman, E. (1942) 'Uber die Bedingungen der Mykorrhizabildung bei Kiefer und Fichte.' *Symb. bot. Upsal.*, **6**(2), 1—191.

Björkman, E. (1970) 'Mycorrhiza and tree nutrition in poor forest soils.' *Stud. For. Suec.* No. 83, 24 pp.

Bowen, G. D. and Rovira, A. D. (1969) 'The influence of micro-organisms on growth and metabolism of roots' in *Root Growth*, ed. W. J. Whittington, pp. 170–201. Butterworth.

Bowen, G. D. and Theodorou, C. (1967) 'Studies on phosphate uptake by mycorrhizas.' *Proc. 14th IUFRO Congr., Munich*, 24, 116–38.

Carrodus, B. B. (1967) 'Absorption of nitrogen by mycorrhizal roots of beech. II. Ammonium and nitrate as sources of nitrogen.' *New Phytol.*, 66, 1–4.

Chilvers, G. A. and Pryor, L. D. (1965) 'The structure of eucalypt mycorrhizas.' *Aust. J. Bot.*, 13, 245–59.

Clowes, F. A. L. (1951) 'The structure of mycorrhizal roots of *Fagus sylvatica*.' *New Phytol.*, 50, 1–16.

Daft, M. J. and Nicolson, T. H. (1966) 'Effect of *Endogone* mycorrhiza on plant growth.' *New Phytol.*, 65, 343–50.

Gerdemann, J. W. (1955) 'Relation of a large soil-borne spore to phyco-mycetous mycorrhizal infections.' *Mycologia*, 47, 619–32.

Gerdemann, J. W. (1964) 'The effect of mycorrhizas on the growth of maize.' *Mycologia*, 56, 342–9.

Harley, J. L. (1965) 'Mycorrhiza' in *Ecology of Soil-borne Plant Pathogens*, eds. K. F. Baker and W. C. Snyder, pp. 218–29. University of California Press.

Harley, J. L. (1968) 'Mycorrhiza' in *The Fungi*, eds. G. C. Ainsworth and A. S. Sussman. Vol. III. *The Fungal Population*, pp. 139–78. Academic Press.

Harley, J. L. (1971a) 'Fungi in ecosystems.' *J. appl. Ecol.*, 8, 627–42.

Harley, J. L. (1971b) 'Associations of microbes and roots' in *Microbes and Biological Productivity* (21st Symp. Soc. Gen. Microbiol.), eds. D. E. Hughes and A. H. Rose, pp. 309–32. Cambridge University Press.

Harley, J. L. and Lewis D. H. (1969) 'The physiology of ectotrophic mycorrhizas.' *Adv. microb. Physiol.*, 3, 53–81.

Hatch, A. B. (1937) 'The physical basis of mycotrophy in *Pinus*.' *Black Rock Forest Bull.*, 6, pp. 168.

Kramer, P. J. and Wilbur, K. M. (1949) 'Absorption of radioactive phosphorus by mycorrhizal roots of pine.' *Science*, 110, 8–9.

Lamb, R. J. and Richards, B. N. (1970) 'Some mycorrhizal fungi of *Pinus radiata* D. Don and *P. elliottii* var. *elliottii* Little and Dorman in Australia.' *Trans. Br. mycol. Soc.*, 54, 371–8.

Lamb, R. J. and Richards, B. N. (1971) 'Effect of mycorrhizal fungi on the growth and nutrient status of slash and radiata pine seedlings.' *Aust. For.*, 35, 1–7.

Lewis, D. H. and Harley, J. L. (1965) 'Carbohydrate physiology of mycorrhizal roots of beech. III. Movement of sugars between host and fungus.' *New Phytol.,* 64, 256—69.

Lister, G. R., Slankis, V., Krotov, G. and Nelson, C. D. (1968) 'The growth and physiology of *Pinus strobus* L. seedlings as affected by various nutritional levels of nitrogen and phosphorus.' *Ann. Bot.,* 32, 33—43.

Marx, D. H. and Davey, C. B. (1969) 'The influence of ectotrophic mycorrhizal fungi on the resistance of pine roots to pathogenic infections. III. Resistance of aseptically formed mycorrhizae to infection by *Phytophthora cinnamomi.*' *Phytopathology,* 59, 549—58.

Marx, D. H. and Davey, C. B. (1969) 'The influence of ectotrophic fungi on the resistance of pine roots to pathogenic infections. IV. Resistance of naturally occurring mycorrhizae to infections by *Phytophthora cinnamomi.*' *Phytopathology,* 59, 559—65.

Mejstrik, V. (1970) 'The uptake of ^{32}P by different kinds of ectotrophic mycorrhiza of *Pinus.*' *New Phytol.,* 69, 295—8.

Melin, E. (1962) 'Physiological aspects of mycorrhizae of forest trees' in *Tree Growth,* ed. T. T. Kozlowski, pp. 247—63. Ronald Press.

Melin, E. (1963) 'Some effects of forest tree roots on mycorrhizal Basidiomycetes' in *Symbiotic Associations* (13th Symp. Soc. Gen. Microbiol.), eds. P. S. Nutman and B. Mosse, pp. 125—45. Cambridge University Press.

Melin, E. and Nilsson, H. (1950) 'Transfer of radioactive phosphorus to pine seedlings by means of mycorrhizal hyphae.' *Physiologia Pl.,* 3, 88—92.

Melin, E. and Nilsson, H. (1957) 'Transport of ^{14}C-labelled photosynthate to the fungal associate of pine mycorrhiza.' *Svensk bot. Tidskr.,* 51, 166—86.

Morrison, T. M. (1962a) 'Absorption of phosphorus from soils by mycorrhizal plants.' *New Phytol.,* 61, 10—20.

Morrison, T. M. (1962b) 'Uptake of sulphur by mycorrhizal plants.' *New Phytol.,* 61, 21—7.

Morrison, T. M. and English, D. A. (1967) 'The significance of mycorrhizal nodules of *Agathis australis.*' *New Phytol.,* 66, 245—50.

Mosse, B. (1953) 'Fructifications associated with mycorrhizal strawberry roots.' *Nature, Lond.,* 171, 974.

Mosse, B. (1957) 'Growth and chemical composition of mycorrhizal and non-mycorrhizal apples.' *Nature, Lond.,* 179, 922—4.

Mosse, B. (1962) 'The establishment of vesicular-arbuscular mycorrhiza under aseptic conditions.' *J. gen. Microbiol.,* 27, 509—20.

Mosse, B. (1963) 'Vesicular-arbuscular mycorrhiza: an extreme form of fungal adaptation' in *Symbiotic Associations* (13th Symp. Soc. Gen. Microbiol.), eds. P. S. Nutman and B. Mosse, pp. 146–70. Cambridge University Press.

Mosse, B. and Bowen, G. D. (1968) 'The distribution of *Endogone* spores in some Australian and New Zealand soils, and in an experimental field soil at Rothamsted.' *Trans Br. mycol. Soc.*, 51, 485–92.

Nicolson, T. H. (1967) 'Vesicular-arbuscular mycorrhiza – a universal plant symbiosis.' *Sci. Progr., Oxf.*, 55, 561–81.

Nicolson, T. H. and Gerdemann, J. W. (1968) 'Mycorrhizal *Endogone* species.' *Mycologia*, 60, 313–75.

Richards, B. N. and Wilson, G. L. (1963) 'Nutrient supply and mycorrhiza development in Caribbean pine.' *For. Sci.*, 9, 405–12.

Robertson, N. F. (1954) 'Studies on the mycorrhiza of *Pinus sylvestris.*' *New Phytol.*, 53, 253–83.

Routien, J. B. and Dawson, R. F. (1943) 'Some interrelationships of growth, salt absorption, respiration and mycorrhizal development in *Pinus echinata.*' *Am. J. Bot.*, 30, 440–51.

Rovira, A. D. and Bowen, G. D. (1966) 'The effects of microorganisms upon plant growth. II. Detoxication of heat-sterilized soils by fungi and bacteria.' *Plant Soil*, 25, 129–42.

Smith, D., Muscatine, L. and Lewis, D. (1969) 'Carbohydrate movement from autotrophs to heterotrophs in parasitic and mutualistic symbiosis.' *Biol. Rev.*, 44, 17–90.

Theodorou, C. and Bowen, G. D. (1969) 'The influence of pH and nitrate on mycorrhizal associations of *Pinus radiata* D. Don.' *Aust. J. Bot.*, 17, 59–67.

Zak, B. (1964) 'Role of mycorrhiza in root disease.' *A. Rev. Phytopath.*, 2, 377–92.

Zak, B. and Bryan, W. C. (1963) 'Isolation of fungal symbionts from pine mycorrhizae.' *For. Sci.*, 9, 270–8.

Zak, B. and Marx, D. H. (1964) 'Isolation of mycorrhizal fungi from roots of individual slash pines.' *For. Sci.*, 10, 214–21.

9 Root nodule symbioses and the nitrogen cycle

The roots of some plants bear nodules which are the visible manifestation of a symbiotic association between these plants and certain bacteria. In contrast to mycorrhizas, whose main function appears to be to use an existing supply of nutrients more efficiently, this symbiosis is able to 'fix' atmospheric nitrogen, i.e. to utilize the molecular nitrogen of the atmosphere for biosynthesis and growth. Except for certain free-living microbes, no other organisms can assimilate gaseous nitrogen. Fixation of nitrogen is therefore one of the fundamental reactions of the biosphere (see p. 230 ff.).

Two broad groups of angiosperms possess root nodules, one comprising legumes and the other certain non-legumes, the bacterial component being different in the two symbioses.

The legume—rhizobium association

The legume—rhizobium symbiosis is of great significance in agriculture, for the growth of crop plants is limited more frequently by a deficiency of nitrogen than of any other element. Efficiently nodulated and properly managed leguminous crops can fix between 100 and 175 kg N/ha/yr; indeed there are authenticated records of fixation rates, under the stimulus of mowing or grazing, exceeding 500 kg per hectare each year. Highest rates of fixation are usually found in association with herbaceous legumes, but some woody species have considerable potential also, for example *Acacia mollissima*, when introduced to South Africa, is reported to have fixed nearly 200 kg N/ha/yr over a thirty year period.

The ability of legumes to maintain or restore soil fertility was known to the ancient Romans, but it is less than 100 years since this has been attributed to the presence of the peculiar nodular structures found on their roots. Around the middle of the nineteenth century it was learned that the growth of most non-leguminous plants depended on the supply of inorganic nitrogen from the soil but this was not necessarily so for legumes. In the 1880s, H. Hellriegel and H. Wilfarth found that when quartz sand, a medium free of nitrogen, was inoculated with a small quantity of soil from an area where legumes grew well, and then sown with legume seed, the seeds developed into healthy plants bearing root nodules and gained considerable amounts of nitrogen. Oats treated in the same way did not develop nodules and grew poorly. When a sterile soil inoculum was used the legumes failed to nodulate, made poor growth, and gained no nitrogen (Table 9.1).

TABLE 9.1 Effect of inoculation with soil containing *Rhizobium* on growth of legumes (peas) and non-legumes (oats)*

Treatment	*Yield*	
	Oats (g)	*Peas* (g)
No N added		
Uninoculated	0.6	0.8
Inoculated with soil which had grown legumes	0.7	16.4
Inoculated with sterile soil	–	0.9
112 mg N added as NO_3^-		
Uninoculated	12.0	12.9
Inoculated	11.6	15.3

* Based on the data of Hellriegel, H. and Wilfarth, H. (1888). *Z. Rübenzucker-Ind*, Beilageheft.

On the basis of these results, Hellriegel and Wilfarth postulated that bacteria in the root nodules assimilated elemental nitrogen from the air and that the pea plants used the nitrogenous compounds formed by the bacteria. This hypothesis gained support when T. Schloesing and E. Laurent found, in 1892, that any gain in the nitrogen content of legumes was balanced by a corresponding loss from the atmosphere. Direct evidence that root nodules were the site of fixation had to await the advent of isotopic tracer techniques, and even then was not obtained until 1952, when W. H. Aprison, and R. H. Burris demonstrated that excised root nodules of soybean could fix $^{15}N_2$ for a short period, although they rapidly lost the capacity to do so. The root nodule organism was first isolated by M. W. Beijerinck in 1888. He named it *Bacillus radicicola*, but several species are now recognized, all of which are placed in the genus *Rhizobium*. Specific rank has in the past been conferred on many strains of rhizobia on the basis of their

FIG. 9.1 Effect of inoculation with various strains of *Rhizobium* on the growth of *Stylosanthes guyanensis*, showing the varying degrees of effectiveness of the different strains, con, uninoculated control; nit, uninoculated control plus nitrate; eff, inoculated with highly effective rhizobia; inef, inoculated with completely ineffective strain. (Photo by CSIRO, Division of Tropical Agronomy.)

constant association with a particular legume, but recent taxonomic evidence indicates that *Rhizobium,* as now constituted, probably contains only two or three distinctive groups which might properly be regarded as separate species. The effect of inoculation with *Rhizobium* on the growth of legumes is shown in Fig. 9.1.

Incidence and specificity of nodulation

The Leguminosae contains three large subdivisions or families. These are the Mimosaceae and the Caesalpiniaceae, which are mostly tropical in distribution, and the Papilionaceae, which contains both tropical and temperate species. Not all legumes will nodulate, the ability to do so being least pronounced in the Caesalpiniaceae: about three-quarters of the species examined in this family are reported as lacking nodules. In contrast, nodulation is almost universal among papilionate species, while the Mimosaceae occupy an intermediate position. Nodule shape and size varies considerably from species to species (Fig. 9.2). Annuals usually have large nodules grouped about the taproot or the first order laterals. The nodules of perennial species tend to be smaller and more widely distributed over the root system. New nodules are formed throughout the growing season and old nodules are sloughed off. Nodulation is affected by seasonal conditions and by the growth patterns of the plant so that nodules may be absent at any given time, even from plants which normally nodulate abundantly. As several workers have pointed out, it is probably unwise to generalize about the incidence of nodulation in the Leguminosae, since only a little more than 10 per cent of the total number of species has ever been examined to determine whether root nodules are present.

D. O. Norris suggested in 1956 that any general description of the legume—rhizobium symbiosis should be based on the fact that the vast majority of legumes are tropical plants, and that their ancestral ecological habitat was probably the strongly leached, acid soils of tropical rainforests. The temperate genera evolved from tropical forebears and some of them, particularly the genera *Trifolium, Medicago, Melilotus* and *Trigonella* of the tribe Vicieae, have become adapted to neutral or calcareous soils of higher nutrient status. Although other workers have challenged Norris' hypothesis concerning the evolution of the Leguminosae, it is indisputable that the bulk of research done on symbiotic nitrogen fixation in legumes deals with the Trifolieae and the Vicieae, and caution must be exercised in generalizing from the results of this research until such time as more is known about the tropical species. This is particularly true when we come to consider the significance of the legume—rhizobium symbiosis in the geochemical cycle of nitrogen (p. 231).

There is a certain degree of specificity in nodulation, and legumes may be arranged in groups, the members of one group generally forming nodules with the same strain of *Rhizobium*, but for the most part not nodulating with rhizobia from other groups. Seven such 'cross-inoculation' groups, and a number of small so-called 'strain-specific' groups, have been recognized. The seven major groups are the field pea *(Pisum)*, medic *(Medicago)*, clover *(Trifolium)*, lupin *(Lupinus)*, garden bean *(Phaseolus)*, soybean *(Soya)* and cowpea *(Vigna)* groups. Within

(a)

the various cross-inoculation groups, sub-groups may be distinguished which are specific in their requirements for particular strains of rhizobia; for example, three sub-groups are recognized in the clover cross-inoculation group. The scheme is of such limited applicability to the Leguminosae as a whole that it has fallen into disfavour. Nowadays, the last four groups, together with a number of the strain-specific groups, are considered as a 'tropical legume miscellany'. This miscellany of species contains some forming more or less discrete groups, some which will nodulate with a wide range of rhizobial strains, and others which will nodulate only when infected with specific strains of bacteria.

Rhizobium strains not only differ in their ability to form nodules

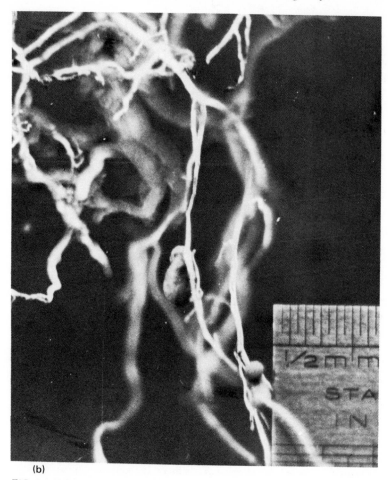

(b)

FIG. 9.2 Root nodules of legumes. (*a*) Broad bean, *Vicia faba.* (*b*) Wyalong wattle, *Acacia cardiophylla.*

with a given legume, but also in their capacity to fix nitrogen in association with the particular host. The property of nitrogen fixation is a function of both host and bacterium, and a strain of *Rhizobium* may be highly efficient, that is 'effective', on one host yet serve no useful purpose, in other words be 'ineffective', on another. Effective nodules are generally larger than ineffective nodules, and can also be distinguished by their pink coloration, which is due to a red internal pigment, haemoglobin. The effectiveness of rhizobia is an important factor to be taken into account when legumes are used in agriculture (Fig. 9.1). When new legumes are being introduced to a region for the first time, care must be taken to ensure that effective strains of rhizobia are present in the soil in sufficient numbers to form nodules on the developing seedlings. In many cases, the native rhizobia are not effective for the introduced plant, and inoculation of the seed with an effective strain of *Rhizobium* can mean the difference between a successful introduction and complete failure of the crop, especially if the soil is low in available nitrogen. The causes of the host—bacterium specificity in nodulation and nodule effectiveness are not known for certain but there is some evidence that they are controlled by genetic factors in the host.

Effect of edaphic factors on nodulation

Nodulation is affected by a variety of edaphic factors, some of which act via their influence on the nutrition of the host. For example, infection is conditioned by the carbohydrate and nutrient status of the plant, in a manner analogous to their effect on mycorrhiza development in pine seedlings (p. 189). Plants which are grossly nitrogen deficient nodulate sparingly or not at all, while a high level of availability of soil nitrogen depresses nodulation and reduces fixation. Many other factors are however involved in the nodulation process and these will be discussed later.

Calcium and phosphorus play an important part in the legume—rhizobium relationship. Phosphorus deficient plants do not nodulate properly and in addition an adequate supply of soil phosphorus helps to maintain the population of nodule bacteria in the soil at a high level. Calcium is important for the nutrition of both legumes and bacteria. Most specialized temperate legumes of the clover, medic or field pea type have a high calcium requirement, and frequently do not nodulate well on acid soils, unless these are limed. In contrast lupins, though confined to temperate regions, have retained the ability to nodulate on acid soils even in the absence of lime. The effect of lime on the root nodule symbiosis of temperate legumes in acid soils is confounded by its effect on the availability of molybdenum. Adequate molybdenum is necessary for the functioning of the fixation process, and its availability is increased by adding lime. Work with subterranean clover on the Southern Tablelands of New South Wales has shown, however, that the amount of lime needed to induce nodulation is less than that needed to correct any molybdenum deficiency. Substantial economies can be effected, in this instance, by using molybdenum-superphosphate to correct molybdenum deficiency and drilling in small quantities of lime (about 220 kg per hectare) with the seed. Furthermore, since superphosphate contains sufficient calcium to overcome any calcium deficiency on these soils, the effect of lime in promoting nodulation is not due to an increase in the supply of molybdenum or calcium. The increase in nodulation brought about by liming is in fact caused by an increase in rhizobial numbers resulting from a decrease in soil acidity. When it was realized that it was necessary only to increase soil pH in the rhizosphere to ensure good nodulation, the technique of 'lime-pelleting' of subterranean clover seed was developed: seed pelleted with a small amount of finely ground calcium carbonate produces as vigorous a pasture as that obtained when much larger quantities of lime are applied in the drill rows.

It should not be assumed, on the basis of these results with temperate species, that all legumes will nodulate better on acid soils if these are limed. D. O. Norris pointed out in 1965 that the well known legumes of temperate agriculture, such as the clovers, peas, vetches and lucerne, all have highly specialized, fast-growing rhizobia which produce acid when grown on appropriate media in the laboratory, whereas all the tropical legumes have slower growing, alkali-producing rhizobia. Norris postulated that this enables the tropical strains of rhizobia to resist acid soil conditions, whereas unless the rhizosphere of temperate legumes is ameliorated with lime, their acid-producing rhizobia fail to cause nodulation. Lime should not, therefore, be applied indiscriminately to tropical legumes, for not only are their rhizobia well adapted to growing in acid soils but in addition there is evidence that they are more efficient than temperate species in extracting calcium from soils of low calcium status.

The specific role of calcium in nodulation, and the importance of its interaction with hydrogen ion concentration, were clarified in 1958 by J. L. Loneragan and E. J. Dowling. They found that the amount of calcium required for nodulation of subterranean clover was greater than that which produced maximum growth of *Rhizobium*, and also was in excess of plant requirement when nitrogen was supplied as potassium nitrate. They concluded that the effects of H^+ and Ca^{2+} on nodulation could best be explained in terms of their influence on the level of calcium in the plant. C. S. Andrew and D. O. Norris came to a similar conclusion in 1961, after experimenting with several tropical and temperate species. A leguminous tree of the Australian semi-arid zone, mulga *(Acacia aneura)*, has maximum nodule development associated with a clearly defined optimum level of calcium in the phyllodes of 0.56 per cent: nodulation declines rapidly as phyllode calcium concentration deviates from the optimum in either direction (Fig. 9.3).

Soil temperature is another environmental variable which has been extensively studied. The temperature of the rooting medium affects

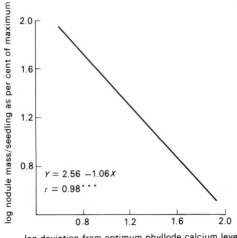

FIG. 9.3 Effect of plant calcium status on the extent of nodulation in *Acacia aneura*. (From O'Hagan, B. J. (1966) MSc thesis, University of New England.)

both the initiation of infection and the subsequent development of nodules. As might be expected, tropical legumes have a higher temperature requirement for nodulation than temperate species. Soil temperature (and probably other edaphic factors as well) exerts its influence on the nitrogen fixing system through its effect on the symbiotic association. In other words, the symbiosis does not necessarily react to environmental variables in the same way as the plant or bacterium growing separately.

Infection and nodule development

Rhizobia are facultative symbionts able to live as normal components of the soil microflora in the temporary absence of their hosts, but their continued existence as free-living heterotrophs depends on the presence of the host root. Whereas nodule bacteria are little affected by the roots of most non-legumes, they are greatly stimulated in the rhizosphere of their particular host, and R/S ratios almost always exceed 1 000/1. The cause of this large and specific rhizosphere effect is unknown. The population of *Rhizobium* in the rhizosphere of legumes may reach 10^6 cells per gram or larger. Such large population densities are not needed to initiate infection in axenic culture, where fewer than 100 bacteria in the whole rhizosphere may be sufficient to start infection. Why such high numbers are necessary in nature remains to be determined.

The process of nodule development involves three stages, which have

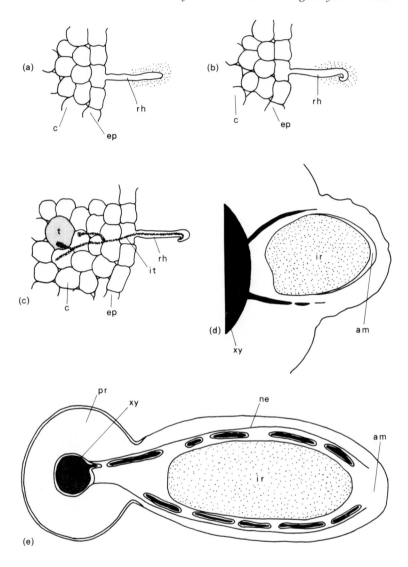

FIG. 9.4 Initiation and structure of pea nodules. (a) Aggregation of rhizobia around root hair. (b) Curling of root hairs. (c) Rhizobia move through infection thread towards tetraploid cell. (d) Differentiation of young nodule into central infected region and apical meristem. (e) Longitudinal section through mature nodule. am, apical meristem; c, cortex; ep, epidermis; ir, infected region; it, infection thread; ne, nodule endodermis; pr, primary root; rh, root hair; t, tetraploid cell; xy, xylem. (From Stewart, W. D. P. (1966) *Nitrogen Fixation in Plants,* Athlone Press.)

been clearly described by P. S. Nutman (Fig. 9.4). The first stage includes the events up to and including infection of the root. Nodules seem to be initiated at predetermined sites on the root, in the case of many herbaceous species via root hairs. In the pre-infection phase, important interactions take place between root exudates and nodule bacteria. Among the exudates is tryptophan which is converted by nodule bacteria to indoleacetic acid (IAA). A characteristic curling of the root hairs, apparently brought about by IAA, precedes the actual infection. It should be noted that the exudation of tryptophan, its conversion to IAA, and root hair curling, can all occur whether or not the *Rhizobium* strain involved can nodulate with the host in question. The next event is the exudation of polygalacturonase by the plant, which is apparently induced by the presence of the extracellular polysaccharide slime layer of the bacterium, although this latter point is in dispute. The function of this pectic enzyme is uncertain, but it is thought to act in conjunction with IAA to increase the plasticity of the primary wall of the root hair and thus facilitate penetration. The infection stage is terminated by the formation of an infection thread, a hypha-like tube containing the bacteria and composed mainly of cellulose secreted by the host. The infection thread appears to be initiated by invagination of the root hair wall, and it grows at its tip, which is free of cellulose, into the root cortex. Not all legumes possess infection threads, and in such hosts the bacteria apparently spread from cell to cell in the root and developing nodule by the division of already infected cells. In those species in which rhizobia do not enter via root hairs, the infection process is less well understood.

The second stage in nodulation concerns the initiation and organization of the nodule. It begins when the penetrating infection thread approaches a pre-existing tetraploid cell in the cortex. This cell and the neighbouring diploid cells are stimulated to repeated division, and the mass of cells so formed rapidly differentiates into the young nodule. The infection thread branches and the branches penetrate the tetraploid cells as they are formed but do not enter the cells of the apical meristem which are diploid. The central infected zone is separated from the rest of the nodule by an endodermis. The uninfected diploid tissue differentiates into nodule cortex, and into vascular strands (each enclosed by an endodermis) which connect the nodule to the main vascular system of the root.

The third and final stage of nodule development as described by Nutman is the intracellular stage. Vesicles are seen to form on the infection threads within the tetraploid cells of the central zone of the nodule. Until recently, it was believed that these vesicles ruptured, releasing the bacteria into the cells, where they multiplied in the host cytoplasm and became transformed to 'bacteroids'. Bacteroids are irregularly shaped, and in some legumes even branched to produce X and Y shapes. Electron micrographs however show that bacteroids do not develop free in the host cytoplasm as was formerly thought. Rather, the bacteria from the infection thread vesicles are enclosed, singly or in small groups according to host, within folds of the outer cytoplasmic membrane of the root cell, where they multiply and

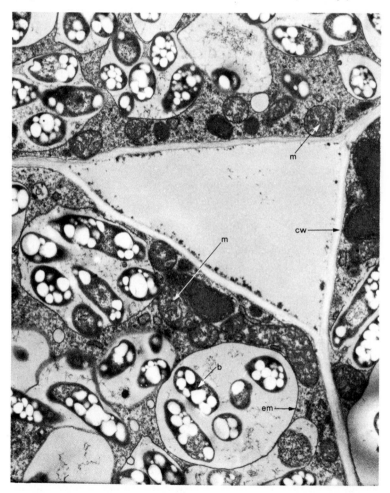

FIG. 9.5 Electron micrograph of mature cell of soybean nodule, showing groups of bacteroids enclosed in membrane envelopes. cw, cell wall; m, mitochondrion; em, membrane envelope. (From Goodchild, D. J. and Bergersen, F. J. (1966) *J. Bact.*, **92**, 204–13.)

change to bacteroids. The mature, infected nodule cell thus contains a very complex system of host membrane envelopes, each one surrounding one or several bacteroids (Fig. 9.5).

The process by which bacteria in the infection thread enter the host cell appears to be similar to the endocytotic process for passage of particles and macromolecules across cell membranes. The bacteria are first adsorbed onto the outer surface of the cell's boundary membrane, which then invaginates to enclose them in a vacuole. It has been estimated that each central tissue cell of a mature soybean nodule contains up to 500 000 bacteroids, and that there are some 10 000–40 000 such cells in each nodule.

Bacteroids do not divide within the nodule and have not so far been cultivated on laboratory media. Concomitant with bacteroid formation, the pigment haemoglobin is produced, and nitrogen fixation begins. After a period of weeks or months (except in those species with perennial nodules) haemoglobin is replaced by bile pigments, the bacteroids lyse, and degenerative processes spread throughout the nodule. Rod-shaped bacteria, which have meanwhile lain dormant in the infection thread, invade and multiply in the old nodule which then decays, permitting the bacteria to escape into the soil.

The site of fixation within the nodule

All effective nodules contain bacteroids, the amount of nitrogen fixed being strongly correlated with the amount of bacteroid containing tissue. This suggests that the bacteroids themselves fix nitrogen which is then transferred to the host. A positive correlation also exists between the amount of haemoglobin and the nitrogen fixing ability of nodules. The pigment changes from red to green when nitrogen fixation ceases in annual plants at the end of vegetative growth or when they are placed in the dark for a few days.

Although the relationship between the presence of bacteroids and nitrogen fixation was known for many years, all efforts to obtain *in vitro* fixation by bacteroids failed; even in excised nodules it continues only briefly. It now appears that this is due to the sensitivity of the nitrogen fixing process to oxygen: the bacteroids require oxygen for respiration but too much oxygen inhibits fixation. Thus F. J. Bergersen and G. L. Turner found it possible to demonstrate fixation in bacteroids by studying the process in breis extracted from nodules crushed under an atmosphere of argon. The problem of providing sufficient oxygen for bacteroid respiration at oxygen tensions low enough to permit nitrogen fixation to proceed is apparently solved through the agency of haemoglobin, which is able to transport oxygen to the bacteroids at many times the rate of simple diffusion.

Non-legume root nodules

Root nodules are found in seven angiosperm families other than those of the Leguminosae (Table 9.2), and thirteen genera have been proven to fix atmospheric nitrogen. These nodulated non-legume genera have a world-wide distribution, from the arctic to the tropics, and comprise about 300 species in all. About one-third of these species have been examined, and the majority though not all are found to possess nodules. Most of these nodulated plants are trees or shrubs, and they often occur on infertile soils. Their ecological significance, and their contribution to the geochemical cycle of nitrogen, will be discussed later (p. 232).

TABLE 9.2 Non-leguminous plants with root nodules that fix molecular nitrogen*

Order	*Family*	*Genus*
Coriariales	Coriariaceae	*Coriaria*
Rosales	Rosaceae	*Cercocarpus†, Dryas, Purshia*
Myricales	Myricaceae	*Comptonia, Gale, Myrica*
Fagales	Betulaceae	*Alnus*
Casuarinales	Casuarinaceae	*Casuarina*
Rhamnales	Eleagnaceae	*Eleagnus, Hippophaë, Shepherdia*
	Rhamnaceae	*Ceanothus, Discaria*

* After Becking, J. H. (1970) *Pl. Soil*, **32**, 611−54.
† N_2-fixing ability not yet confirmed by ^{15}N technique.

Identity of the endophyte

The nodule endophytes are not seed borne, so that plants of each generation must be infected afresh from the soil. Since most attempts to synthesize nodules in axenic culture, using microorganisms isolated from naturally occurring nodules as inocula, have failed, the evidence concerning the nature of the endophyte has perforce been derived from cytological studies. Many conflicting reports have come from investigations with the light microscope, but electron microscopy has revealed that the nodule endophyte is an actinomycete, occurring as fine, branched, septate hyphae less than 1 μm in diameter. A prominent feature of infected nodules, under the light microscope, is the presence in some cells of club shaped or spherical structures known as vesicles;

they are prevalent in nodule tissue which is actively fixing nitrogen but it is not known whether they are essential for the fixation process or not. In electron micrographs, the vesicles are seen to be terminal cells of hyphae, 3—4 μm in diameter, with a complex internal structure. They have not been described from the nodules of all non-legumes examined, however. In some species, irrespective of whether vesicles are produced or not, the hyphae appear to fragment into bacteroid-like segments; the significance of these structures is unknown.

J. H. Becking has recently proposed that a new family of bacteria be established (Frankiaceae) to include all those actinomycetes which form nodules on the roots of non-leguminous dicotyledons. On the basis of host specificity (see below) he recognizes ten species within a single genus, *Frankia.*

Incidence and specificity of nodulation

Good nodule development depends on favourable environmental conditions. For most genera, nodulation is best in a substrate with a pH around neutrality. The numbers of nodules per plant decline as the level of combined nitrogen in the rooting medium increases; nodule weight however increases, except at very high levels of available nitrogen, when it too is depressed.

Organisms from one genus will not necessarily infect plants in another genus. Using crushed nodule suspensions as inocula, it has been shown that *Eleagnus, Hippophaë* and *Shepherdia,* all members of the Eleagnaceae, cross-inoculate while the inocula from various species of *Alnus* (Betulaceae) will not nodulate *Gale palustris* syn. *Myrica gale* (Myricaceae) or representatives of the families Casuarinaceae, Rhamnaceae and Coriariaceae. Compatibility within genera is not invariable, either: cross-inoculation is possible between various species of *Casuarina* whereas *Coriaria japonica* from Japan will not nodulate with the endophyte of the European species, *C. myrtifolia.* Thus while some degree of specificity in nodulation exists, probably due to geographical isolation, there appears to be nothing like the marked specificity found in the legumes and especially in the Papilionaceae.

Infection and nodule development

The nodules of non-legumes are perennial. Externally they are fairly distinct from those of legumes. At first they appear as lateral swellings on the roots and later become strongly lobed, producing large nodule clusters up to 5 cm in diameter (Fig. 9.6). *Casuarina* and *Myrica* are

FIG. 9.6 Root nodules of non-legumes. *(a) Casuarina cunninghamiana*, showing the negatively geotrophic roots that arise from the lobes of some nodules. *(b) Hippophaë rhamnoides*, detached nodule.

distinctive in that the apex of each lobe gives rise to a root which is negatively geotropic. Infection occurs at discrete points on the root and is often associated with the distortion of root hairs. Because of the crude inocula used however, it is not possible to ascribe root hair distortion to the endophyte, nor is it certain that infection always takes place via the root hairs. Where it does, an infection thread develops apparently by invagination of the outer cytoplasmic membrane of the root hair cell, as in legumes. In *Myrica* the nodule originates from the pericycle and thus has affinities with a lateral root. A similar finding has been reported for *Alnus*, although some workers believe that nodules in this genus arise from both pericycle and cortex of the parent root. Anatomically, all non-legumes root nodules are characterized by a well-developed cork layer, an infected cortex and a central stele which shows secondary thickening. The presence of the endophyte in the cortex contrasts markedly with the infected region in legume nodules, which is internal to the vascular system.

The nitrogen-fixing process

There is no doubt that the nodules are the site of fixation. This has been clearly shown by the investigations of G. Bond in Scotland. If the nodules are removed from a plant, it soon develops symptoms of nitrogen deficiency which persist until new nodules are formed. When nodulated plants are allowed to fix nitrogen labelled with ^{15}N, the label is found mainly in the nodules; and if the nodules are removed before the test and they and the rest of the root systems are then gassed separately, only the nodules show this evidence of fixation.

The amount of nitrogen fixed is proportional to the volume of infected tissue and the site of fixation is within the infected cells, but it has not yet been determined whether fixation occurs within the endophyte or extracellularly to it. The presence of haemoglobin in non-legume nodules has been reported, but its existence is disputed by many workers; if it occurs then it may be firmly attached to cellular materials rather than free in solution as in legumes. J. H. Becking and his colleagues showed in 1964, by means of electron microscopy, that the endophyte of non-legumes is surrounded by a membrane of host plant origin, and in this sense the symbiosis is structurally similar to the legume–rhizobium association. Other similarities with legumes are a requirement for molybdenum and cobalt in the fixation process.

Significance of root nodule symbioses: biogeochemistry of nitrogen

As a constituent of proteins, nitrogen is of paramount importance to organisms. Despite the fact that there are some 30 000 tons of nitrogen in the air over every acre of the Earth's surface (755 g/cm^2), most plants and animals, including a large proportion of the world's human population, suffer from the effects of nitrogen deficiency at some stage of their lives. The great reservoir of nitrogen in the atmosphere is the ultimate source of nitrogen for the biosphere, so that the significance of root nodule symbioses is best gauged by considering their role in fixing gaseous nitrogen relative to that of other agents for removing this element from the air. These agents may be either biological or physical, and their several contributions will be considered in turn.

Biological nitrogen fixation

Biological nitrogen fixing systems involve either symbiotic or free-living soil microbes. The former include root nodule symbioses and some lichens.

Legume—rhizobium symbiosis

The cultivation of leguminous crops is a basic feature of most of the permanent agricultural systems of the world. From the point of view of the agronomist, the legume—rhizobium symbiosis is undoubtedly the most important biological mechanism for adding nitrogen to the soil—plant system. While none would deny its agronomic importance, its significance from the geochemical viewpoint is another matter. G. E. Hutchinson, following a critical review of the available data in 1954, concluded that legumes are responsible for only 3—4 per cent of the nitrogen fixed at the surface of the Earth each year.

As previously indicated (p. 217), knowledge of the role of legumes in nitrogen fixation is restricted to a few tribes of the family Papilionaceae. These are cultivated herbaceous legumes capable of fixing nitrogen at rates of the order of 100 kg/ha annually. Under intensive agriculture in temperate climates, even higher rates of fixation have been achieved. However, it would be unwise to assume that fixation rates attained by these herbaceous species in cultivation apply also to the vast numbers of wild legumes. Taking into account that one-third of the land surface is sparsely vegetated, and that the cultivation of legumes is practised on but a small fraction of the remainder, Hutchinson estimated that the total annual contribution of legumes is slightly less than 0.3 kg/ha of fixed nitrogen for the Earth's surface as a whole. This estimate might be enlarged if more data were available on nitrogen fixation in the Leguminosae as a whole, for it is not inconceivable that the woody perennial legumes of the tropics and subtropics contribute far more to the nitrogen cycle than the handful of herbaceous species that have been intensively studied. It must be remembered, however, that many tropical legumes apparently do not nodulate (p. 217), and therefore presumably do not fix nitrogen at all.

Non-legume—actinomycete symbiosis

Perhaps of greater geochemical significance than legumes are the symbioses involving nodulated non-leguminous plants. The ability of plants such as alder *(Alnus)* to act as soil improvers has been known for almost as long as that of legumes, however quantitative data on their contribution to the nitrogen cycle is meagre. *Gale palustris* (syn. *Myrica gale*), which grows in acid peat bogs, fixes about 9 kg N/ha/yr in the field, whereas in artificial culture its nitrogen fixing ability may surpass that of red clover and other annual legumes. Under appropriate ecological conditions, non-legumes may achieve quite high fixation rates, for example 62—164 kg N/ha/yr for *Alnus crispa* in Alaska and 58 kg N/ha/yr for *Casuarina equisetifolia* in Africa. An average value for vigorous stands of non-leguminous nodule bearing angiosperms would lie in the range 50—100 kg N/ha/yr. The contribution of these plants to the nitrogen economy of many forest ecosystems is widely recognized, and bearing in mind their broad distribution, it is likely that nodulated plants other than legumes will prove to be among the major contributors to the geochemical cycle of nitrogen.

Other root nodule symbioses

In addition to the angiosperms discussed above, nodules of a very different kind have been reported in the gymnosperm family Cycadaceae, and nitrogen fixation in cycads has been confirmed by the ^{15}N technique for *Cycas* and *Macrozamia*. In these plants, the endophyte is a blue-green alga, probably *Anabaena* or *Nostoc,* contained within negatively geotropic coralloid roots which arise from the surface of the swollen hypocotyl and taproot. The contribution of these symbioses to the geochemical cycle of nitrogen is probably negligible, however they might well be significant in the nitrogen economy of particular ecosystems, *M. communis,* for instance, is a prominent understorey plant of the spotted gum *(Eucalyptus maculata)* forests on the south coast of New South Wales.

Lichens

One other symbiotic system remains to be discussed, viz. the lichen symbiosis. A lichen is an association between a fungus which is usually a discomycete and an alga which may be green or blue-green (see p. 94). About 8 per cent of all lichens contain blue-green algae, and it is likely that most of these fix atmospheric nitrogen. Fixation has been demonstrated by the ^{15}N technique in several genera. Quantitative data on the contribution of lichens to the nitrogen cycle is lacking, but they no doubt play an important role in vegetating specific habitats such as bare rock surfaces. They are also abundant on the bark of many rain-forest trees in the tropics and subtropics and it is conceivable that they play a significant role in the nitrogen economy of such ecosystems. Their overall geochemical significance is difficult to assess but is probably slight.

Non-symbiotic fixation: bacteria

Turning now to non-symbiotic nitrogen fixation, the organisms concerned here are, with the possible exception of some yeasts, either bacteria or blue-green algae, i.e. lower protists. The bacteria fall into two broad groups, heterotrophic and autotrophic. Among the heterotrophic nitrogen fixing bacteria, both aerobic and anaerobic species are known. Two closely related aerobic genera are *Azotobacter* and *Beijerinckia,* the generic name *Beijerinckia* having been given by H. G. Derx in 1950 to a species previously isolated and described by R. L. Starkey and P. K. De in 1939 as *Azotobacter indicum. Azotobacter* has a world-wide distribution, especially in neutral and alkaline soils. *Beijerinckia* is restricted mainly to acid, lateritic soils of tropical and extra-tropical regions. In 1960 a new nitrogen fixing genus *(Derxia)* was described by H. L. Jensen and his colleagues: it appears to be confined to the tropics.

Azotobacter was first isolated by Beijerinck in 1901. Since then, innumerable papers have been written on its nitrogen fixing ability, ' . . . their number and volume directly related to the ease and convenience of working with this aerobic organism, and almost unrelated to its real importance in world nitrogen economy'.* The contribution of heterotrophic nitrogen fixers to the nitrogen cycle is limited by the availability of a suitable organic substrate. *Azotobacter,* for example, is most abundant in fertile soils with a high organic matter content, although numbers rarely exceed 200 cells per gram. The presence of

* Henzell and Norris, 1962.

Azotobacter does not however mean that it is making any significant contribution to the nitrogen economy of such soils, since these will normally contain some mineralized nitrogen, such as ammonium, which *Azotobacter* is known to utilize in preference to molecular nitrogen.

Several other heterotrophs are known to fix nitrogen aerobically, for example certain species or strains of *Pseudomonas, Bacillus, Klebsiella, Mycobacterium* and possibly *Spirillum*; in some species fixation proceeds most rapidly at very low oxygen levels. G. Metcalf and M. E. Brown reported in 1957 that the actinomycete *Nocardia* fixes atmospheric nitrogen, but this has not yet been confirmed. Many of these genera are widespread in soils, and are therefore likely to be more important geochemically than *Azotobacter*; they are however subject to the same restrictions in respect of energy substrates.

The best known anaerobic nitrogen fixer is *Clostridium*. This was the first bacterial genus shown to fix nitrogen in pure culture, and some twelve species are recognized as having this ability. Like *Azotobacter, Clostridium* is dependent upon a suitable energy supply and its nitrogen fixing capacity is inhibited by small amounts of ammonium or nitrate. Knowledge of the role of *Clostridium* in nature is even more speculative than of *Azotobacter,* for the reason that it is difficult and tedious to work with an organism that is an obligate anaerobe. It is known to be more widespread in distribution than *Azotobacter*, being much more tolerant of acid conditions. Its contribution to the nitrogen cycle is therefore likely to be greater than that of *Azotobacter.*

There are several facultative anaerobes which fix N_2 when growing anaerobically, for example certain strains of *Bacillus, Klebsiella* and *Pseudomonas.* Because of the limitations imposed by their energy requirements, and their preferential use of mineral nitrogen, the agronomic value of these and other heterotrophic nitrogen fixing bacteria in cultivated soils is thought to be slight. The same may be true of their geochemical significance; however as pointed out by H. L. Jensen in 1950, the efficiency of nitrogen fixing heterotrophs may be greater in the field than in the laboratory. Thus in uncultivated soils, where crops are not removed but where plants are allowed to die and decompose *in situ,* it is conceivable that chemoheterotrophic bacteria, both aerobic and anaerobic, make a substantial contribution to the nitrogen cycle. In 1936, J. G. Lipman and A. B. Coneybeare published a detailed analysis of the nutrient budget of the USA and estimated that the mean rate of nitrogen fixation by non-symbiotic bacteria was 6.7 kg/ha/yr. G. E. Hutchinson has accepted this figure as a reasonable estimate for the Earth's land area as a whole. Assuming that the land occupies 29 per cent of the Earth's surface, we arrive at a figure of 2.8 kg/ha/yr as the contribution of free-living heterotrophs to the nitrogen budget of the Earth.

Several kinds of autotrophic nitrogen fixing bacteria are known, such as the chemoautotrophic *Methanobacterium omelianskii* and the photoautotrophic green and purple sulphur bacteria. It would seem that all photosynthetic bacteria, including the photoheterotrophic non-sulphur purple bacteria, are capable of fixing nitrogen. Some are able to fix nitrogen also in the dark, when growing chemoheterotrophically, but their efficiency of fixation is then much lower. It should be kept in mind that the environmental conditions for bacterial photosynthesis are very restrictive. The bacteria require both sunlight and anaerobic conditions, thus are likely to be active only in shallow waters and estuarine muds. Although their local importance in such ecosystems may be considerable, their contribution to the geochemical cycle of nitrogen is probably very small.

Non-symbiotic fixation: blue-green algae

A group of autotrophic microorganisms whose geochemical significance may be greater than any of the free-living bacteria is the blue-green algae (Cyanophyta). The first evidence of nitrogen fixation by these microbes was obtained by B. Frank in 1889. Frank's cultures however were not free of bacteria, and when it was later shown that pure cultures of green algae (Chlorophyta) could not fix nitrogen, his results were discounted as being due to bacterial contamination. It was not until 1928 that K. Drewes was able to prove conclusively that nitrogen fixation occurred in pure cultures of the blue-green algae *Nostoc* and *Anabaena*. Since then, at least fourteen genera and about forty species, from terrestrial, marine and freshwater habitats, from the antarctic to the tropics, have been shown to fix nitrogen. Fixation in blue-green algae was first confirmed using the ^{15}N technique by R. H. Burris *et al.* in 1943. Nitrogen fixing ability is widespread in the group but by no means universal. With one possible exception, all the blue-greens that fix nitrogen have a common peculiarity, they form thick-walled cells called **heterocysts** at intervals along their filaments so that the proportion of species with heterocysts in a mixed algal population is an index of the nitrogen fixing potential of that population. Recent evidence supports an earlier view that heterocysts take part in nitrogen fixation but this has not been proven unequivocally.

Blue-green algae have a recognized role in the nitrogen economy of rice paddies. During the rainy season there is profuse growth in most paddy fields of many nitrogen fixing genera, and P. K. De and

L. N. Mandal in 1956 found that 15–50 kg N/ha were fixed in six weeks. As primary colonizers in desert regions, they make significant contributions also, for example Y. T. Tchan and N. C. W. Beadle estimated in 1955 that blue-green algae fixed about 3 kg/ha/yr in the arid zone of New South Wales, a substantial amount for such a difficult environment. In the antarctic, *Nostoc* is common and is the chief component of so-called 'algal peat'. In the littoral zone, W. D. P. Stewart in 1965 found that fixation by blue-green algae increased from little or none in mid-winter to 8 kg/ha/mo in spring. Nitrogen fixation in lakes by blue-green algae is well established, reaching a peak in late summer when the algal bloom is commencing, and it is probable that it occurs in the open ocean as well. Although quantitative data on the contribution of these microorganisms to the overall nitrogen economy of the Earth is not available, it is clear that they make important contributions to a diverse group of ecosystems. Their geochemical significance remains to be properly assessed, but it is no doubt considerable.

Other agents of biological nitrogen fixation

Many claims for nitrogen fixation by fungi have been made, especially among students of mycorrhiza, but in no instance can fixation be positively ascribed to the presence of the fungal endophyte. Until unequivocal evidence to the contrary is available, nitrogen fixation occurring in association with the root systems of mycorrhizal plants should be ascribed to the activities of free-living bacteria in the rhizosphere. The only fungi which have been shown to fix nitrogen by the sensitive ^{15}N technique are the soil-inhabiting yeasts, *Saccharomyces*, *Rhodotorula* and the yeast-like organism *Pullularia (Aureobasidium)*. Since these are the only eucaryotic organisms reputed to have this capacity, even this report should be accepted with caution. Nitrogen fixation would appear to be a property of the procaryotic cell.

There are other plant–microbe associations which may be of some significance in the nitrogen economy of certain ecosystems, and these are the so-called leaf glands or nodules on leaves. G. Stevenson in 1959 demonstrated fixation of ^{15}N$_2$ by leafy shoots of *Coprosma*, a genus of the family Rubiaceae which possesses stipular glands inhabited by bacteria. Three other genera in this family, viz. *Psychotria, Pavetta* and *Chomelia*, bear leaf nodules, which are sub-epidermal cavities filled with slime and bacteria. Of these, reliable evidence of fixation has been obtained only for *Psychotria*. W. S. Silver and co-workers found in 1963 that homogenates of the leaves of *Psychotria* fixed ^{15}N$_2$; they isolated from the nodules the bacterium *Klebsiella*, and showed that it could fix $^{15}N_2$ in pure culture. Nitrogen fixation is apparently not the only function of the endophyte, because although nodulated plants can grow normally in a nitrogen-free medium, non-nodulated plants are abnormal even when supplied with mineral nitrogen. It has been suggested that the bacteria supply an essential growth factor in addition to fixing nitrogen, and this is supported by the finding that gibberellic acid partially replaces the bacteria in allowing normal growth on combined nitrogen. Leaf nodules also occur in *Ardisia,* a widely distributed tropical genus of the family Myrsinaceae, but the evidence for nitrogen fixation in this instance is contradictory.

Non-biological nitrogen fixation

In addition to the fixation of molecular nitrogen by microorganisms, nitrogen may pass from the atmosphere to the biosphere as nitrogen compounds dissolved in rainwater. A variety of nitrogenous compounds is found in rain. A certain amount of organic nitrogen is always present; it is frequently referred to as 'albuminoid' nitrogen and is associated with particulate matter — dust and organic debris — suspended in the atmosphere. The two major nitrogen components in rain are however, ammonium and nitrate. E. Eriksson in 1952 made a detailed study of the nitrogen content of rain from a large number of meterological stations throughout the world. Average values for the northern hemisphere were 0.78 mg/l NH_4-N and 0.27 mg/l NO_3-N, and for the southern hemisphere 0.36 mg/l NH_4-N and 0.21 mg/l NO_3-N. The higher values for NH_4^+ in the northern hemisphere are believed to be due to increased industrial and agricultural activities in that hemisphere. The amount of nitrogen removed from the atmosphere each year in rain depends not only on the concentration of nitrogen compounds in rainwater but also on the annual precipitation. G. E. Hutchinson estimated that the rate of delivery of nitrogen in rain, averaged over the Earth's surface, is 1.3–3.2 kg/ha/yr. For individual land masses, the values are higher, and Eriksson's estimates are 7.5 and 8.1 kg/ha/yr for inorganic nitrogen in North America and Europe respectively, and 2.3 kg/ha/yr for organic nitrogen.

Origin of nitrogen in rainwater

Nitrogen in rainwater could be either cyclical or newly fixed. As Hutchinson has pointed out, it is important to distinguish between these because newly fixed nitrogen represents an addition to the nitrogen cycle whereas cyclical nitrogen does not. By cyclical nitrogen we mean nitrogen originating from organisms. Ammonium is cyclical nitrogen, that portion which is not clearly anthropogenic being derived from the normal respiratory activities of organisms. The crux of the problem of differentiating between the two kinds of nitrogen lies in determining the source of nitrate. If this is cyclical, then it must be formed from ammonium by oxidation. If on the other hand it is newly fixed nitrogen, the mechanism by which fixation occurs must be established.

It has long been held that nitrate in rain is fixed by lightning discharges during thunderstorms, an idea first put forward by Justus von Liebig in 1827. This question was thoroughly explored by Hutchinson in 1954. He concluded, on theoretical grounds, that the major part of the nitrate in rainwater is not fixed electrically. That such fixation can and does occur is undoubtedly true, but its contribution to the nitrogen cycle is minor. This conclusion is confirmed by the knowledge that there is often no correlation between the occurrence of lightning and the presence of nitrate in rain, and indeed sometimes the reverse is true. At Katherine, NT, where the average annual thunder day is the highest in Australia, R. Wetselaar and J. T. Hutton found in 1963 that the nitrate content of rain on days when lightning occurred was 30 per cent lower than on days when no lightning was observed.

If most of the nitrate in rain is not fixed by lightning discharges, it can only have been formed by photochemical oxidation of ammonium derived from the mineralization of organic nitrogen. In other words, it is derived from organisms and is being returned to them; as such it is cyclical nitrogen and does not add any newly fixed nitrogen to the cycle. The photochemical oxidation of ammonium proceeds according to the reaction:

$$NH_4^+ + OH^- + \tfrac{3}{2}O_2 \longrightarrow H^+ + NO_2^- + 2H_2O; \qquad \Delta F = -59\,000 \text{ cal/mole}$$

Being accompanied by a large decrease in free energy, this reaction can proceed practically to completion if suitably activated. K. Rao and N. R. Dhar suggested in 1931 that it is catalysed by the presence of certain oxides, notably silica (SiO_2). Their suggestion is supported by the finding that fluctuations in the nitrate concentration in rain are closely paralleled by fluctuations in the silica concentration.

There is much additional evidence which points to the soil and the soil—vegetation system as the ultimate source of nitrate in precipitation. In the vast majority of cases, the NH_4^+/NO_3^- ratio in rainwater is very close to 2/1. This is consistent with the hypothesis that NO_3^- is formed by photochemical oxidation of NH_4^+ and is inconsistent with the fixation of nitrate *de novo* from O_2 and N_2. Furthermore, reports from stations all over the world indicate that the NH_4^+

and NO_3^- content of rain decreases as the amount of precipitation increases. This points to the existence of both NH_4^+ and NO_3^- in the atmosphere before precipitation occurs, and indicates increasing dilution as more and more rain falls. Again, the ammonium level in precipitation and in the air is greatest at seasons when the decomposition rate of soil organic matter is highest, that is in the summer in regions with pronounced seasonal temperature fluctuations. This was clearly shown in a detailed study by C. E. Junge in 1958 of the distribution pattern of NH_4^+ and NO_3^- in precipitation over the USA. Finally, both NO_3^- and NH_4^+ levels in precipitation are high when there are high levels of solid and/or liquid particles in the air, for example in the dry season in monsoon climates. This not only implicates soil as the source of NH_4^+ but supports the contention that photo-oxidation of NH_4^+ takes place in moisture films on the surface of dust or silica particles.

The relative contributions of nitrogen fixing agents: a summing-up

G. E. Hutchinson in 1954 calculated 7 kg N/ha as the maximum annual rate of nitrogen fixation for the Earth's surface as a whole. C. C. Delwiche subsequently (in 1965) gave a revised estimate of 0.1 mg/cm^2 (10 kg/ha/yr). Of this total, lichens and autotrophic bacteria probably contribute a negligible amount, herbaceous legumes considerably less than 1 kg, heterotrophic non-symbiotic bacteria slightly less than 3 kg, leaving more than half to be fixed annually by woody legumes, nodulated non-legumes and blue-green algae (Fig. 9.7). These latter three groups seem to be the major agents of fixation from the geochemical viewpoint. Other mechanisms may of course be of paramount importance in any given ecosystem.

It has been suggested that the role of free-living heterotrophic bacteria might be enhanced in special habitats such as in the neighbourhood of roots (the rhizosphere) or on the surfaces of leaves (the phyllosphere). In such habitats, plant exudates could conceivably permit heterotrophs to escape some of the limitations placed on them by their dependence upon a readily available substrate. Indeed there is some experimental evidence that nitrogen fixation is stimulated in the rhizosphere of certain plants, and the microbial inhabitants of the phyllosphere commonly include nitrogen fixing genera such as *Beijerinckia* and *Azotobacter*. It is not known for certain however whether such plant—microbe associations make an effective contribution to the nitrogen economy of any ecosystem.

In conclusion, it should be noted that there are many ecosystems in

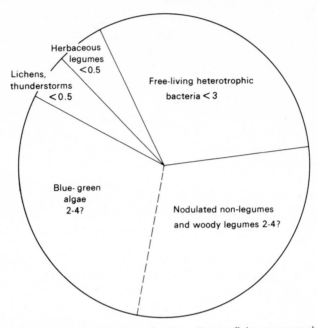

FIG. 9.7 The relative contributions of various nitrogen-fixing agents to the geo-chemical cycle of nitrogen. The figures represent the amounts fixed in kg/ha/yr for the Earth's surface as a whole, the total being 10 kg/ha/yr.

which unexplained gains of nitrogen have been recorded, gains of the order of 50 kg/ha/yr, for example in soil beneath pure grass swards and in pure stands of pines and other conifers. These ecosystems contain no symbiotic associations known to fix molecular nitrogen, yet the measured rates of fixation far exceed the accepted contributions of free-living microorganisms. It follows that either the activities of the non-symbiotic nitrogen fixers are capable of great stimulation in some as yet unexplained fashion (in the rhizosphere perhaps), or that nitrogen fixation in such ecosystems is accomplished by hitherto un-recognized processes. One possibility is the direct absorption of ammonia from the atmosphere, but free ammonia occurs at such low concentrations ($10^{-5}-10^{-7}$ g/m^3) that this could hardly account for more than a small fraction of the observed increases. In any event, this is cyclical nitrogen and if accepted as a gain to one ecosystem then it represents a loss to another.

The nitrogen cycle

The nitrogen incorporated by organisms is eventually returned to the inorganic state by a complex series of reactions involving its stepwise oxidation to NH_4^+, NO_2^- and NO_3^- (Chapter 6). In terrestrial ecosystems, the ammonium ion is normally adsorbed on colloidal matter near the soil surface, there to be reabsorbed by plants or microbes or further oxidized by the nitrifying bacteria. Although the efficiency of the nitrifiers is not great, they are nevertheless effective biogeochemical agents and have been known to produce several hundred ppm NO_3-N in soils in the space of a few weeks. The nitrate ion is mobile and as a result some nitrate is lost to ground waters by leaching and eventually reaches the sea. Nitrate which is not leached is either assimilated by organisms or else denitrified, i.e. reduced to gaseous form, and this is the ultimate fate of most of the nitrate that reaches the sea also. Denitrification is the major process by which nitrogen is returned to the atmosphere (Chapter 6), and so constitutes the opposite half of the nitrogen cycle to fixation.

Another way of looking at the geochemical cycle of nitrogen is to consider the equilibrium between it and oxygen, the other major gaseous constituent of the atmosphere:

$$2H_2O + 2N_2 + 5O_2 \rightleftharpoons 4HNO_3; \qquad \Delta F = 1\ 780 \text{ cal/mole}$$

Because the free energy of formation of nitric acid is quite small, one would not expect this reaction to go to completion in either direction, and theoretically (as G. E. Hutchinson has pointed out), the two major atmospheric gases ought to be in equilibrium with an appreciable quantity of nitric acid. The extreme stability of the N–N bond however, prevents the production of nitrate in detectable amounts at any ordinary temperature and pressure, except by a series of biological processes, viz. fixation of N_2 followed by ammonification and subsequent nitrification. Once nitrate has been produced however, it is thermodynamically possible, in accordance with the above equation, for a considerable amount to accumulate in the biosphere. In point of fact it does not, except as isolated deposits in arid regions, for example the Chilean nitrate deposits. It follows that there must be mechanisms operating which are continually returning nitrogen to the atmosphere, the principal one being denitrification.

The whole series of processes whereby the molecular nitrogen of the air enters into other compounds, and is finally delivered again to the atmosphere, is what constitutes the nitrogen cycle. It is illustrated diagrammatically in Fig. 9.8. No attempt is made to indicate in this diagram the relative contributions of the various processes to the overall cycle, except to omit those considered to be insignificant, e.g. electrical fixation of nitrate in thunderstorms. In many elementary text books,

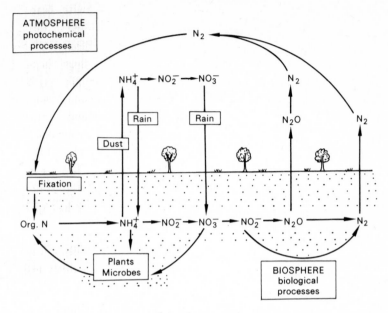

FIG. 9.8 Generalized diagram of the nitrogen cycle.

undue and even improper emphasis is sometimes placed on certain facets of the cycle. Thus discussion is usually centred on the classical nitrogen-fixing bacteria *Rhizobium* and *Azotobacter,* and furthermore, the contribution of nitrogen dissolved in rainwater is frequently stressed. In point of fact, with the possible exception of *Rhizobium,* not one of these agents is particularly important from the geochemical viewpoint. Certainly *Rhizobium* achieves considerable local significance by adding substantial amounts of newly fixed nitrogen to ecosystems dominated by herbaceous legumes, but whether the woody perennial legumes of the tropical and warm temperate zones contribute more to the world nitrogen budget than the nodulated non-legumes remains an open question.

In energy circuit language (Fig. 9.9), nitrogen fixation is seen as the key to the productivity of the biosphere. Ultimately, the rate of capture of solar energy by autotrophic nitrogen fixers, both symbiotic and free-living, determines the amount of nitrogen fixed, but it is this fixed nitrogen which permits accumulation of the organic residues that in turn serve as energy sources for further fixation by heterotrophic nitrogen fixers, and for the mineralization processes which provide nitrogen in a form available to non-fixing green plants. Although the interrelationships among the components of the cycle are complex, the productivity of the latter group is clearly governed by the supply of

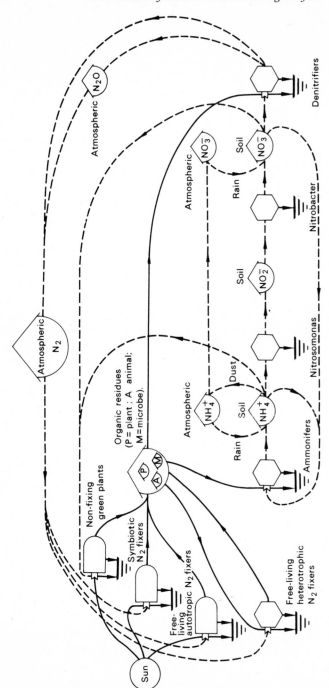

FIG. 9.9 Energy network diagram of the geochemical cycle of nitrogen.

mineral nitrogen at the work gate through which solar energy flows. This then serves as a basis for the complex series of food webs that characterize the biosphere.

Selected references

Mishustin, E. N. and Shil'nikova, V. K. (1971) *Biological Fixation of Atmospheric Nitrogen,* tr. A. Crozy. Macmillan.

Russell, E. W. (1961) *Soil Conditions and Plant Growth,* 9th edn. Longman.

Stewart, W. D. P. (1966) *Nitrogen Fixation in Plants.* Athlone Press.

Allison, F. E. (1965) 'Evaluation of incoming and outgoing processes that affect soil nitrogen' in *Soil Nitrogen,* eds. W. V. Bartholomew and F. E. Clark, pp. 573—606. American Society of Agronomy.

Anderson, A. J. and Moye, D. V. (1952) 'Lime and molybdenum in clover development on acid soils.' *Aust. J. agric. Res.,* 3, 95—110.

Andrews, C. S. and Norris, D. O. (1961) 'Comparative responses to calcium of five tropical and four temperate pasture legume species.' *Aust. J. agric. Res.,* 12, 40—55.

Becking, J. H. (1970a) 'Plant—endophyte symbiosis in non-leguminous plants.' *Plant Soil,* 32, 611—54.

Becking, J. H. (1970b) '*Frankiaceae* Fam. Nov. *(Actinomycetales)* with one new combination and six new species of the genus *Frankia* Brunchorst 1886, 174.' *Int. J. syst. Bact.,* 20, 201—20.

Becking, J. H., Boer, W. E. and Houwink, A. L. (1964) 'Electron microscopy of the endophyte of *Alnus glutinosa.*' *Antonie van Leeuwenhoek,* 30, 343—76.

Bergersen, F. J. and Briggs, M. J. (1958) 'Studies on the bacterial component of soybean root nodules: cytology and organization in the host tissue.' *J. gen. Microbiol.,* 19, 482—90.

Bergersen, F. J., Kennedy, G. S. and Wittman, W. (1965) 'Nitrogen fixation in the coralloid roots of *Macrozamia communis* L. Johnson.' *Aust. J. biol. Sci.,* 18, 1135—42.

Bergersen, F. J. and Turner, G. L. (1967) 'Nitrogen fixation by the bacteroid fraction of breis of soybean root nodules.' *Biochim. Biophys. Acta,* 141, 507—15.

Biggens, D. R. and Postgate, J. R. (1969) 'Nitrogen fixation by cultures and cell-free extracts of *Mycobacterium flavum* 301.' *J. gen. Microbiol.,* 56, 181—93.

Bond, G. (1951) 'The fixation of nitrogen associated with the root nodules of *Myrica gale* L., with special reference to its pH relation and ecological significance.' *Ann. Bot.,* 15, 447–59.

Bond, G. (1963) 'The root nodules of non-leguminous angiosperms' in *Symbiotic Associations* (13th Symp. Soc. Gen. Microbiol.), eds. P. S. Nutman and B. Mosse, pp. 72–91. Cambridge University Press.

Bond, G. (1967) 'Fixation of nitrogen by higher plants other than legumes.' *A. Rev. Pl. Physiol.,* 18, 107–26.

Bond, G. (1968) 'Some biological aspects of nitrogen fixation' in *Recent Aspects of Nitrogen Metabolism in Plants,* eds. E. J. Hewitt and C. V. Cutting, pp. 15–25. Academic Press.

Bond, G. and Scott, G. D. (1955) 'An examination of some symbiotic systems for fixation of nitrogen.' *Ann. Bot.,* 19, 57–77.

Burris, R. H. (1966) 'Biological nitrogen fixation.' *A. Rev. Pl. Physiol.,* 17, 155–84.

Burris, R. H., Eppling, F. J., Wahlin, H. B. and Wilson, P. W. (1943) 'Detection of nitrogen fixation with isotopic nitrogen.' *J. biol. Chem.,* 148, 349–57.

Crocker, R. L. and Major J. (1955) 'Soil development in relation to vegetation and surface age at Glacier Bay, Alaska.' *J. Ecol.,* 43, 427–48.

Delwiche, C. C. (1965) 'The cycling of carbon and nitrogen in the biosphere' in *Microbiology and Soil Fertility,* eds. C. M. Gilmour and O. N. Allen, pp. 29–58. Oregon State University Press.

Dixon, R. O. D. (1969) 'Rhizobia (with particular reference to relationships with host plants).' *A. Rev. Microbiol.,* 23, 137–58.

Döbereiner, J. (1961) 'Nitrogen-fixing bacteria of the genus *Beijerinckia* Derx in the rhizosphere of sugar cane.' *Plant Soil,* 14, 211–17.

Dommergues, Y. (1963) 'Evaluation du taux de fixation de l'azote dans un sol dunaire reboisé en filao *(Casuarina equisetifolia).' Agrochimica,* 7, 335–40.

Eriksson, E. (1952) 'Composition of atmospheric precipitation. I. Nitrogen compounds.' *Tellus,* 4, 215–32.

Fogg, G. E. and Stewart W. D. P. (1965) 'Nitrogen fixation in blue-green algae.' *Sci. Progr., Oxf.,* 53, 191–201.

Goodchild, D. J. and Bergersen, F. J. (1966) 'Electron microscopy of the infection and subsequent development of soybean nodule cells.' *J. Bact.,* 92, 204–13.

Henzell, E. F. and Norris, D. O. (1962) 'Processes by which nitrogen is added to the soil–plant system.' *Commonw. Bur. Pastures and Field Crops. Bull.,* 46, 1–18.

Hutchinson, G. E. (1954) 'The biogeochemistry of the terrestrial atmosphere' in *The Earth as a Planet*, ed. G. P. Kuiper, pp. 371–433, University of Chicago Press.

Jensen, H. L. (1950) 'A survey of biological nitrogen fixation in relation to the world supply of nitrogen.' *Trans 4th Int. Congr. Soil Sci.,* 1. 165–72.

Jensen, H. L. (1965) 'Nonsymbiotic nitrogen fixation' in *Soil Nitrogen,* eds. W. V. Bartholomew and F. E. Clark, pp. 436–80. American Society of Agronomy.

Junge, C. E. (1958) 'The distribution of ammonia and nitrate in rainwater over the United States.' *Trans Am. geophys. Union,* **39,** 241–8.

Kass, D. L., Drosdoff, M. and Alexander, M. (1971) 'Nitrogen fixation by *Azotobacter paspali* in association with bahiagrass *(Paspalum notatum).' Soil Sci. Soc. Am. Proc.,* **35,** 286–9.

Lawrence, D. B., Schoenike, R. E., Quispel, A. and Bond, G. (1967) 'The role of *Dryas drummondii* in vegetation development following ice recession at Glacier Bay, Alaska, with special reference to its nitrogen fixation by root nodules.' *J. Ecol.,* **55,** 793–813.

Loneragan, J. F., Meyer, D., Fawcett, F. G. and Anderson, A. J. (1955) 'Lime pelleted clover seeds for nodulation on acid soils.' *J. Aust. Inst. agric. Sci.,* **21,** 264–5.

Moore, A. W. (1966) 'Non-symbiotic nitrogen fixation in soil and soil–plant systems.' *Soils and Ferts.,* **29,** 113–28.

Norris, D. O. (1956) 'Legumes and the rhizobium symbiosis.' *Emp. J. exp. Agric.,* **24,** 247–70.

Norris, D. O. (1965) 'Acid production by *Rhizobium.* A unifying concept.' *Plant Soil,* **22,** 143–66.

Nutman, P. S. (1963) 'Factors influencing the balance of mutual advantage in legume symbiosis' in *Symbiotic Associations* (13th Symp. Soc. Gen. Microbiol.), eds. P. S. Nutman and B. Mosse, pp. 51–71. Cambridge University Press.

Nutman, P. S. (1965) 'Symbiotic nitrogen fixation' in *Soil Nitrogen,* eds. W. V. Bartholomew and F. E. Clark, pp. 360–83. American Society of Agronomy.

Parker, C. A. (1968) 'On the evolution of symbiosis in legumes' in *Festskrift til Hans Lauritis Jensen,* pp. 107–66. Publ. Gadgaard Nielsens Bogtrykkeri, Lemvig, Denmark.

Postgate, J. (1971) 'Relevant aspects of the physiological chemistry of nitrogen fixation' in *Microbes and Biological Productivity* (21st Symp. Soc. Gen. Microbiol.), eds. D. E. Hughes and A. H. Rose, pp. 287–307. Cambridge University Press.

Richards, B. N. (1964) 'Fixation of atmospheric nitrogen in coniferous forests.' *Aust. For.*, **28**, 68—74.

Ruinen, J. (1965) 'The phyllosphere. III. Nitrogen fixation in the phyllosphere.' *Plant Soil*, **22**, 375—94.

Silver, W. S., Centrifanto, Y. M. and Nicholas, D. J. D. (1963) 'Nitrogen fixation by the leaf-nodule endophyte of *Psychotria bacteriophila.*' *Nature, Lond.*, **199**, 396—7.

Stevenson, F. J. (1965) 'Origin and distribution of nitrogen in soil' in *Soil Nitrogen*, eds. W. V. Bartholomew and F. E. Clark, pp. 1—41. American Society of Agronomy.

Stewart, W. D. P. (1970) 'Algal fixation of atmospheric nitrogen.' *Plant Soil*, **32**, 555—88.

Thompson, J. P. (1968) 'The occurrence of nitrogen-fixing bacteria of the genus *Beijerinckia* in Australia outside the tropical zone.' *Trans. 9th Int. Congr. Soil Sci.*, **2**, 129—37.

Vincent, J. M. (1965) 'Environmental factors in the fixation of nitrogen by the legume' in *Soil Nitrogen*, eds. W. V. Bartholomew and F. E. Clark, pp. 384—435. American Society of Agronomy.

Virtanen, A. I. (1962) 'On the fixation of molecular nitrogen in nature.' *Communs. Inst. Forest. Fenniae*, **55**(22), 1—11.

Webster, S. R., Youngberg, C. T. and Wollum II, A. G. (1967) 'Fixation of nitrogen by bitterbrush (*Purshia tridentata* (Pursh) DC).' *Nature, Lond.*, **216**, 392—3.

Wetselaar, R. and Hutton, J. T. (1963) 'The ionic composition of rainwater at Katherine, NT, and its part in the cycling of plant nutrients.' *Aust. J. agric. Res.*, **14**, 319—29.

Appendix I   Modules of the energy circuit language

Appendix I copied from H. T. Odum: 'Environment, Power and Society', Wiley, 1971, Figs. 2–4 on pp. 38–9.

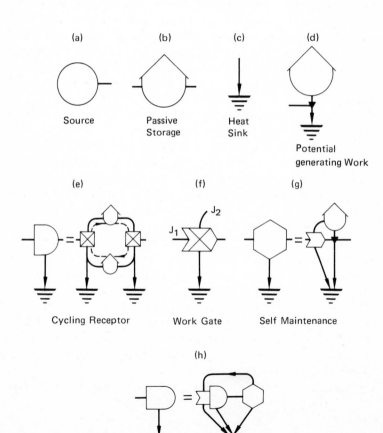

Appendix I Modules of the energy circuit language. *(a)* Circular symbol represents a source of energy such as the sun, fossil fuel, or the water from a reservoir. A full description of this source would require supplementary description indicating if the source were constant force, constant flux, or programmed in a particular sequence with, for example, a square wave or sine wave. *(b)* Passive storage symbol showing location in a system for passive storage such as moving potatoes into a grocery store or fuel into a tank. No new potential energy is generated and some work must be done in the process of moving the potential energy in and out of the storage by some other unit. *(c)* Heat sink required according to the second law of thermodynamics for all processes that are real and spontaneous. All processes deliver some potential energy into heat. Heat is the random wandering of molecules that have kinetic energy and it is this wandering from a less probable to a more probable state that pulls and drives real processes connected to such flows. *(d)* Combination of *(b)* and *(c)* that represents the storage of new potential energy against some storage force, and such work requires a dispersal of some potential energy into heat to be spontaneous. If this storing is done at the maximum possible rate, then 50 per cent must be delivered into the heat sink. *(e)* The bullet-shaped symbol represents the reception of pure wave energy such as sound, light, and water waves. In this module energy interacts with some cycling material producing an energy-activated state, which then returns to its deactivated state passing energy on to the next step in a chain of processes. The kinetics of this module was first discovered in a reaction of an enzyme with its substrate and is called a Michaelis-Menton reaction. *(f)* Work gate module at which a flow of energy (J_2) makes possible another flow of energy (J_1). This action may be as simple as a person turning a valve, or it may be the interaction of limiting fertilizer in photosynthesis. *(g)* Hexagonal symbol represents the combination of *(d)* and *(f)* by which potential energy stored in one or more sites in a subsystem is fed back to do work on the successful processing and work of that unit. In its simple form this module is sometimes said to be autocatalytic. Its growth when graphed has a sigmoid pattern. *(h)* This symbol is a combination of *(g)* and *(e)*. Energy captured by a cycling receptor unit is passed to self-maintaining unit that also keeps the cycling receptor machinery working, and returns necessary materials to it. The green plant is an example.

Appendix II Techniques of soil microbiology

The following account is but a brief introduction to some of the principal methods which may be used in studying the microbial ecology of the soil. For a more detailed treatment, the reader is referred to IBP Handbook No. 19, *Methods for Studying the Ecology of Soil Micro-organisms* by D. Parkinson, T. R. G. Gray and S. T. Williams, Blackwell Scientific Publications, 1971.

Because they cannot usually see the organisms they are studying, soil microbiologists face certain problems which are not experienced by ecologists who deal with plants and animals. Even when a micro-organism can be seen with the naked eye, it is difficult and often impossible to identify the species *in situ*. For example, fungi in soil can be discerned by the presence of visible mycelium, but normally they must be isolated and grown in the laboratory before they can be identified with any degree of certainty. A variety of techniques has been devised in attempts to overcome these difficulties. They may be grouped into two broad categories: firstly, those methods which involve the direct microscopic examination of microbes in the soil; and secondly, those which involve the isolation and study of micro-organisms in pure culture.

Microscopic examination of soil microorganisms without isolation in pure culture

About fifty years ago there was much controversy among micro-biologists concerning the relative importance of bacteria and fungi in decomposition processes in the soil. Some bacteriologists asserted that fungi were not normal inhabitants of soil but were merely present as dormant spores originating from fungi which parasitized plants. One such bacteriologist, the American H. J. Conn, devised a method for determining the relative abundance of soil microorganisms by direct microscopic examination of **soil smears**. A suspension of soil in water is prepared, smeared on a glass slide, fixed with dilute hydrochloric acid, then dried and stained with an appropriate stain. Upon examining such smears under the microscope, Conn found that fungal hyphae were quite common, thus indicating that fungi do in fact grow actively in the soil.

It will be readily appreciated that soil smears cannot give us a picture of the relative distribution of soil particles and microorganisms as they occur in the soil. The **buried slide** technique, developed in a simplified form by the Italians G. M. Rossi and S. Riccardo in 1927, and refined by the Russian N. Cholodny in 1930, overcomes this disadvantage to some extent. The method consists of burying a glass slide in soil for a period of days or weeks then fixing and staining the soil that adheres to it, and examining it under the microscope. This very simple yet elegant technique gave soil microbiologists their first view of what the soil microflora actually looks like *in situ*. Rossi–Cholodny slides clearly demonstrate that bacteria do not exist in the soil as isolated cells in the soil solution but rather as colonies associated with particulate organic or mineral matter.

Buried slides are used primarily to give a qualitative picture of the soil population. However H. L. Jensen, in a survey of the microbial populations of Australian soils during the 1930s, used them to provide quantitative information on the soil fungi. Jensen examined a large number of microscopic fields (*ca.* 500 per slide) and recorded the numbers of fungal spores and the percentage of fields showing fungal hyphae. A further modification of the buried slide method is the **nylon mesh** technique of J. S. Waid and M. J. Woodman, introduced in 1957, which also permits a quantitative estimate of the growth of fungal hyphae in soil. Instead of glass slides, nylon gauze is used and buried in the soil for some months before examination; fungal activity is then measured by counting the number of hyphal fragments per mesh. It overcomes some of the criticisms which have been levelled at the buried slide method, in that nylon mesh provides a discontinuous surface: this prevents the formation of a surface water film which might otherwise artificially stimulate the growth of fungi; it permits hyphae to grow through the mesh; and it interferes but slightly with the passage of soil mesofauna, water and gases.

Yet another advance was made in 1957, when H. T. Tribe replaced the Rossi–Cholodny slide with a thin, transparent cellulose film marketed as 'cellophane'. Pieces of cellophane are mounted on glass cover slips and buried in soil; on recovery, they are stained and mounted for microscopic observation. Tribe's method provides a picture of microbial succession developing on a clearly defined substrate in the soil. On cellophane, fungi were found to be the first colonizers, but after a time were replaced by bacteria. Micro- and meso-fauna also develop on the cellophane, and the activity of mites devouring fungal hyphae can be clearly observed.

Isolation of microorganisms from soil by cultural methods

Some of the most significant early discoveries in soil microbiology were made by the use of a simple technique known as **elective** or **enrichment culture,** which depends for its success on the principle of natural selection. It consists of exposing a mixed culture of many different kinds of microorganisms to conditions which allow one species to outgrow all the others to such an extent that its identification and isolation in pure culture becomes relatively easy. For example, if one wishes to study microbes which can satisfy their energy requirements by oxidizing ammonium compounds, it is necessary only to prepare a simple medium containing a source of ammonium ions but no organic matter. If this medium is inoculated with a pinch of soil, then the only organisms which can develop are the bacteria which oxidize ammonium to nitrite and subsequently to nitrate.

Enrichment culture was used extensively, during the last decade of the nineteenth century, by the great pioneer microbiologists S. Winogradsky and M. W. Beijernick. It remains a valuable tool, provided its limitations are clearly appreciated. Because a mixed population is used as the inoculum a chain of events occurs with different organisms predominating at different stages. For example, the enrichment medium for nitrifiers just described actually causes two distinct groups of organisms to develop. The first, comprising members of the genus *Nitrosomonas,* oxidizes ammonium only to nitrite, which in turn provides the energy substrate for the second group, *Nitrobacter.* Again, if a liquid glucose medium containing a complex organic nitrogen source is inoculated with soil and incubated aerobically, a thin layer of pseudomonads frequently develops at the surface. This causes the bulk of the solution to become anaerobic, thus permitting the growth of the microaerophilic lactic acid bacteria or anaerobic bacilli. If either of these latter two groups of organisms is now isolated in pure culture and used to inoculate the original medium under aerobic conditions, it may be prevented from growing by the presence of oxygen. One must always take the precaution of re-inoculating the original medium with any organism isolated by the enrichment method, otherwise quite false conclusions might be drawn concerning its metabolism.

Enrichment culture tells us nothing of the original soil population, except that it contained at least one viable cell of the organism which eventually predominates. The most widely used technique for estimating the numbers of bacteria, actinomycetes and fungi in soil is known as the **dilution plate** method. A known weight of soil is shaken up with sterile water or saline solution, and progressively diluted with the sterile shake medium. From one or more of the higher dilutions, 1 ml aliquots are taken and dispersed with cooled but still liquid agar in sterile petri dishes. If the appropriate dilution is chosen, discrete colonies of microorganisms will develop on the plates, and these may be counted and multiplied by the appropriate dilution factor to obtain an estimate of the number of microbes contained in the original soil sample.

By varying the composition of the medium, selected groups of microorganisms can be encouraged at the expense of others. For example, to be able to count fungi on dilution plates, it is necessary to make the medium unsuitable for bacteria so that these will not interfere with the development of fungal colonies. This may be done by making the medium too acid for the growth of bacteria, or by incorporating an antibiotic, such as streptomycin, to suppress them.

Although it is used frequently by soil microbiologists, it is important to realize that the dilution plate method does have serious limitations. Since no single medium is suitable for culturing all the diverse metabolic groups of microbes, only a small fraction of those actually present in the soil appear on the plates. Furthermore, rare species may not be found even though the medium is suitable, because their population numbers are too low. Many common soil fungi, like the higher basidiomycetes, are slow growing and do not appear on dilution plates because their propagules are inhibited at an earlier stage by faster growing fungi such as *Trichoderma, Mucor* and *Rhizopus.*

Another disability arises because, in the preparation of a dilution series, the heavier fraction of the soil settles before the sample aliquot can be pipetted off. The samples actually plated out are suspensions of the finer mineral and organic particles together with bacterial and actinomycete cells and fungal spores. Fragments of fungal hyphae are poorly represented, as was clearly shown by the investigations of J. H. Warcup during the 1950s. By careful microscopic examination, Warcup identified the source of fungal colonies on soil dilution plates, and found that 75 per cent arose from spores, 20 per cent grew out of humus particles, and only 5 per cent developed from visible fragments of hyphae. Hence any fungus that is sporing heavily in the original soil sample will be represented on dilution plates at a frequency grossly in excess of the volume of its active mycelium.

While not always providing a very useful population statistic for fungi, soil dilution plates are reasonably satisfactory for counting bacteria since these are unicellular. They have also proved generally adequate for actinomycetes because the hyphae of these organisms, unlike those of fungi, fragment fairly readily into individual cells.

In 1916, S. A. Waksman attempted to overcome some of the disadvantages of the soil dilution plate by placing soil crumbs or small lumps of soil directly on the surface of the agar medium. Bacteria develop rapidly in the film of water that soon surrounds the soil particles, which makes the technique unsatisfactory for isolating fungi. It was not until 1950 that Warcup found that he could overcome this problem by burying the soil crumbs in the agar, and **Warcup's soil plate** method, as it became known, is designed specifically for the isolation of soil fungi. Small soil samples (5—15 mg) are carried on the flattened tip of a sterile inoculating needle to a sterile petri dish where they are crushed and covered with about 10 ml of melted but cooled agar medium; the dish is rotated gently to disperse the soil particles.

Soil plates are much less tedious to prepare than dilution plates, and they permit the isolation of fungi which are discarded with the soil residue in a dilution series. This is shown in a comparison of the two methods made by Warcup himself (see table). Soil plates reduce though they do not eliminate the advantage of heavily sporing fungi. However, they still tend to favour medium to fast growing fungi present in the soil in relatively low numbers. They do not permit ready development of slow growing fungi of low competitive ability.

Comparison of fungi isolated from soil by different methods*

Number of species isolated	Method		
	Warcup's soil plate	Dilution plate	
		Suspension	Residue
Average per plate	15	10	15
Total per sample	24	21	24

* After Warcup, J. H. (1950) 'The soil-plate method for isolation of fungi from soil.' *Nature, Lond.,* **166**, 117—18.

Warcup's data, as tabulated, clearly indicate that when soil suspensions are prepared, many fungal propagules remain behind with the heavier soil particles in the residue. If this heavier fraction is separated from the fine material in suspension by sedimentation or sieving, and examined under a dissecting microscope, fungal hyphae can be recognized and transferred individually to an agar medium. This **hyphal isolation** method thus combines direct microscopic examination with cultural techniques, and was first described by Warcup in 1955. In the same year, I. Levisohn used a similar method to isolate mycorrhizal fungi from rhizomorphs and mycelial strands.

The hyphal isolation method gives a completely different picture of the fungal inhabitants of the soil from that obtained by dilution plates or soil plates, and apparently samples a different section of the population. In one study, for example, Warcup found that about two-thirds of the species isolated by hyphal transfer did not appear on dilution plates or even on soil plates. Furthermore, it was apparent that the most abundant species on dilution or soil plates were isolated only rarely by hyphal transfer. Many of the species isolated by hyphal transfer were non-sporing forms, and remained sterile in culture.

Index

See also, Ectomycorrhiza, Endomycorrhiza
Mycorrhizal fungi, 6, 66, 83, 189, 194
Mycostasis, 89
Myriapod, *see* Myriapoda
Myriapoda, 50
See also, Centipedes, Millipedes
Myrica, 228, 230
 M. gale, 228, 232
Myxobacteria, 37, 38
Myxomycetes, 37

Nematoda, *see* Nematodes
Nematodes, 45, 46, 47, 105 ff., 122
Net immobilization, 140, 142, 143, 144
Net mineralization, 140, 142, 144
Niche, 85—6
Nitrate reduction, 158—60
Nitrification, 150 ff., 158, 241
Nitrifying bacteria, 60, 86, 150 ff., 241
Nitrite toxicity, 145, 151
Nitrobacter, 42, 86, 87, 91, 145, 151, 252
Nitrogen,
 as nutrient, 64
 geochemistry, *see* Geochemistry
 mineralization—immobilization cycle, 143 ff.
Nitrogen fixation, 38, 42, 137, 162, 182, 206, 214—15, 226—7, 230 ff.
Nitrosomonas, 42, 86, 91, 145, 150, 151, 252
Nocardia, 43, 146, 234
Non-legume root nodules,
 identity of endophyte, 227—8
 incidence and specificity of nodulation, 228
 infection and nodule development, 228—30
 nitrogen fixing process, 230

role in geochemistry, 232
Non-sulphur purple bacteria, 59
Nostoc, 232, 235, 236
Nucleic acids, 64
Nucelotides, 64
Nutrient cycle, 4, 7
Nutrients, 64 ff.
 availability of, 176 ff.
 limiting, 11
Nutrient uptake process, 67 ff.
Nylon gauze, 142
Nylon mesh, 251
 See also, Nylon gauze

Oidia, 28
Oidiodendron, 77
Oligochaeta, 48 ff.
 See also, Annelids, Enchytraeids
Oomycetes, 31
Organic matter decomposition, 4, 5, 108 ff.
Organic nitrogen, in soils, 144—5
Osmosis, 66
Osmotrophs, 61, 62, 66
Outer free space, 173
Oxygen, as nutrient, 63
Oxygen relationships, 62

Parasitism, 90—1, 107
Partitioning energy flow, 121 ff.
Passive uptake, 67
Pavetta, 236
Peat, 63
Penicillium, 32, 34, 69, 78, 80, 100, 142, 149
 P. frequentans, 89
Peptidase, 69
Permanent wilting point, 17
Permease, 67
Peritrichous flagella, 40
Petroleum, 131, 312
pF, 16
Phage, *see* Bacteriophage